RELIGION IN AMERICA

A DIRECTORY

RELIGION IN AMERICA

A DIRECTORY

COMPILED AND EDITED

BY

JAMES V. GEISENDORFER

LEIDEN
E. J. BRILL
1983

ISBN   90 04 06910 0

A Candle (*Adventist*), P.O. Box 2325, Lehigh Valley, PA 18001.
Aaronic Order (*Mormon*), c/o Robert J. Conrad, P.O. Box 7095, Salt Lake City, UT 84107.
The Abibical Society (*New Age*), 1335 Phelps Avenue, San Jose, CA 95117.
Abraham Lincoln Centre (*Unitarian Universalist*), 3858 South Cottage Grove Avenue, Chicago, IL 60653.
Academic Committee on Soviet Jewry, 345 East 46th Street, New York, NY 10017.
Academy of American Franciscan History (*Catholic*) P.O. Box 34440, Washington, DC 20034.
Academy of California Church History (*Catholic*), P.O. Box 1668, Fresno, CA 93717.
Academy of Homiletics, c/o Dr. Donald Macleod, Princeton Theological Seminary, Princeton, NJ 08540.
Academy of Infinite Metaphysics (*New Age*), 4321 Voltaire Street, San Diego, CA 92107.
Academy of Mind Dynamics, (See Today Church).
Academy of Parish Clergy, Inc., P.O. Box 86, Princeton, NJ 08540.
Academy of Religion and Mental Health, (See Institutes of Religion and Health).
Academy of Religion and Psychical Research, 326 Tunxis Avenue, Bloomfield, CT 06002.
Academy of Universal Truth, Inc. (*New Thought*), c/o Dr. Anna Maye Dahl, President, 4710 University Way, N.E. — Suite 215, Seattle WA 98105.
Academy of Yoga and Psychical Research (*New Age*), 4827 Forest Avenue, Mercer Island, WA 98040.
Accelerated Christian Education, Inc., P.O. Box 2205, Garland, TX 75041.
Accrediting Association of Bible Colleges, (See American Association of Bible Colleges).
Accrediting Association of Bible Institutes and Bible Colleges, (See American Association of Bible Colleges).
Accrediting Association of Christian Colleges and Seminaries, P.O. Box 4174, Sarasota, FL 33578.
Action International Ministries, P.O. Box 2068, Lynwood, WA 98036.
ACTS 17, P.O. Box 2183, La Mesa, CA 92041.
Admatha Tape Ministry, (See Angelus Temple Tape Ministry).
Adult Christian Education Foundation, P.O. Box 5305, Madison, WI 53705.
Advanced Spiritual Church (*New Age*), 4446 Ledge Avenue, North Hollywood, CA 91602.
The Advent Christian Association, (See Advent Christian Church).
Advent Christian Church, P.O. Box 23152, Charlotte, NC 28212.
The Aetherius Society (*Psychic*), 6202 Afton Place, Hollywood, CA 90028.
Afghan Border Crusade, c/o W. H. Webb, 73 Windermere Avenue, Lansdowne, PA 19050.
Africa Evangelical Fellowship, P.O. Box 109, Glen Ridge, NJ 07028.
Africa Inland Mission, P.O. Box 178, Pearl River, NY 10965.
Africa Inter Mennonite Mission, Inc., c/o Dr. James E. Bentsche, Executive Director, 224 West High Street, Elkhart, IN 46514.

African Enterprise, Inc., P.O. Box 988, Pasadena, CA 91102.

African Methodist Episcopal Church, c/o Dr. Richard A. Chappelle, General Secretary, P.O. Box 183, St. Louis, MO 63166.

African Methodist Episcopal Church, Department of Christian Education, 500 8th Avenue South, Nashville, TN 37203.

African Methodist Episcopal Church, Lay Organization, c/o Mr. J. D. Williams, President, 3232 East 30th Street, Kansas City, MO 64128.

African Methodist Episcopal Church, Women's Missionary Society, c/o Mrs. Wilhelmina Lawrence, President, 2311 M Street, N.W., Washington, DC 20037.

African Methodist Episcopal Zion Church, P.O. Box 32843, Charlotte, NC 28232.

African Methodist Episcopal Zion Church, Department of Foreign Missions, 475 Riverside Drive — Room 1910, New York, NY 10115.

African Methodist Episcopal Zion Church, Woman's Home and Overseas Missionary Society, c/o Mrs. Alcestis Coleman, General President, 120-19 Nashville Avenue, St. Albans, NY 11412.

African Mission Services, Inc., 1012 City Avenue, Philadelphia, PA 19151.

African Orthodox Church, 122 West 129th Street, New York, NY 10027.

African Union First Colored Methodist Protestant Church of the United States of America or Elsewhere, Inc., (See African Union Methodist Protestant Church).

African Union Methodist Protestant Church, c/o Bishop Robert F. Walters, 515 Jefferson Street, Plymouth Township, Norristown, PA 19401.

African Universal Church (*Pentecostal*), 14 Webster Place, East Orange, NJ 07018.

The Agape Association, P.O. Box 506, Casselberry, FL 32707.

Agasha Temple of Wisdom, Inc. (*Psychic*), 460 North Western Avenue, Los Angeles, CA 90004.

Agni Yoga Society (*New Age*), 319 West 107th Street, New York, NY 10025.

Agora Ministries, Inc. (*Pentecostal*), P.O. Box 2467, Costa Mesa, CA 92626.

Agricultural Missions (*National Council of Churches*), 475 Riverside Drive, New York, NY 10115.

Agricultural Missions Foundation, (See Agricultural Missions).

Agropolitan Ministries, c/o Rev. Keith L. Inskeep, P.O. Box 145, Merom, IN 47861.

Agudas Israel World Organization (*Jewish*), 471 West End Avenue, New York, NY 10024.

Agudath Harabonim (*Jewish*), (See Union of Orthodox Rabbis of the U.S. and Canada).

Agudath Israel of America (*Jewish-Orthodox*), 5 Beekman Street, New York, NY 10038.

Ah Kin Gnostic Temple (*Witchcraft*), c/o Norman Kaeseberg, 2550 North Southport, Chicago, IL 60614.

The Ahmadiyya Movement in Islam, 103 Chilton Street, Cambridge, MA 02138.

Aid Association for Lutherans, Appleton, WI 54919.

AIM, Inc., c/o Barton A. Buhtz, President, 9003 Terhune Avenue, Sun Valley, CA 91352.

Ajapa Yoga Foundation (*Hindu*), c/o Shri Janardan Ajapa Yoga Ashram, P.O. Box 1731, Placerville, CA 95667.

The Akashic Organization of Los Angeles, California, Inc. (*New Age*), 20110 Needles Street, Chatsworth, CA 91311.

The Alan Watts Society for Comparative Philosophy, Inc., P.O. Box 857, Sausalito, CA 94965.

Alaska Christian Conference, P.O. Box 441, Fairbanks, AK 99707.

Alaska Yearly Meeting of Friends (*Unaffiliated*), P.O. Box 687, Kotzebue, AK 99752.

The Alban Institute, Inc., Wisconsin Avenue and Woodley Road, N.W., Washington, DC 20016.

Albanian Orthodox Archdiocese in America, 529 East Broadway, South Boston, MA 02127.

Albanian Orthodox Diocese of America, 54 Burroughs Street, Jamaica Plain, MA 02130.

Albert Cardinal Meyer Institute (*Catholic*), 3257 South Lake Drive, Milwaukee, WI 53207.

Albert Schweitzer Center, c/o Stephen C. Rose, Executive Director, Great Barrington, MA 01230.

Albert Schweitzer Fellowship, 866 United Nations Plaza, New York, NY 10017.

Albertus Magnus Guild (*Catholic*), c/o Rev. William D. Sullivan, Boston College, 140 Commonwealth Avenue, Chestnut Hill, MA 02167.

Aletheia Psycho-Physical Foundation (*New Age*), c/o Jack Schwarz, Founder-President, 515 N.E. 8th Street, Grants Pass, OR 97526.

Alexandrian Temple of Light, 2581 Piedmont Road, N.E., Atlanta, GA 30324.

Algard Wicca (*Witchcraft*), c/o Mary Nesnick, 520 East 20th Street, New York, NY 10009.

All Nations Frontier Missions, c/o Dr. Morris Watkins, Faith Evangelical Lutheran Seminary, P.O. Box 7186, Tacoma, WA 98407.

All-One-Faith-in-One-God State, 2915 Berryessa Road, San Jose, CA 95133.

All Saints Church of Mystic Science (*Psychic*), P.O. Box 42461, Las Vegas, NV 89104.

All Saints Sisters of the Poor (*Episcopal*), P.O. Box 3127, Catonsville, MD 21228.

Allegheny Wesleyan Methodist Connection (*Holiness*), 413 East Main Street, Titusville, PA 16354.

Alliance for Health and Wholeness, Inc. (*New Age*), P.O. Box 3752, Station D, Albuquerque, NM 87190.

The Alliance for the Preservation of Religious Liberty, P.O. Box 99568, San Diego, CA 92109.

Alliance of Unitarian Women, (See Unitarian Universalist Women's Federation).

Alliance to End Repression, 1000 Old Colony Bldg., 407 South Dearborn Street, Chicago, IL 60605.

Alpha and Omega Christian Church and Bible School (*Pentecostal*), 96-171 Kamehameha Highway, Pearl City, Honolulu, HI 96782.

Alpha and Omega Pentecostal Church of America, Inc., 3023 Clifton Avenue, Baltimore, MD 21216.

Alphan Society (*New Age*), c/o Rev. A. D. Bethany, 11831 Ayres Avenue, Los Angeles, CA 90064.

Alternative Religions Center, P.O. Box 443, Bloomington, IN 47402.

Amana Church Society (*Communal*), Amana, IA 52203.

Amana Community of Inspirationists, (See Amana Church Society).

Ambassadors for Christ National Ministries, P.O. Box 7115, Jacksonville, FL 32210.

Ambassadors of Mary (*Catholic*), 6003 West Diversey Avenue, Chicago, IL 60639.

America for Jesus, (See One Nation Under God).

America-Israel Cultural Foundation, 485 Madison Avenue, New York, NY 10022.

American Academy for Jewish Research, 3080 Broadway, New York, NY 10027.

American Academy of Asian Studies, 134 Church Street, San Francisco, CA 94114.

American Academy of Homiletics, (See Academy of Homiletics).

American Academy of Religion, c/o Charles Winquist, Executive Director, California State University, Chico, CA 95929.

American Advent Mission Society, (See Advent Christian Church).

American and European Friends of ORT (*Jewish*), 817 Broadway, New York, NY 10003.

American and Foreign Christian Union, c/o World Council of Churches, 475 Riverside Drive — Room 1062, New York, NY 10115.

American Association for Jewish Education, 114 Fifth Avenue, New York, NY 10011.

American Association for Jewish Evangelism, Inc., 5860 North Lincoln Avenue, Chicago, IL 60659.

American Association for the Advancement of Atheism, Inc., (See Atheist Association).

American Association of Bible Colleges, P.O. Box 1523, Fayetteville, AR 72701.

American Association of Christian Counselors, 20 Green Bay, Winnetka, IL 60093.

American Association of Christian Schools of Higher Learning, P.O. Box 35139, Greenville, SC 29614.

American Association of English Jewish Newspapers, (See American Jewish Press Association).

American Association of Evangelical Students, P.O. Box 306, Winona Lake, IN 46590.

American Association of Pastoral Counselors, 3000 Connecticut Avenue, N.W. — Suite 300, Washington, DC 20008.

The American Association of Religious Counselors, 6213 North Highland, Gladstone, MO 64118.

American Association of Religious Therapists, 5800 S.W. 130th Avenue, Ft. Lauderdale, FL 33330.

American Association of Schools of Religious Education, (See Association of Theological Schools in the United States and Canada).

American Association of Theological School Funds, (See Fund for Theological Education).

American Association of Theological Schools, (See Association of Theological Schools in the United States and Canada).

American Association of Women Ministers, (See International Association of Women Ministers).

American Atheist Women, P.O. Box 2117, Austin, TX 78768.

American Atheists, P.O. Box 2117, Austin, TX 78768

American Baptist Assembly (*American Baptist Churches in the USA*), Green Lake, WI 54941.

American Baptist Association, 4605 North State Line Avenue, Texarkana, TX 75503.

American Baptist Churches in the USA, Valley Forge, PA 19481.

American Baptist Convention, (See American Baptist Churches in the USA).

American Baptist Foreign Mission Society (*American Baptist Churches in the USA*), Valley Forge, PA 19481.

American Baptist Historical Society, 1106 South Goodman Street, Rochester, NY 14620.

American Baptist Men (*American Baptist Churches in the USA*) Valley Forge, PA 19481.

American Baptist Relief, (See Baptist World Relief).

American Baptist Women (*American Baptist Churches in the USA*) Valley Forge, PA 19481.

American Benedictine Academy (*Catholic*), St. Meinrad Abbey, St. Meinrad, IN 47577.

American Bible Churches, (See American Evangelical Christian Churches).

American Bible Society, 1865 Broadway, New York, NY 10023.

American Biblical Encyclopedia Society, 24 West Maple Avenue, Monsey, NY 10952.

American Board of Commissioners for Foreign Missions (*United Church of Christ*), (See United Church Board for World Ministries).

American Board of Missions to the Jews, P.O. Box 2000, Orangeburg, NY 10962.

American Buddhist Academy, 331 Riverside Drive, New York, NY 10025.

American Buddhist Association, 1151 West Leland Avenue, Chicago, IL 60640.

American Buddhist Mission, P.O. Box 536, Atlantic Beach, FL 32233.

American Buddhist Society and Fellowship, Inc., c/o Dr. Robert E. Dickhoff, 600 West 157th Street — Apt. 56, New York, NY 10032.

The American Carpatho-Russian Orthodox Greek Catholic Church, Johnstown, PA 15906.

American Catholic Church, c/o Most Rev. Simon E. Talarczyk, 430 Park Avenue, Laguna Beach, CA 92651.

American Catholic Church, Archdiocese of New York, c/o Most Rev. James F. Lashley, Primate, 457 West 144th Street, New York, NY 10031.

American Catholic Church (Lines Succession), (See Church of Antioch, Malabar Rite).

The American Catholic Church (Syro-Antiochian), c/o Most Rev. Archbishop H. Francis Wilkie, St. Mary Magdalene Catholic Church, 189 Lenox Avenue, New York, NY 10026.

American Catholic Correctional Chaplains Association, c/o Rev. Dismas Boeff, Secretary, 2900 East Blvd., Cleveland, OH 44104.

American Catholic Esperanto Society, 7605 Winona Lane, Sebastopol, CA 95472.

American Catholic Historical Association, Catholic University of America, 620 Michigan Avenue, N.E., Washington, DC 20064.

American Catholic Historical Society, 263 South Fourth, Philadelphia, PA 19106.

American Catholic Philosophical Association, Catholic University of America, 620 Michigan Avenue, N.E., Washington, DC 20064.

American Catholic Prison Chaplains Association, (See American Catholic Correctional Chaplains Association).

American Catholic Psychological Association, c/o American Psychological Association, 1200 17th Street, N.W., Washington, DC 20036.

American Catholic Sociological Society, (See Association for the Sociology of Religion).

"American Celtic", (See American Order of the Brotherhood of Wicca).

American Chinese Christian Alliance, (See World Council of Christians).

American Christian Association for Israel, (See America-Israel Cultural Foundation).

American Christian Council, 756 Haddon Avenue, Collingswood, NJ 08108.

The American Church Union (*Episcopal*), 6013 Lawton Avenue, Oakland, CA 94618.

American Commission on Ministerial Training, P.O. Box 1252, York, PA 17405.

American Committee for Rescue and Resettlement of Iraqi Jews (*Jewish*), 1200 Fifth Avenue, New York, NY 10029.

American Committee for the Evangelization of the Greeks, (See AMG International).

American Committee on Italian Migration (*Catholic*), 373 Fifth Avenue, New York, NY 10016.

American Conference of Cantors (*Jewish*), 838 Fifth Avenue, New York, NY 10021.

American Conference of Certified Cantors (*Jewish*), (See American Conference of Cantors).

American Conference of Undenominational Churches, (See Independant Fundamental Churches of America).

American Congregation of Jews from Austria, 118 West 95th Street, New York, NY 10025.

American Congregational Association, 14 Beacon Street, Boston, MA 02108.

American Correctional Chaplains' Association, c/o Rev. Huey D. Perry, Secretary, 1311 Winewood Blvd., Tallahassee, FL 32301.

American Council for Judaism, 307 Fifth Avenue, New York, NY 10016.

American Council of Christian Churches, P.O. Box 816, Valley Forge, PA 19481.

American Council of Christian Laymen, (See Laymen's Commission of the American Council of Christian Churches).

American Council of Executives in Religion, P.O. Box 511, Huntington, NY 11743.

The American Council of the Ramabai Mukti Mission, 55 Leigh Street, P.O. Box 4912, Clinton, NJ 08809.

American Eastern Orthodox Church, c/o Most Rev. Thomas Martin, 1580 Bledsoe Lane, Las Vegas, NV 89110.

American Episcopal Church, c/o Rt. Rev. Anthony F. M. Clavier, P.O. Box 373, 1416 S.E. 2nd Terrace, Deerfield Beach, FL 33441.

American Ethical Union, Two West 64th Street, New York, NY 10023.

American-European Bethel Mission, Inc., P.O. Box 30562, Santa Barbara, CA 93105.

American Evangelical Christian Churches, Waterfront Drive, Pineland, FL 33945.

American Evangelical Lutheran Church, (See Lutheran Church in America).

American Evangelistic Association (*Pentecostal*), P.O. Box 63, Dallas, TX 75221.

American Family Foundation, Inc., P.O. Box 343, Lexington, MA 02173.

American Federation of Catholic Workers for the Blind and Visually Handicapped, 154 East 23rd Street, New York, NY 10010.

American Federation of Italian Evangelicals, (See Association of Evangelicals for Italian Mission).

American Federation of Jewish Fighters, Camp Inmates and Nazi Victims, Inc., 315 Lexington Avenue, New York, NY 10016.

American Federation of Jews from Central Europe, 570 Seventh Avenue, New York, NY 10018.

American Federation of Polish Jews, 342 Madison Avenue, New York, NY 10017.

American Federation of Reformed Young Men Societies, (See Young Calvinist Federation).

American Federation of Reformed Young Women Societies, (See Young Calvinist Federation).

American Fellowship Church, 469 Pacific, Monterey, CA 93940.

American Festival of Evangelism, P.O. Box 17093, Washington, DC 20041.

American Foundation for the Science of Creative Intelligence, (See International Meditation Society).

American Foundation of Religion and Psychiatry, (See Institutes of Religion and Health).

American Franciscan Society for Vocations (*Catholic*), (See Franciscan Vocation Conference).

American Friends of Israel (*Jewish*), 850 Third Avenue, New York, NY 10022.

American Friends of Religious Freedom in Israel (*Jewish*), P.O. Box 5888, Washington, DC 20014.

American Friends of the Alliance Israelite Universelle (*Jewish*), 61 Broadway — Room 811, New York, NY 10006.

American Friends of the Hebrew University (*Jewish*), 1140 Avenue of the Americas, New York, NY 10036.

American Friends of the Mirrer Yeshivah in Jerusalem (*Jewish*), 1133 Broadway, New York, NY 10010.

American Friends Service Committee, Inc., 1501 Cherry Street, Philadelphia, PA 19102.

American Fund for Israel Institutions, (See America-Israel Cultural Foundation).

American Fund for Palestine Institutions, (See America-Israel Cultural Foundation).

The American Greyfriars (*Anglican*), P.O. Box 396, Old Chelsea Station, New York, NY 10011.

American Healing Association (*New Age*), 6311 Yucca Street, Los Angeles, CA 90028.

American Histadrut Development Foundation (*Jewish*), (See Israel Histadrut Foundation).

American Holy Orthodox Catholic Apostolic Eastern Church, 247 East 126th Street, New York, NY 10035.

American Humanist Association, Seven Harwood Drive, Amherst, NY 14226.

American Hungarian Catholic Society, 11800 Shaker Blvd. — No. 105, Cleveland, OH 44120.

American Indian Evangelical Church (*Pentecostal*), 1823 Emerson Avenue North, Minneapolis, MN 55411.

American Institute of Buddhist Studies, 233 South Pleasant Street, Amherst, MA 01002.

American Institute of Holy Land Studies, Mt. Zion, Jerusalem, Israel.

American Institute of Islamic Studies, P.O. Box 10191, Denver, CO 80210.

American Institute of Theology, P.O. Box 336, Newhall, CA 91321.

American-Israel Society, (See America-Israel Cultural Foundation).

American Jesuit Missionary Association (*Catholic*), (See Jesuit Missions).

American Jewish Alternatives to Zionism, 133 East 73rd Street — Suite 404, New York, NY 10021.

American Jewish Archives, 3101 Clifton Avenue, Cincinnati, OH 45220.

American Jewish Committee, 165 East 56th Street, New York, NY 10022.

American Jewish Conference on Soviet Jewry, (See National Conference on Soviet Jewry).

American Jewish Congress, 15 East 84th Street, New York, NY 10028.

American Jewish Correctional Chaplains Association, 10 East 73rd Street, New York, NY 10021.

American Jewish Historical Society, Two Thornton Road, Waltham, MA 02154.

American Jewish History Center of the Jewish Theological Seminary, 3080 Broadway, New York, NY 10027.

American Jewish Institute, (See Jewish Information Bureau).

American Jewish Joint Distribution Committee, 60 East 42nd Street — Room 1914, New York, NY 10017.

American Jewish League Against Communism, 39 East 68th Street, New York, NY 10021.

American Jewish League for Israel, 595 Madison Avenue, New York, NY 10022.

American Jewish Periodical Center, 3101 Clifton Avenue, Cincinnati, OH 45220.

American Jewish Physicians' Committee, (See American Friends of the Hebrew University).

American Jewish Press Association, c/o Jewish Exponent, 226 South 16th Street, Philadelphia, PA 19102.

American Jewish Public Relations Society, c/o Ms. Riki E. Kosut, P.O. Box 6117, Long Island City, NY 11106.

American Jewish Society for Service, 15 East 26th Street — Room 1302, New York, NY 10010.

American Labor ORT (*Jewish*), 817 Broadway, New York, NY 10003.

American Leprosy Missions, Inc., 1262 Broad Street, Bloomfield, NJ 07003.

American Lithuanian Catholic Federation Ateitis, One South 561 Cotuit, Glen Ellyn, IL 60137.

American-Lithuanian Roman Catholic Federation, c/o Dr. Joseph B. Jerome, 9050 South Troy Avenue, Evergreen Park, IL 60642.

American Lithuanian Roman Catholic Federation Ateitis, (See American Lithuanian Catholic Federation Ateitis).

American Lithuanian Roman Catholic Organist Alliance, c/o Anthony P. Giedraitis, 7310 South California Avenue, Chicago, IL 60629.

The American Lutheran Church, 422 South Fifth Street, Minneapolis, MN 55415.

American Lutheran Church Men, 422 South Fifth Street, Minneapolis, MN 55415.

American Lutheran Church Women, 422 South Fifth Street, Minneapolis, MN 55415.

American Lutheran Education Association, c/o Mr. Ronald E. Fiebig, Secretary, St. John Lutheran School, 725 West Washington Blvd., Fort Wayne, IN 46804.

American Lutheran Publicity Bureau, 155 East 22nd Street, New York, NY 10010.

American Messianic Fellowship, 7448 North Damen Avenue, Chicago, IL 60645.

American Millennial Association, (See Advent Christian Church).

American Ministerial Association, P.O. Box 1252, York, PA 17405.

American Mission for Opening Churches, 6419 East Lake Road, Olcott, NY 14126.

American Mission for Opening Closed Churches, (See American Mission for Opening Churches).

American Mission to Greeks, (See AMG International).

American Mission to Lepers, (See American Leprosy Missions, Inc.).

American Mission to the Chinese, (See American Mission to the Chinese and Asian).

American Mission to the Chinese and Asian, c/o Rev. Peter P. S. Ching, 144-25 Roosevelt Avenue, Flushing, NY 11354.

American Missionary Fellowship, 672 Conestoga Road, P.O. Box 368, Villanova, PA 19085.

American Mizrachi Women (*Jewish*), 817 Broadway, New York, NY 10003.

American Mohammedan Society, (See Moslem Mosque).

American Mountain Center (*New Age*), 9449 West Jefferson Blvd., Culver City, CA 90230.

American National Church, Roman Catholic Ultrajectine, c/o Shrine of Our Lady of the Holy Rosary Mediatrix of Peace, Necedah, WI 54646.

American Old Catholic Church, c/o Monastery of The Holy Protection of The Blessed Virgin Mary, 3500 Coltrane Road, Oklahoma City, OK 73121.

American Order of the Brotherhood of Wicca (*Witchcraft*), P.O. Box 3383, St. Paul, MN 55165.

American ORT Federation (*Jewish*), 817 Broadway, New York, NY 10003.

American Orthodox Catholic Church, c/o Bishop Robert S. Zeiger, 12033 West Maryland Drive, Denver, CO 80228.

American Orthodox Catholic Church, Diocese of Wisconsin, c/o Most Rev. Michael Bent, D.D., 300 South Maple Avenue, Green Bay, WI 54303.

American Orthodox Church, 316 South First, Rogers, AR 72756.

American Palestine Fund, (See America-Israel Cultural Foundation).

American Parapsychological Research Foundation, 15446 Sherman Way, P.O. Box 5395, Sherman Oaks, CA 91413.

American Protestant Correctional Chaplains Association, c/o South Carolina Department of Corrections, P.O. Box 11159, Columbia, SC 29211.

American Protestant Hospital Association, 840 North Lake Shore Drive — Room 607, Chicago, IL 60611.

American Raelian Movement (*Psychic*), P.O. Box 39488, Griffith Station, Los Angeles, CA 90039.

American Rationalist Federation, c/o Mr. George B. Kisslinger, 515 Tuxedo Blvd., St. Louis, MO 63119.
American Remnant Mission, Inc. (*National Association of Evangelicals*), c/o Rev. Jacob Spiegel, President, 2100 Monument Blvd. — Suite 17, Pleasant Hill, CA 94523.
American Rescue Workers (*Holiness*), 2827 Frankford Avenue, Philadelphia, PA 19134.
American Romanian Orthodox Youth, 2522 Grey Tower Road, Jackson, MI 49201.
American Sabbath Tract Society (*Seventh Day Baptist General Conference*), 510 Watchung Avenue, Plainfield, NJ 07060.
The American Saint Hill Organization (*Church of Scientology*), 1413 North Berendo Street, Los Angeles, CA 90027.
American Salvation Army (*Holiness*), (See American Rescue Workers).
American School of Mentalvivology (*New Thought*), Cedar Heart of the Ozarks, Thornfield, MO 65762.
American Schools of Oriental Research, c/o Roger S. Boraas, 50 Fernwood Road, East Orange, N.J. 07017.
American Scientific Affiliation, 500 Melrose Court, Elgin, IL 60120.
American Scripture Gift Mission, 1211 Arch Street — Room T, Philadelphia, PA 19107.
American Society for Church Architecture, (See Interfaith Forum on Religion, Art and Architecture).
American Society for Psychical Research, Five West 73rd Street, New York, NY 10023.
American Society for Reformation Research, c/o Daniel Augsburger, Secretary, Andrews University, Berrien Springs, MI 49104.
American Society for the Defense of Tradition, Family and Property, P.O. Box 1281, New Rochelle, NY 10802.
American Society for the Study of Religion, c/o Department of Religious Studies, Rice University, Houston, TX 77005.
The American Society of Christian Ethics, (See The Society of Christian Ethics).
American Society of Christian Social Ethics in the United States and Canada, (See The Society of Christian Ethics).
American Society of Church History, c/o William B. Miller, Secretary-Treasurer, 305 East Country Club Lane, Wallingford, PA 19086.
American Society of Mature Catholics, c/o Merlin Victora, 1100 West Wells Street, Milwaukee, WI 53233.
American Society of Missiology, c/o Wilbert R. Shenk, Secretary-Treasurer, P.O. Box 370, Elkhart, IN 46515.
American Society of St. Caecilia (*Catholic*), (See Church Music Association of America).
American Spiritual Healing Association, P.O. Box 1189, Six Bridle Path Circle, Framingham, MA 01701.
American Sunday School Union, (See American Missionary Fellowship).
The American Synod of the Holy Orthodox Church, 70 West 6th Avenue, Denver, CO 80204.
American Teilhard Association for the Future of Man, P.O. Box 67, White Plains, NY 10604.
American Teilhard de Chardin Association, (See American Teilhard Association for the Future of Man).

American Temperance Society (*Seventh-day Adventist Church*), 6840 Eastern Avenue, N.W., Washington, DC 20012.

American Theological Library Association, c/o David J. Wartluft, Executive Secretary, Lutheran Theological Seminary, 7301 Germantown Avenue, Philadelphia, PA 19119.

American Theological Society, c/o Lutheran School of Theology, 1100 East 55th Street, Chicago, IL 60615.

American Torah Shelemah Committee (*Jewish*), 24 West Maple Avenue, Monsey, NY 10952.

American Tract Society, c/o Dr. S. E. Slocum, Jr., President, 1624 North First Street, Garland, TX 75040.

American Trade Union Council for Histadrut (*Jewish*), 33 East 67th Street, New York, NY 10021.

American Unitarian Association, (See Unitarian Universalist Association).

American Unitarian Youth, (See Liberal Religious Youth).

American Vegan Society (*Hindu*), 501 Old Harding Hwy. — Box H, Malaga, NJ 08328.

American Veterans of Israel, 548 East Walnut Street, Long Beach, NY 11561.

American Waldensian Aid Society, 475 Riverside Drive — Room 1850, New York, NY 10115.

American World Patriarchs (*Eastern Orthodox*), c/o Most Rev. E. J. Ryzy, 19 Aquaduct Street, Ossining, NY 10562.

American Youth Foundation, 3460 Hampton Avenue, St. Louis, MO 63139.

American Zionist Council (*Jewish*), (See American Zionist Federation).

American Zionist Emergency Council (*Jewish*), (See American Zionist Federation).

American Zionist Federation (*Jewish*), 515 Park Avenue, New York, NY 10022.

American Zionist Youth Commission (*Jewish*), (See Hadassah Zionist Youth Commission).

American Zionist Youth Council (*Jewish*), 515 Park Avenue, New York, NY 10022.

American Zionist Youth Foundation (*Jewish*), 515 Park Avenue, New York, NY 10022.

Americans Against Abortion, c/o Maxine Secrest, P.O. Box 977, Tulsa, OK 74102.

Americans for Progressive Israel (*Jewish*) 150 Fifth Avenue, New York, NY 10011.

Americans United for Separation of Church and State, 8120 Fenton Street, Silver Spring, MD 20910.

Americans United Research Foundation, 900 Silver Spring Avenue, Silver Spring, MD 20910.

America's Promise, (See Lord's Covenant Church, Inc.).

AMG International, (Advancing the Ministries of the Gospel), 6815 Shallowford Road, Chattanooga, TN 37421.

Amica Temple of Radiance (*Psychic*), P.O. Box 304, Ojai, CA 93023.

AMORC (*Occult*), (See Ancient and Mystic Order of Rosae Crucis).

AMORE, (See Astrological, Metaphysical, Occult, Revelatory, Enlightenment Church).

Ananda Ashram World Yoga University (*Hindu*), P.O. Box 805, Monroe, NY 10950.

Ananda Ashrama (*Hindu*), P.O. Box 8555, La Crescenta, CA 91214.
Ananda Marga (*Hindu*), 854 Pearl Street, Denver, CO 80203.
Ananda Marga Yoga Society, (See Ananda Marga).
Ananda Meditation Retreat (*Hindu*), 900 Alleghany Star Route, Nevada City, CA 95959.
Anchor Bay Evangelistic Association (*Pentecostal*), P.O. Box 188, New Baltimore, MI 48047.
Ancient and Mystic Order of Rosae Crucis (AMORC) (*Occult*), Rosicrucian Park, San Jose, CA 95191.
Ancient Order of Hibernians in America (*Catholic*), P.O. Box 700, Riverdale Station, Bronx, NY 10471.
Ancient Order of Oriental Templars, (See Neo-Pythagorean Gnostic Church).
Andes Evangelical Mission, P.O. Box 155, Whiting, NJ 08759.
Angelic Warfare Confraternity (*Catholic*), 141 East 65th Street, New York, NY 10021.
Angelus Temple Tape Ministry, 1100 Glendale Blvd., Los Angeles, CA 90026.
Anglican Catholic Church, c/o Rt. Rev. William O. Lewis, Anglican Diocese of the Midwest, 1616 Merrill Street, Kalamazoo, MI 49008.
Anglican Church in America, c/o Rt. Rev. Robert S. Morse, St. Peter's Church, 6013 Lawton Avenue, Oakland, CA 94618.
Anglican Church of North America, (See Anglican Catholic Church).
Anglican Episcopal Church, P.O. Box 11782, Santa Ana, CA 92711.
The Anglican Episcopal Church of North America, P.O. Box 52702, Atlanta, GA 30355.
The Anglican Episcopal Council of Churches, P.O. Box 52702, Atlanta, GA 30355.
Anglican Fellowship of Prayer (*Episcopal*), c/o Rev. Donald M. Hulstrand, Executive Director, 529 East King Street, Lancaster, PA 17602.
Anglican Orthodox Church, c/o Bishop James Parker Dees, 323 East Walnut Street, Statesville, NC 28677.
The Anglican Society, c/o Rt. Rev. Robert Terwilliger, President, St. John's Church, 61 Broad Street, Elizabeth, NJ 07201.
Anglo-Saxon Federation of America, Haverhill, MA 01830.
Anita Bryant Ministries, (See Successful Life Ministries).
Annwn Temple of Gwynfyd (*Witchcraft*), P.O. Box 27895, Tucson, AZ 85726.
Antahkarna Circle (*New Age*), P.O. Box 308, Manson, WA 98831.
Antarctica Development Interests (*Mormon*), P. O. Box 417, Port Angeles, WA 98362.
Anthroposophical Society in America, 211 Madison Avenue, New York, NY 10016.
Antichrist Information Center, c/o Dr. Alberto M. R. Rivera, P.O. Box 1076, Alta Loma, CA 91701.
Ant-Defamation League of B'nai B'rith (*Jewish*), 823 United Nations Plaza, New York, NY 10017.
Antiochian Orthodox Archdiocese of Toledo, Ohio and Dependencies in North America, (See The Antiochian Orthodox Christian Archdiocese of North America).
The Antiochian Orthodox Christian Archdiocese of New York and All North America, (See The Antiochian Orthodox Christian Archdiocese of North America).

The Antiochian Orthodox Christian Archdiocese of North America, 358 Mountain Road, Englewood, NJ 07631.

The Antiochian Orthodox Christian Archdiocese of North America — Western Rite, c/o Very Rev. Paul W. S. Schneirla, 8005 Ridge Blvd., Brooklyn, NY 11209.

Anubhava School of Enlightenment, (See Dyad School of Enlightenment).

Apostleship of Prayer (*Catholic*), 114 East 13th Street, New York, NY 10003.

Apostleship of the Sea in the United States (*Catholic*), P.O. Box 12824, Pensacola, FL 32575.

Apostolate for Family Consecration (*Catholic*), c/o The House of St. Joseph, P.O. Box 220, Kenosha, WI 53141.

Apostolate of Christian Action (*Catholic*), P.O. Box 24, Fresno, CA 93707.

Apostolate to Assist Dying Non-Catholics (*Catholic*), (See Markham Prayer Card Apostolate).

Apostolic Christian Church — Nazarean, P.O. Box 151, Tremont, IL 61568.

Apostolic Christian Churches of America (*Holiness*), c/o Elder Roy L. Sauder, 1100 East St. Luke Court, Peoria, IL 61614.

The Apostolic Church (*Pentecostal*), 10841 Chapman Avenue, Garden Grove, CA 92640.

The Apostolic Church, Inc. (*Pentecostal*), P.O. Box 427, Ottumwa, IA 52501.

Apostolic Church of Jesus (*Pentecostal*), c/o Rev. Raymond P. Vigil, Secretary, 1818 East First Street, Pueblo, CO 81001.

Apostolic Episcopal Church, c/o Rev. Francis C. Spatano, 86-11 Common-wealth Blvd., Bellerose, NY 11426.

Apostolic Episcopal Church, c/o Most Rev. Robert Ramm, 1052 Sonora Avenue, Glendale, CA 91201.

Apostolic Faith (*Pentecostal*), c/o Apostolic Faith Bible School, 1009 Lincoln Avenue, Baxter Springs, KS 66713.

The Apostolic Faith (*Pentecostal*), S.E. 52nd and Duke Street, Portland, OR 97206.

The Apostolic Faith Church (*Pentecostal*), 1043 Middle Street, Kalihi, Honolulu, HI 96819.

Apostolic Gospel Church of Jesus Christ (*Pentecostal*), 1767 Thomas Terrace, Decatur, GA 30032.

Apostolic Lutheran Church of America, c/o James Johnson, Secretary, Route 2 — Box 99, L'Anse, MI 49946.

The Apostolic Methodist Church (*Holiness*), c/o Elder E. H. Crowson, P.O. Box 1106, Kissimmee, FL 32741.

Apostolic Overcoming Holy Church of God (*Pentecostal*), c/o Mrs. Juanita R. Arrington, Secretary, 909 Jasper Road West, Birmingham, AL 35204.

Apostolic United Brethren (*Mormon*), c/o Owen Allred, 2936 Curry Circle, Granger, UT 84118.

Appalachian Ministries (*Episcopal*), 815 Second Avenue, New York, NY 10017.

The Appeal of Conscience Foundation, 119 West 57th Street, New York, NY 10019.

Aquarian Academy, c/o Robert E. Birdsong, P.O. Box 6294, Eureka, CA 95501.

Aquarian Age (*New Age*), 355 West Olive Avenue, Sunnyvale, CA 94086.

Aquarian Age Yoga Center, P.O. Box 965, 620 14th Street, Virginia Beach, VA 23451.

The Aquarian Church of Universal Service (*New Age*), P.O. Box 144, Colton, OR 97017.

Aquarian Educational Group (*New Age*), 30188 Mulholland Hwy., Agoura, CA 91301.

Aquarian Fellowship Church (*Psychic*), 965 Park Avenue, San Jose, CA 95126.

The Aquarian Foundation (*New Age*) 315 15th Avenue East, Seattle, WA 98112.

"Aquarian Metaphysics", (See International Church of Spiritual Vision).

Aquarian Minyan (*New Age*), c/o Robert Goldfarb, 918 Ensenada, Berkeley, CA 94707.

Aquarian Order of the Restoration, P.O. Box 352, Berkeley, CA 94701.

Aquarian Radio Teaching, Inc. (*New Age*), P.O. Box 30127, Santa Barbara, CA 93105.

Aquarian Research Foundation (*New Age*), 5620 Morton Street, Philadelphia, PA 19144.

Aquarian Service Groups (*New Age*), P.O. Box 1341, Grants Pass, OR 97526.

Aquarian Tabernacle (*Neo-Paganism*), P.O. Box 73, Index, WA 98256.

The Aquarian Wisdom School (*New Age*), 13133 Julian Avenue, Lakeside, CA 92040.

Aquarian World Servers (*New Age*), Route 9 — Box 2370, Brooksville, FL 33512.

Aquarius School of the Masters, (See American School of Mentalvivology).

Aquarius Spiritus Templum (*New Age*), 1603 Perkins Street, Elkhart, IN 46514.

Aquarius Workshops, Inc. (*New Age*), P.O. Box 556, Encino, CA 91426.

Aquinas Institute of Theology (*Catholic*), 2570 Asbury, Dubuque, IA 52001.

The Aramaic Bible Society, Inc., 334 Corey Avenue, P.O. Box 6406, St. Petersburg Beach, FL 33736.

Arbutus Youth Association, P.O. Box 143, San Jose, CA 95103.

Arcana Workshops (*New Age*), 407 North Maple Drive — Suite 214, P.O. Box 5105, Beverly Hills, CA 90210.

Arcane Order (*New Age*), Studio of Contemplation, 2904 Rosemary Lane East, Falls Church, VA 22042.

Arcane School (*New Age*), 866 United Nations Plaza — Suite 566-7, New York, NY 10164.

Archconfraternity of Christian Mothers (*Catholic*), 220 37th Street, Pittsburgh, PA 15201.

Archconfraternity of Our Lady of Perpetual Help and St. Alphonsus (*Catholic*), 526 59th Street, Brooklyn, NY 11220.

Archconfraternity of Perpetual Adoration (*Catholic*), c/o St. John's Abbey, Collegeville, MN 56321.

Archconfraternity of the Holy Ghost (*Catholic*), c/o Holy Ghost Preparatory School, Cornwells Heights, PA 19020.

The Archdiocese of New York of the American Catholic Church, 457 West 144th Street, New York, NY 10031.

Archdiocese of the American Orthodox Catholic Church in the U.S. and Canada, c/o Monastery of St. Gregory, 2803 10th Street, Wyandotte, MI 48192.

Archdiocese of the Old Catholic Church in America, c/o Most Rev. Walter Xavier Brown, 2915 West Highland Blvd., Milwaukee, WI 53208.

ARCHE International (*New Age*), 212 South Marion Street — Suite 27, Oak Park, IL 60302.

Archives of Cooperative Lutheranism, c/o Library of the Lutheran Council in the U.S.A., 315 Park Avenue South, New York, NY 10010.

Archives of the American Catholic Historical Society of Philadelphia, c/o St. Charles Boromeo Seminary, Overbrook, Philadelphia, PA 19151.

Archives of the American Lutheran Church, c/o Wartburg Theological Seminary, 333 Wartburg Place, Dubuque, IA 52001.

Archives of the Brethren in Christ Church, c/o Messiah College, Grantham, PA 17027.

Archives of the Evangelical Lutheran Synod, c/o Bethany Lutheran Theological Seminary, 447 North Division Street, Mankato, MN 56001.

Archives of the Lutheran Church in America, c/o Lutheran School of Theology at Chicago, 1100 East 55th Street, Chicago, IL 60615.

Archives of the Mennonite Church, 1700 South Main, Goshen, IN 46526.

Archives of the Moravian Church, 1228 Main Street, Bethlehem, PA 18018.

Archives of the National Council of the Churches of Christ in the U.S.A., c/o Presbyterian Historical Society, 425 Lombard Street, Philadelphia, PA 19147.

Archives of the Unitarian-Universalist Association, 25 Beacon Street, Boston, MA 02108.

Archives of the United Church of Christ, 555 West James Street, Lancaster, PA 17603.

Archives of the Wisconsin Evangelical Lutheran Synod, 3512 West North Avenue, Milwaukee, WI 53208.

Arctic Missions, Inc., P.O. Box 512, Gresham, OR 97030.

Arianhu Church of Wicca (*Witchcraft*), P.O. Box 69, Dimmitt, TX 79027.

Arica at Pyramid West (*New Age*), P.O. Box 57261, Los Angeles, CA 90057.

Arica Institute (*New Age*), 235 Park Avenue South, New York, NY 10019.

Arithmosophical Society, (See Neo-Pythagorean Gnostic Church).

Arizona Metaphysical Society, 3639 East Clarendon Road, Phoenix, AZ 85018.

Arkansas Council of Churches, 715 West 22nd Street, P.O. Box 6011, Little Rock, AR 72216.

Armenian Apostolic Church of America, 138 East 39th Street, New York, NY 10016.

Armenian Church of North America — Eastern Diocese, 630 Second Avenue, New York, NY 10016.

Armenian Church of North America — Western Diocese, 1201 North Vine Street, Hollywood, CA 90038.

Armenian Church Youth Organization of America, 630 Second Avenue, New York, NY 10016.

Armenian Missionary Association of America, 140 Forest Avenue, Paramus, NJ 07652.

The Arthur Bradford Evangelistic Association, 729 Cleveland Street, Brooklyn, NY 11208.

Arunachala Ashrama (*Hindu*), c/o Bhagavan Sri Ramana Maharshi Center, Inc., 342 East 6th Street, New York, NY 10003.

Arya Maitreya Mandala (*Buddhist*), 214 Sir Francis Drake Blvd., San Anselmo, CA 94960.

Arya Samaj of Southern California (*Hindu*), c/o Mr. B. K. Sharma, President, 1375 Fircroft Avenue North, Covina, CA 91722.

Asatru Free Assembly (*Norse Paganism*), c/o Stephen McNallen, 3400 Village Avenue, Denair, CA 95316.

Asbury Bible Churches, c/o Rev. Jack Tondee, P.O. Box 1021, Dublin, GA 31021.

Ascended Masters Fellowship (*Psychic*), P.O. Box 603, 162 Look-a-Way, Yarnell, AZ 85362.

Ashram West (*New Age*), P.O. Box 5602, Everett, WA 98206.

Assemblies of God (*Pentecostal*), 1445 Boonville Avenue, Springfield, MO 65802.

Assemblies of "The Called Out Ones" of "Yah", 231 Cedar Street, Jackson, TN 38301.

Assemblies of the Church of Jesus Christ (*Pentecostal*), (See Assemblies of the Lord Jesus Christ).

Assemblies of the Lord Jesus Christ (*Pentecostal*), 3034 Summer Avenue, Memphis, TN 38112.

Assemblies of Yahweh, c/o Jacob O. Meyer, Route 1 — Box 200, Bethel, PA 19507.

Assembly of Christian Churches, Inc. (*Pentecostal*), c/o Bethel Christian Temple, Seven West 110th Street, New York, NY 10026.

Assembly of Episcopal Hospitals and Chaplains, c/o Rev. Charles K. Treivhella, Good Samaritan Hospital and Medical Center, 1015 N.W. 22nd Avenue, Portland, OR 97210.

Assembly of Wicca (*Witchcraft*), c/o Duane Landziak, 4715 Franklin Blvd., Sacramento, CA 95820.

The Assembly of Yahvah, 6th and Elm Streets, Junction City, OR 97448.

Assembly of Yahweh, 1010 North Gunnel Road, Eaton Rapids, MI 48827.

Associate Presbyterian Church of North America, (See Reformed Presbyterian Church of North America).

Associate Reformed Presbyterian Church — General Synod, c/o Associate Reformed Presbyterian Center, One Cleveland Street, Greenville, SC 29601.

Associate Reformed Synod (*Presbyterian*), (See Associate Reformed Presbyterian Church — General Synod).

Associated Boards for Christian Colleges in China, (See United Board for Christian Higher Education in Asia).

Associated Brotherhood of Christians (*Pentecostal*), 1151 Fries Avenue, Wilmington, CA 90744.

The Associated Church Press, P.O. Box 306, Geneva, IL 60134.

Associated Churches of Christ Holiness, 1302 East Adams Blvd., Los Angeles, CA 90011.

Associated Churches of God (*Adventist*), (See Association for Christian Development).

Associated Committee of Friends on Indian Affairs (*Religious Society of Friends*), c/o Sterrett Nash, 612 Plum Street, P.O. Box 161, Frankton, IN 46044.

Associated Gospel Churches, P.O. Box 427, South Lyon, MI 48178.

Associated Ministers of Jesus Christ (*Pentecostal*), (See Associated Brotherhood of Christians).

Associated Missionaries, c/o Dr. Luther Davis, 1755 Mabel Street, Ottumwa, IA 52501.

Associated Parishes (*Episcopal*), 3606 Mt. Vernon Avenue, Alexandria, VA 22305.

Associates for Biblical Research, 3328 Paper Mill Road, Huntingdon Valley, PA 19006.

Associates of the Graymoor Ecumenical Institute, Graymoor Ecumenical Institute, Garrison, NY 10524.

Association for Christian Development (*Adventist*), P.O. Box 10903, Winslow Station, Seattle, WA 98110.

Association for Christian Schools, P.O. Box 35096, 4900 Jackwood, Houston, TX 77035.

Association for Christian Training and Service, 1001 18th Avenue South, Nashville, TN 37212.

Association for Clinical Pastoral Education, 475 Riverside Drive — Suite 450, New York, NY 10115.

Association for Creative Change Within Religious and Other Social Systems, P.O. Box 2212, Syracuse, NY 13220.

Association for Holistic Health (*New Age*), P.O. Box 9532, San Diego, CA 92109.

Association for Human Development (*New Age*), c/o Katherine R. Reynolds, P.O. Box 75175, Los Angeles, CA 90075.

Association for Jewish Demography and Statistics, P.O. Box 38190, Wilcox Station, Hollywood, CA 90038.

Association for Jewish Studies, c/o Widener Library, Harvard University, Cambridge, MA 02138.

Association for Professional Education for Ministry, c/o Oliver F. Williams, University of Notre Dame, Notre Dame, IN 46556.

Association for Religious and Value Issues in Counseling, c/o Iona College, 715 North Avenue, New Rochelle, NY 10801.

Association for Research and Enlightenment, Inc. (*Psychic*), P.O. Box 595, 215 67th Street, Virginia Beach, VA 23451.

Association for Social Economics (*Catholic*), c/o DePaul University, 25 East Jackson Blvd., Chicago, IL 60604.

Association for the Coordination of University Religious Affairs, c/o Graham L. Hales, P.O. Box 118, Southern Station, Hattiesburg, MS 39401.

Association for the Development of Religious Information Systems, c/o Department of Theology, Loyola University of Chicago, 6525 North Sheridan Road, Chicago, IL 60626.

Association for the Promotion of Christian Unity, (See Council on Christian Unity).

Association for the Rights of Catholics in the Church, P.O. Box 3932, Philadelphia, PA 19146.

Association for the Sociological Study of Jewry, c/o Department of Sociology, University College, Rutgers University, New Brunswick, NJ 08903.

Association for the Sociology of Religion (*Catholic*), c/o Loyola University of Chicago, 6525 North Sheridan Road, Chicago, IL 60626.

Association for the Understanding of Man (*Psychic*), c/o Ray Stanford, P.O. Box 5310, Austin, TX 78763.

Association for Theological Field Education, P.O. Box 130, Vandalia, OH 45377.

Association of Baptist Professors of Religion, c/o Watson Mills, Department of Christianity, Mercer University, Macon, GA 31207.

Association of Baptists for Evangelism in the Orient, (See Association of Baptists for World Evangelism).

Association of Baptists for World Evangelism, 1720 Springdale Road, P.O. Box 5000, Cherry Hill, NJ 08034.

Association of Catholic Trade Unionists, 58 Washington Square South, New York, NY 10012.

Association of Catholic TV and Radio Syndicators, 1229 South Santee Street, Los Angeles, CA 90015.

Association of Christian Church Educators (*Disciples of Christ*), P.O. Box 1986, Indianapolis, IN 46206.

Association of Christian Churches, 200 West 18th Street, Sioux Falls, SD 57104.

Association of Christian Television Stations, c/o Dr. Lester Sumrall, President, P.O. Box 50250, Indianapolis, IN 46250.

Association of Christians in Secular Careers, P.O. Box 395, Cedar Falls, IA 50613.

Association of Church Missions Committees, 1620 South Myrtle Avenue, Monrovia, CA 91016.

Association of Churches of The Tolerants, P.O. Box 36099, Houston, TX 77036.

Association of Contemplative Sisters (*Catholic*), 920 Centre Street, Jamaica Plain, MA 02130.

Association of Council Secretaries, (See National Association of Ecumenical Staff).

Association of Cymry Wicca (*Witchcraft*), P.O. Box 4152, Athens, GA 30602.

Association of Disciples for Theological Discussion (*Disciples of Christ*), c/o Division of Higher Education, 119 North Jefferson Avenue, St. Louis, MO 63103.

Association of Eastern Religious (*Catholic*), c/o Very Rev. Anthony Skurla, Sybertsville, PA 18251.

Association of Episcopal Colleges, 815 Second Avenue, New York, NY 10017.

Association of Evangelical Friends, (See Evangelical Friends Alliance).

Association of Evangelical Lutheran Churches, 12015 Manchester Road, St. Louis, MO 63131.

Association of Evangelical Presbyterian Churches, (See Evangelical Presbyterian Church — Trenton, MI).

Association of Evangelicals for Italian Mission (*Baptist*), 314 Richfield Road, Upper Darby, PA 19082.

Association of Evangelicals for Missions, c/o Rev. Charles A. Hodgman, 24 Granby Road, Worcester, MA 01604.

Association of Former Christian Scientists, 1550 South Anaheim Blvd., Anaheim, CA 92805.

Association of Free Lutheran Congregations, 3110 East Medicine Lake Blvd., Minneapolis, MN 55441.

Association of Fundamental Gospel Churches (*Brethren*), 9189 Grubb Court, Canton, OH 44721.

Association of Fundamental Ministers and Churches, Inc., 8605 East 55th Street, Kansas City, MO 64129.

Association of Independent Baptist Churches of Illinois, 406 West Kelsey Street, Bloomington, IL 61701.

Association of Independent Methodist Churches, c/o John R. Wright, P.O. Box 4274, Jackson, MS 39216.

Association of International Dianologists, (See Eductivism).

Association of Jesuit Colleges and Universities (*Catholic*), 1717 Massachusetts Avenue, N.W., Washington, DC 20036.

Association of Jewish Anti-Poverty Workers, 18 East 41st Street — Room 806, New York, NY 10017.

Association of Jewish Book Publishers, c/o Dr. Michael Stanislavski, 838 Fifth Avenue, New York, NY 10021.

Association of Jewish Center Workers, 15 East 26th Street, New York, NY 10010.

Association of Jewish Chaplains of the Armed Forces, 15 East 26th Street — Room 1423, New York, NY 10010.

Association of Jewish Community, Municipal and Anti-Poverty Employees, (See Association of Jewish Anti-Poverty Workers).

Association of Jewish Community Relations Workers, 55 West 42nd Street — Suite 1530, New York, NY 10036.

Association of Jewish Libraries, c/o National Foundation for Jewish Culture, 122 East 42nd Street — Room 1512, New York, NY 10017.

Association of Jewish Sponsored Camps, 130 East 59th Street, New York, NY 10022.

Association of Ladies of Charity of the United States (*Catholic*), 7806 Natural Bridge Road, P.O. Box 5730, St. Louis, MO 63121.

Association of Lutheran College Faculties, c/o Carthage College, Kenosha, WI 53141.

Association of Lutheran Secondary Schools, c/o Richard Klatt, Secretary-Treasurer, 3201 West Arizona Avenue, Denver, CO 80219.

Association of Marian Helpers (*Catholic*), c/o Eden Hall, Stockbridge, MA 01262.

Association of Mental Health Clergy, Inc., c/o Rev. George E. Doebler, Executive Director, Lakeshore Mental Health Institute, 5908 Lyons View Drive, Knoxville, TN 37919.

Association of Mental Hospital Chaplains, (See Association of Mental Health Clergy, Inc.).

Association of Methodist Historical Societies, (See Commission on Archives and History of the United Methodist Church).

Association of Orthodox Church Publications, c/o Mrs. Victoria Trbuhovich, P.O. Box 368, Sewickley, PA 15143.

Association of Orthodox Jewish Scientists, 116 East 27th Street, New York, NY 10016.

Association of Orthodox Jewish Teachers, 1577 Coney Island Avenue, Brooklyn, NY 11230.

Association of Pentecostal Assemblies, (See The International Pentecostal Church of Christ).

Association of Presbyterian University Pastors, (See National Campus Ministry Association).

Association of Professional Directors, Young Men's Christian Associations in the United States, 40 West Long Street, Columbus, OH 43215.

Association of Professors and Researchers in Religious Education, c/o Donald F. Williams, Executive Secretary, Chicago Cluster of Theological Schools, 1100 East 55th Street, Chicago, IL 60615.

Association of Professors of Missions, c/o Rev. Robert Schreiter, Catholic Theological Union, 5401 South Cornell Avenue, Chicago, IL 60615.

Association of Reform Zionists in America (*Jewish*), 838 Fifth Avenue, New York, NY 10021.

Association of Regional Religious Communicators, c/o J. G. Taylor, Secretary, Religious Broadcasting Commission of the Pacific Northwest, 521 Wall Street, Seattle, WA 98121.

Association of Religion and Applied Behavioral Science, (See Association for Creative Change Within Religious and Other Social Systems).

Association of Romanian-American Orthodox Ladies' Auxiliaries, 1336 North Plainview Drive, Copley, OH 44321.

Association of Romanian Catholics of America, 4309 Olcott Avenue, East Chicago, IN 46312.

The Association of Sananda and Sanat Kumara (*New Age*), P.O. Box 35, Mt. Shasta, CA 96067.

Association of Secretaries, Young Men's Christian Associations of North America, (See Association of Professional Directors, YMCA's in the U.S.).

Association of Secular Institutes (*Catholic*), (See United States Conference of Secular Institutes).

Association of Seminary Professors in the Practical Fields, (See Association for Professional Education for Ministry).

Association of Seventh-day Adventist Educators, c/o General Conference, Department of Education, 6840 Eastern Avenue, N.W., Washington, DC 20012.

Association of Seventh-day Adventist Institutions of Higher Education of Secondary Schools, (See Association of Seventh-day Adventist Educators).

Association of Seventh-Day Pentecostal Assemblies, 4700 N.E. 119th Street, Vancouver, WA 98665.

Association of Southern Baptist Colleges and Schools, 460 James Robertson Parkway, Nashville, TN 37219.

Association of Statisticians of American Religious Bodies, c/o Otto K. Finkbeiner, Secretary, United Presbyterian Church in the U.S.A., 475 Riverside Drive — Room 1201, New York, NY 10115.

Association of Theological Schools, (See Association of Theological Schools in the United States and Canada).

Association of Theological Schools in the United States and Canada, P.O. Box 130, Vandalia, OH 45377.

Association of Universal Philosophy, Inc. (*New Age*), 309 East Bailey Street, Globe, AZ 85501.

Association of Universalist Women, (See Unitarian Universalist Women's Federation).

Association of Yugoslav Jews in the U.S.A., 247 West 99th Street, New York, NY 10025.

Assumption Guild (*Catholic*), 329 West 108th Street, New York, NY 10025.

Assyrian Orthodox Church, (Archdiocese of the Syrian Church of Antioch), c/o Rev. Elias Sugar, 701 87th Street, North Bergen, NJ 07047.

Assyrian Orthodox Church, (See Holy Apostolic and Catholic Church of the East — Assyrian).

Astara (*New Age*), 800 West Arrow Highway, Upland, CA 91786.

Astara Foundation, (See Astara).

Astral Assembly (*Witchcraft*), c/o Morgan Parrish. Nine Wellington, Everett, MA 02149.

Astra's Garden (*New Age*), 1813 S.W. 23rd Street, Gainesville, FL 32608.

Astro Consciousness Institute (*New Age*), 1627 South Emerson Street, Denver, CO 80210.

Astrological, Metaphysical, Occult, Revelatory, Enlightenment Church (*New Age*), c/o Charles Robert Gordon, Professional Bldg. — Suite 211-212, 147 West Main Street, Meriden, CT 06450.

The Ataraxian Society (*New Age*), P.O. Box 13042-A, Sacramento, CA 95813.

Ateitininkai (*Catholic*), 1443 South 50th Avenue, Cicero, IL 60650.

Ateitis Association of Lithuanian Catholic Intellectuals, 7235 South Sacramento, Chicago, IL 60629.

The Athanor Fellowship (*Neo-Paganism*), P.O. Box 464, Allston, MA 02134.

Atheist Association, P.O. Box 2832, San Diego, CA 92112.

Athletes in Action (*Campus Crusade for Christ*), 1451 East Irvine Blvd. — No. 12, Tustin, CA 92680.

Atlan Foundation, (See Church of All Worlds).

Atlanta Institute of Metaphysics, 5229 Roswell Road, Atlanta, GA 30342.

Atmaniketan Ashram Research Library (*Hindu*), 785 Alcott Avenue, Pomona, CA 91766.

Augustana Evangelical Lutheran Church, (See Lutheran Church in America).

Augustana Historical Society (*Lutheran*), c/o Augustana College, Rock Island, IL 61201.

Augustana Lutheran Church Women, (See Lutheran Church Women).

Augustana Swedish Institute (*Lutheran*), (See Augustana Historical Society).

Augustinian Educational Association (*Catholic*), c/o Villanova University, Villanova, PA 19085.

AUM Center (*New Age*), 9999 Palm Street, Bellflower, CA 90706.

AUM Esoteric Study Center (*New Age*), (See Savitria).

AUM Temple of Universal Truth (*New Age*), 45837 Deva Lane, Newberry Springs, CA 92365.

Autocephalous Slavonic Orthodox Catholic Church (In Exile), c/o Metropolitan-Archbishop Andrew, 2213 Hunter Avenue, Bronx, NY 10475.

Auxiliaries of Our Lady of the Cenacle (*Catholic*), c/o Sr. Agnes Sauer, P.O. Box 494, Carmichael, CA 95608.

Avalon (and Related Jesus People Communities), 174 Portage Drive, Akron, OH 44303.

Avatar Meher Baba Center of Southern California (*Sufism*), 10808 Santa Monica Blvd., Los Angeles, CA 90025.

Awareness Ashram (*New Age*), c/o Patricia James, 2101 Cove Avenue, Los Angeles, CA 90039.

The Awareness Research Foundation, Inc. (*Psychic*), 1518 Lee Street, Hollywood, FL 33020.

Babylonian Church, (See Holy Apostolic and Catholic Church of the East — Assyrian).

Bachard Organization (*Jewish*), (See Bnei Akiva of North America).

Back to the Bible Broadcast, (See The Good News Broadcasting Association, Inc.).

Back to the Bible Way, 517 N.E. Second Street, Ft. Lauderdale, FL 33301.

Baha'i Faith, National Spiritual Assembly, 536 Sheridan Road, Wilmette, IL 60091.

Baha'i Publishing Trust, 415 Linden Avenue, Wilmette, IL 60091.

Balance, Inc. (*Lutheran*), c/o Walther Memorial Lutheran Church, 4040 West Fond du Lac Avenue, Milwaukee, WI 53216.

The Banner of Truth Trust, P.O. Box 621, Carlisle, PA 17013.

Baptist Bible Fellowship, International, 730 East Kearney, Springfield, MO 65803.

Baptist Bible Union, (See General Association of Regular Baptist Churches).

Baptist Brotherhood of the South, (See Southern Baptist Convention, Brotherhood Commission).

Baptist Foreign Mission Convention, (See National Baptist Convention, U.S.A.).

Baptist General Conference, 2002 South Arlington Heights Road, Arlington Heights, IL 60005.

Baptist International Missions, Inc., c/o Dr. Tom Wallace, President, Beth Haven Baptist Church, 5515 Johnsontown Road, Louisville, KY 40272.

Baptist Joint Committee on Public Affairs, 200 Maryland Avenue, N.E., Washington, DC 20002.

Baptist Life Association, 8555 Main Street, Buffalo, NY 14221.

Baptist Mid-Missions, 4205 Chester Avenue, Cleveland, OH 44103.

Baptist Missionary Association, (See American Baptist Association).

Baptist Missionary Association of America, c/o Rev. Ralph Cottrell, Secretary, P.O. Box 2866, Texarkana, AR 75501.

Baptist Pacifist Fellowship, (See Baptist Peace Fellowship).

Baptist Peace Fellowship, c/o Olive M. Tiller, 528 Cumberland Avenue, Teaneck, NJ 07666.

Baptist Public Relations Association (*Southern Baptist Convention*), 460 James Robertson Parkway, Nashville, TN 37219.

Baptist World Alliance, 1628 16th Street, N.W., Washington, DC 20009.

Baptist World Mission, 811 2nd Avenue, S.E., Decatur, AL 35601.

Baptist World Relief, 1628 16th Street, N.W., Washington, DC 20009.

Baseball Chapel, Inc., P.O. Box 8382, Madeira Beach, FL 33738.

Basic Bible Church of America, P.O. Box 1708, Twin City Airport, MN 55111.

Bavarian Illuminati (*Occult*), c/o R.A. Wilson, 1437 Polk Street, San Francisco, CA 94109.

Bawa Muhaiyaddeen Fellowship, 5820 Overbrook Avenue — Room 3, Philadelphia, PA 19131.

Beachy Amish Mennonite Churches, c/o Ervin N. Hershberger, R.D. 1, Meyersdale, PA 15552.

Bear Tribe Medicine Society (*Native American*), P.O. Box 9167, Spokane, WA 99209.

Behold, Inc., c/o Ruth Carter Stapleton, Route 1 — Box H, Denton, TX 76201.

Bell Trust (*Church of Christ*), P.O. Box 20097, 2361 Northwest Highway, West, Dallas, TX 75220.

Belz Hasidim (*Jewish*), c/o Rabbi Michael Halberstam, 1523 56th, Brooklyn, NY 11219.

Ben Haden Evangelical Association, P.O. Box 100, Chattanooga, TN 37401.

Ben Israel Ministries, Route 2 — Box 276, Laporte, MN 56461.

Bendheim Foundation (*Jewish*), (See Charles and Els Bendheim Foundation).

Benedictine Liturgical Conference, (See The Liturgical Conference).

The Benevolent Fraternity of Unitarian Churches, 110 Arlington Street, Boston, MA 02116.

Bennu Phoenix Temple of the Hermetic Order of the Golden Dawn (*Occult*), c/o John Phillips Palmer, P.O. Box 36, River Road, Lumberville, PA 18933.

Benny Hinn Evangelistic Association, c/o Calvary Assembly, 1199 Clay Street, Winter Park, FL 32789.

Bentz Foundation (*Catholic*), 2569 Berwick Blvd., Columbus, OH 43209.

Berachah Church, 5139 West Alabama, Houston, TX 77056.

Berean Bible Fellowship, 52nd and East Virginia Streets, Phoenix, AZ 85008.

Berean Bible Society, 7609 West Belmont, Chicago, IL 60635.

Berean Fundamental Church, P.O. Box 628, North Platte, NE 69101.
Berean Gospel Fellowship (*Pentecostal*), P.O. Box 207, Baldwin Park, CA 91706.
Berean Mission, Inc., 3536 Russell Blvd., St. Louis, MO 63104.
Berean Research Fellowship, P.O. Box 708, Carpinteria, CA 93013.
The Berkeley Center for Human Interaction (*New Age*), 1816 Scenic Avenue, Berkeley, CA 94709.
Berkeley Christian Coalition, P.O. Box 2418, Berkeley, CA 94702.
Berkeley Free Church, P.O. Box 9177, Berkeley, CA 94709.
Beth Din of America (*Jewish*), 1250 Broadway, New York, NY 10001.
Beth-Shalom Society, P.O. Box 704, Hamilton, OH 45012.
Bethany Bible Church and Related Independent Bible Churches of the Phoenix (Arizona) Area, 6060 North Seventh Avenue, Phoenix, AZ 85013.
Bethany Christian Services, 901 Eastern, N.E., Grand Rapids, MI 49503.
Bethany Fellowship, Inc., 6820 Auto Club Road, Minneapolis, MN 55438.
Bethany Union for Young Women (*Unitarian Universalist*), 256 Newbury Street, Boston, MA 02116.
Bethel Baptist Assembly, (See Bethel Ministerial Association, Inc.).
"the Bethel Family", (See Jehovah's Witnesses).
Bethel Ministerial Association, Inc. (*Pentecostal*), P.O. Box 5353, Evansville, IN 47715.
Bethel Temple (*Pentecostal*), 2033 Second Avenue, Seattle WA 98121.
Bethesda Christian Center, P.O. Box 1215, Wenatchee, WA 98801.
Bethesda Mission, Inc. (*Grace Gospel Fellowship*), c/o Harry Rosbottom, Executive Director, 3745 26th Avenue South, Minneapolis, MN 55406.
Bethesda Temple Church, Inc., P.O. Box 39, Hot Springs, AR 71901.
The Better Humanity League (*New Age*), P.O. Box 885, Tarzana, CA 91356.
Bhagavan Sri Ramana Maharshi Center (*Hindu*), 342 East 6th Street, New York, NY 10003.
Bible and Medical Missionary Fellowship, 241 Fairfield Avenue, Upper Darby, PA 19082.
Bible Believers' Evangelistic Association, Route 3 — Box 92, Sherman, TX 75090.
Bible Christian Union, P.O. Box 718, Lebanon, PA 17042.
The Bible Church of Christ, Inc., 1358 Morris Avenue, Bronx, NY 10456.
Bible Church of God (*Adventist*), 826 East Ninth Street, Des Moines, IA 50316.
Bible Churches (Classics Expositor), c/o Dr. C. E. McLain, 1429 N.W. 100th, Oklahoma City, OK 73114.
Bible Club Movement, 237 Fairfield Avenue, Upper Darby, PA 19082.
Bible Fellowship Church, 2340 Union Street West, Allentown, PA 18104.
The Bible For You, Inc., c/o Dr. Manford Gutzke, President, P.O. Box 15007, Atlanta, GA 30333.
Bible Holiness Mission, (See Bible Holiness Movement).
Bible Holiness Movement, P.O. Box 714, Kent, WA 98031.
Bible Literature International, P.O. Box 477, Columbus, OH 43216.
Bible Meditation League, (See Bible Literature International).
Bible Memory Association, International, 1298 Pennsylvania Avenue, St. Louis, MO 63130.
Bible Methodist Church (*Holiness*), (See Bible Methodist Connection of Churches).
Bible Methodist Connection of Churches (*Holiness*), c/o Rev. Jarrette D. Young, 1705 Columbia Avenue, Middletown, OH 45042.

Bible Methodist Connection of Tennessee (*Holiness*), P.O. Box 10408, Knoxville, TN 37919.

Bible Missionary Church (*Holiness*), 1824 Jones Street, Duncan, OK 73533.

Bible Missionary Union (*Holiness*), (See Bible Missionary Church).

Bible-Pathway Ministries, c/o John A. Hash, Director, P.O. Box 1515, Murfreesboro, TN 37130.

Bible Presbyterian Church, 756 Haddon Avenue, Collingswood, NJ 08108.

The Bible Protestant Church, c/o Rev. Marshall Weatherby, Executive Secretary, R.D. 1 — Box 12, Port Jervis, NY 12771.

The Bible Sabbath Association, Fairview, OK 73737.

Bible Science Association, 2911 East 42nd Street, Minneapolis, MN 55406.

Bible Standard Church, Inc. (*Pentecostal*), (See Open Bible Standard Churches, Inc.).

Bible Study League of America, 3240 North High Street, Columbus, OH 43202.

Bible Tracts, Inc., P.O. Box 508, Waterloo, IA 50704.

Bible Translations on Tape, Inc., c/o W. Paul Smith, President, 712 Cedar Street, Cedar Hill, TX 75104.

Bible Way Church of Our Lord Jesus Christ World Wide, Inc. (*Pentecostal*), 1130 New Jersey Avenue, N.W., Washington, DC 20001.

Bibles for Africa, Falls Church, VA 22042.

Bibles for the World, 1300 Crescent Street, Wheaton, IL 60187.

Bibles to China, c/o Wesley Smith, P.O. Box 7000, Seymour, IN 47274.

Biblical Archaeology Society, 3111 Rittenhouse Street, N.W., Washington, DC 20015.

Biblical Evangelism, c/o Dr. Robert L. Sumner, Director, P.O. Box 1513, Murfreesboro, TN 37130.

Biblical Research Institute, 799 Broadway, New York, NY 10003.

Biblical Research Society, c/o David L. Cooper, Jr., President, 4005 Verdugo Road, Los Angeles, CA 90065.

Biblical Theologians, c/o Beaver College, Glenside, PA 19038.

Biennial Council of Community Churches, (See National Council of Community Churches).

Big Kahara Association (*Pentecostal*), (See United Holy Church of America, Inc.).

Bill Basansky Ministries, P.O. Box 7333, Tulsa, OK 74105.

Billy Graham Center at Wheaton College, Wheaton, IL 60187.

Billy Graham Evangelistic Association, 1300 Harmon Place, Minneapolis, MN 55403.

Billy James Hargis Ministries, (See Christian Crusade).

Bishop Baraga Association (*Catholic*) 239 Baraga Avenue, Marquette, MI 49855.

Bishops' Commission for Ecumenical Affairs (*Catholic*), (See Bishops' Committee for Ecumenical and Interreligious Affairs).

Bishops's Committee for Ecumenical and Interreligious Affairs (*Catholic*), 1312 Massachusetts Avenue, N.W., Washington, DC 20005.

Bishops' Committee for Migrant Workers (*Catholic*), (See Secretariat for Hispanic Affairs).

Bishops' Committee for the Spanish Speaking (*Catholic*), (See Secretariat for Hispanic Affairs).

Bishops' Committee on Priestly Formation (*Catholic*), 1312 Massachusetts Avenue, N.W., Washington, DC 20005.

Bishops' Committee on Scouting (*Catholic*), (See National Catholic Committee on Scouting).

Bishops' Committee on the Liturgy (*Catholic*), 1312 Massachusetts Avenue, N.W., Washington, DC 20005.

Bishop's Helpers (*Catholic*), c/o Kathleen Toups, President, 732 St. Louis Street, Lafayette, LA 70506.

Black American Baptist Churchmen, c/o Rev. Amos C. Brown, Third Baptist Church, 1399 McAllister, San Francisco, CA 94115.

Black Christian Education Resources Center, 475 Riverside Drive — 7th Floor, New York, NY 10115.

Black Christian Nationalist Church, c/o Shrine of the Black Madonna, 13535 Livernois, Detroit, MI 48238.

Black Educational Resources Center, (See Black Christian Education Resources Center).

Black Methodists for Church Renewal, Inc. (*United Methodist*), c/o Mrs. Thelma D. Barnes, Executive Director, 890 Beckwith Street, S.W., Atlanta, GA 30314.

The Blaisdell Institute (*New Age*), 143 East Tenth Street, Claremont, CA 91711.

Blank Family Foundation (*Jewish*), (See Samuel Blank and Family Foundation).

Blessed Eymard League (*Catholic*), (See Eymard League).

Blessed Martin Guild (*Catholic*), (See St. Martin de Porres Guild).

Blessed Martin Spiritual Church, 694 Pryor Street, S.W., Atlanta, GA 30315.

The Blue Army of Our Lady of Fatima (*Catholic*), c/o Ave Maria Institute, Mountain View Road, Washington, NJ 07882.

Blue Card (*Jewish*), 2121 Broadway, New York, NY 10023.

Blue Mountain Center of Meditation (*Hindu*), P.O. Box 477, Petaluma, CA 94952.

Blue Ridge Christian Writers Conference, c/o Yvonne Lehman, P.O. Box 188, Black Mountain, NC 28711.

Blue Sky Vegetarian Commune (*New Age*), 2523 Toner Avenue, Allison Park, PA 15101.

Blue Star Grove (*Witchcraft*), 3803 Hunterspoint Avenue, Long Island City, Queens, NY 11101.

The Blumenthal Foundation for Charity, Religion, Education and Better Inter-Faith Relations, P.O. Box 10628, Charlotte, NC 28237.

B. M. Woltman Foundation (*Lutheran*), 2200 West Loop South, Houston, TX 77027.

B'nai B'rith Career and Counseling Services (*Jewish*), 1640 Rhode Island Avenue, N.W., Washington, DC 20036.

B'nai B'rith Hillel Foundation (*Jewish*), 1640 Rhode Island Avenue, N.W., Washington, DC 20036.

B'nai B'rith International (*Jewish*), 1640 Rhode Island Avenue, N.W., Washington, DC 20036.

B'nai B'rith Vocational Service (*Jewish*), (See B'nai B'rith Career and Counseling Services).

B'nai B'rith Women (*Jewish*), 1640 Rhode Island Avenue, N.W., Washington, DC 20036.

B'nai B'rith Youth Organization (*Jewish*), 1640 Rhode Island Avenue, N.W., Washington, DC 20036.

B'nai Yiddish Society (*Jewish*), 41 Union Square, New York, NY 10003.

Bnai Zion (*Jewish*), 136 East 39th Street, New York, NY 10016.

Bnei Akiva of North America (*Jewish*), 25 West 26th Street, New York, NY 10010.

Bnei Yeshivos (*Jewish*), G.P.O. Box 2141, Brooklyn, NY 11202.
Board for International Missions of the Evangelical and Reformed Church, (See United Church Board for World Ministries).
Board of Church and Society of the United Methodist Church, 100 Maryland Avenue, N.E., Washington, DC 20002.
Board of Hospitals and Homes of the Methodist Church, (See National Association of Health and Welfare Ministries of the United Methodist Church).
Board of International Ministries (*American Baptist Churches in the U.S.A.*), (See American Baptist Foreign Mission Society).
Board of Jewish Education of Greater New York, 426 West 58th Street, New York, NY 10019.
Bodaiji Mission (*Buddhist*), 1251 Elm, Honolulu, HI 96814.
Bodha Society of America, Inc. (*New Age*), c/o Violet Reed, P.O. Box 144, Long Beach, CA 90801.
Body of Christ (B'nai Shalom) (*Pentecostal*), c/o Gospel of Peace Camp Ground, 5607 South 7th Street, Phoenix, AZ 85040.
Boise Christian Outreach, P.O. Box 3356, Boise, ID 83703.
Bold Bible Living (*Pentecostal*), P.O. Box 2, Blaine, WA 98230.
Bonhoeffer Society, c/o Geffrey B. Kelly, Secretary, Department of Religion, La Salle College, 20th Street and Olney Avenue, Philadelphia, PA 19141.
Book of Mormon Foundation, c/o Robert Maley, 3644 South Louisville, Tulsa, OK 74135.
Born Again Club, 261 N.E. 23rd Street, Miami, FL 33137.
Boston Theological Institute, 210 Herrick Road, Newton Centre, MA 02159.
Boston University Institute for Philosophy and Religion, 745 Commonwealth Avenue, Boston, MA 02215.
Boston Vedanta Center, (See Ananda Ashrama).
The Boston Visionary Cell (*New Age*), c/o Paul Laffoley, President, 36 Bromfield Street — Room 200, Boston, MA 02108.
The Bowery Mission, 40 Overlook Drive, Chappaqua, NY 10514.
Boy Savior Youth Movement (*Catholic*), c/o St. Francis Xavier Church, 30 West 16th Street, New York, NY 10011.
Brahma Kumaris Raja Yoga Center (*Hindu*), 11600 Atlantic Avenue, Lynwood, CA 90262.
Brandeis Institute (*Jewish*), 1101 Peppertree Lane, Brandeis, CA 93064.
Brandeis Institute of the West (*Jewish*), (See Brandeis Institute).
Brant Baker Ministries, P.O. Box 590, Glendale, CA 91209.
Brazil Gospel Fellowship Mission, c/o Larry Lipka, Executive Secretary, 121 North Glenwood, Springfield, IL 62702.
Brazilian Missions, 25283 Cabot Road — Suite 222, Laguna Hills, CA 92653.
Bread for Children, Inc., P.O. Box 1017, Arcadia, FL 33821.
Bread for the World, 32 Union Square East, New York, NY 10003.
Breitenbush Hot Springs Community (*New Age*), P.O. Box 578, Detroit, OR 97342.
Brethren Church (Ashland, Ohio), 524 College Avenue, Ashland, OH 44805.
Brethren in Christ Church, c/o Dr. Arthur M. Climenhaga, General Secretary, 1093 Twp. Road No. 1704, R.D. 4, Ashland, OH 44805.
Brethren in Christ Fellowship, Edmon, PA 15630.
Brethren Peace Fellowship, 777 South Mt. Joy Street, Elizabethtown, PA 17022.
The Bridge Meditation Center, P.O. Box 808, Riverdale, GA 30274.

Bridge to Freedom, Inc. (*New Age*), Kings Park, Hicksville, NY 11754.
"Brinsers", (See United Zion Church).
Brite Christian Writers Conference, c/o Mary Brite, 321 Warbler Drive, Bedford, TX 76021.
Brith Abraham Foundation (*Jewish*), 136 East 39th Street, New York, NY 10016.
Brith Sholom (*Jewish*), 1235 Chestnut Street, Philadelphia, PA 19107.
Broadcasting and Film Commission (*National Council of Churches*), (See Communication Commission).
The Brotherhood of Eternal Truth (*New Age*), 1002 East Market Street, New Albany, IN 47150.
The Brotherhood of the Followers of the Present Jesus (*New Age*), P.O. Box 16264, San Diego, CA 92116.
Brotherhood of Light, (See Church of Light; see also Etherian Religious Society of Universal Brotherhood).
Brohterhood of Peace and Tranquility, (Church of the Brotherhood), P.O. Box 2142, Costa Mesa, CA 92626.
Brotherhood of St. Andrew (*Episcopal*), P.O. Box 21, York, PA 17405.
Brotherhood of the American Lutheran Church, (See American Lutheran Church Men).
Bortherhood of the Evangelical Lutheran Church, (See American Lutheran Church Men).
Brotherhood of the New Order (*New Age*), 543 5th Street, West Des Moines, IA 50265.
Brotherhood of the Pleroma, P.O. Box 5220, Sherman Oaks, CA 91403.
Brotherhood of the Spirit (*Communal*), Shepardson Road, Warwick, MA 01378.
Brotherhood of the Sun (*Communal*), 8080 East Cota Street, Santa Barbara, CA 93103.
Brotherhood of the Way of the Cross (*Episcopal*), c/o Rev. Nigel Lyon Andrews, 81 Elm Street, Concord, MA 01742.
Brotherhood of the White Temple (*Occult*), Sedalia, CO 80135.
Brotherhood of Wicca (*Witchcraft*), (See Association of Cymry Wicca).
Brothers of Saint Francis of Assisi, c/o Regina Pacis Seminary and Devotional Center, 19 Central Avenue, Ravena, NY 12143.
Bubbling Well Church of Universal Love, Inc., c/o Bubbling Well Pet Memorial Park, 2462 Atlas Peak Road, Napa, CA 94558.
Bud Chambers International Revival Crusades, P.O. Box 123, Oklahoma City, OK 73101.
Buddha Yoga Association, 23 East 16th Street, New York, NY 10003.
Buddha's Universal Church, 702 Washington Street, San Francisco, CA 94108.
Buddha's Universal Church and Ch'an Buddhist Sangha, c/o Dr. Calvin Chan Vassallo, 3507¹/₂ Louisiana, Houston, TX 77002.
Buddhist Association of America, 109 Waverly Place, San Francisco, CA 94108.
The Buddhist Association of the United States, 3070 Albany Crescent, Bronx, NY 10463.
Buddhist Churches of America, 1710 Octavia Street, San Francisco, CA 94109.
The Buddhist Cultural Institute, 140 East 63rd Street, New York, NY 10021.
Buddhist Fellowship of New York, c/o Buddhist Church, 331 Riverside Drive, New York, NY 10025.
Buddhist Information Center of San Diego, 4611 Georgia Street — No. 7, San Diego, CA 92116.

Buddhist Mission of North America, (See Buddhist Churches of America).

Buddhist Science, c/o Dr. George L. Messier, III, 1874 Broad Street, Cranston, RI 02910.

Buddhist Society of America, (See First Zen Institute of America, Inc.).

Buddhist Vihara Society, Inc., 5017 16th Street, N.W., Washington, DC 20011.

Buffalo Synod (*Lutheran*), (See The American Lutheran Church).

Builders of the Adytum (*Occult*), 5105 North Figueroa Street, Los Angeles, CA 90042.

Bulgarian Eastern Orthodox Church, Diocese of North and South America and Australia, 1953 Stockbridge Road, Akron, OH 44313.

The Bulgarian Eastern Orthodox Church, Diocese of the U.S.A. and Canada, 519 Brynhaven Drive, Oregon, OH 43616.

Bureau of Catholic Indian Missions, 2021 H Street, N.W., Washington, DC 20006.

Bureau of Jewish Social Research, (See Council of Jewish Federations, Inc.).

Bureau on Jewish Employment Problems, 220 South State Street, Chicago, IL 60604.

Business and Professional ORT (*Jewish*), 817 Broadway, New York, NY 10003.

The Byelorussian Autocephalic Orthodox Church, 401 Atlantic Avenue, Brooklyn, NY 11217.

Byelorussian (White Ruthenian) Patriarchate of St. Andrew the Apostle, the First Called, c/o Most Rev. Uladyslau Ryzy-Ryski, Wren Place, Shrub Oak, NY 10588.

Calcutta Mission of Mercy, 1717 South Puget Sound, Tacoma, WA 98405.

California Babaji Yoga Sangam (*Hindu*), 11305 Alondra Blvd., Norwalk, CA 90650.

California Bosatsukai (*Buddhist*), c/o Nakagawa Soen Roshi, 5632 Green Oak Drive, Los Angeles, CA 90068.

California Church Council, 1300 N Street, Sacramento, CA 95814.

California Council of Spiritualist Ministers, c/o Rev. Gayle Eaton, President, 5819½ Laurel Canyon, North Hollywood, CA 91607.

California Evangelistic Association (*Pentecostal*), 1800 East Anaheim Blvd., Long Beach, CA 90813.

California Institute of Asian Studies (*Hindu*), 3494 21st Street, San Francisco, CA 94110.

California New Age Caucus, 3725 Midvale Avenue — No. 3, Los Angeles, CA 90034.

Calix Society (*Catholic*), c/o R. D. Dickinson, 7601 Wayzata Blvd., Minneapolis, MN 55426.

Calumet Pagan Temple (*Neo-Paganism*), c/o Richard Clarke, 1519 Kenilworth, Calumet City, IL 60409.

Calvary Chapels, P.O. Box 8000, Costa Mesa, CA 92626.

Calvary Crusades (*Baptist*), P.O. Box 2293, Columbus, GA 31902.

Calvary Fellowships, Inc., c/o Woodbrook Soul Winning Bible School, 14815 Spring Street, S.W., Tacoma, WA 98439.

Calvary Grace Christian Churches of Faith, c/o Dr. Herman Keck, Jr., 5610 Tennessee Avenue, Chattanooga, TN 37409.

Calvary Grace Churches of Faith, Inc., P.O. Box 333, Rillton, PA 15678.

Calvary Holiness Church, 3423 North Second Street, Philadelphia, PA 19140.

Calvary Holiness Church of Britain, (See Church of the Nazarene).
CAM International, 8625 LaPrada Drive, Dallas, TX 75228.
Cambridge Buddhist Association, Three Craigie Street, Cambridge, MA 02138.
Cambridge Center for Social Studies, (See Jesuit Center for Social Studies).
Campaign for Human Development (*Catholic*), c/o United States Catholic Conference, 1312 Massachusetts Avenue, N.W., Washington, DC 20005.
Campaign for Surplus Rosaries (*Catholic*), 1821 West Short 17th Street, North Little Rock, AR 72114.
Camps Farthest Out, Inc., 1569 Grand Avenue, St. Paul, MN 55105.
Campus Crusade for Christ International, Arrowhead Springs, San Bernardino, CA 92414.
Campus Ministry Association, (See National Campus Ministry Association).
Campus Ministry Communications, c/o Lutheran Council in the U.S.A., 35 East Wacker Drive — Suite 1847, Chicago, IL 60601.
Campus Ministry Women, 802 Monroe, Ann Arbor, MI 48104.
Canaan Farm, RFD Box 55, Canaan, NY 12029.
Canon Law Society of America (*Catholic*), 1933 Spielbusch Avenue, Toledo, OH 43624.
The Canterbury Guild, c/o St. Timothy's Anglican Church, 68½ Queen Street, Charleston, SC 29401.
Cantors Assembly (*Jewish*), 150 5th Avenue, New York, NY 10011.
Cape Fear Conference of Free Will Baptists, (See The Pentecostal Free Will Baptist Church, Inc.).
Cardinal Mindszenty Foundation (*Catholic*), P.O. Box 11321, St. Louis, MO 63105.
Caring Cancer Ministry, P.O. Box 1315, Abilene, TX 79604.
Carolina Baptist Fellowship, (See South Carolina Baptist Fellowship).
Carolina Evangelistic Association (*Pentecostal*), 200 Tuckaseegee Road, Charlotte, NC 28208.
The Carroll Center for the Blind, 770 Centre Street, Newton, MA 02158.
Carroll Rehabilitation Center for the Visually Handicapped, (See The Carroll Center for the Blind).
Carver Foreign Missions, Inc., c/o Dr. W. D. Hungerpiller, 65 Haynes Street, S.W., P.O. Box 92091, Atlanta, GA 30313.
Cathedral of Tomorrow, (See The Rex Humbard Ministry).
Catholic Actors Guild of America, 227 West 45th Street, New York, NY 10036.
Catholic Aid Association, 49 West Ninth Street, St. Paul, MN 55102.
Catholic Alliance for Communications, c/o Archdiocese of New York, 1011 First Avenue, New York, NY 10022.
Catholic Alumni Clubs, International, 50 Baker Avenue, Quincy, MA 02169.
Catholic Apostolate of Radio, Television and Advertising, 1011 First Avenue, New York, NY 10022.
Catholic Apostolic Church, 417 West 57th Street, New York, NY 10019.
Catholic Apostolic Church — Eastern Orthodox, 3585 Fourth Avenue, San Diego, CA 92103.
Catholic Association of Foresters, 347 Commonwealth Avenue, Boston, MA 02115.
Catholic Audio-Visual Educators Association, P.O. Box 7195, Pittsburgh, PA 15213.
Catholic Bible Society of America, Inc., P.O. Box 2296, Dallas, TX 75221.

Catholic Biblical Association, Catholic University of America, Washington, DC
20064.
Catholic Big Brothers, 1011 First Avenue, New York, NY 10022.
Catholic Big Sisters, Inc., 60 Lafayette Street, New York, NY 10013.
Catholic Board for Mission Work Among the Colored People, (See Catholic
Negro-American Mission Board).
Catholic Business Education Association, (See National Catholic Business Edu-
cation Association).
Catholic Business Educational Association, (See National Catholic Educational
Association).
Catholic Campus Ministry Association, 3700 West 103rd Street, Chicago, IL
60655.
Catholic Central Union, (See Catholic Order of Foresters).
Catholic Central Union of America, 3835 Westminster Place, St. Louis, MO
63108.
Catholic Central Verein of America, (See Catholic Central Union of America).
Catholic Charismatic Renewal, c/o Dr. Kevin Ranaghan, 237 North Michigan
Street, South Bend, IN 46601.
Catholic Church Extension Society, 35 East Wacker Drive, Chicago, IL 60601.
Catholic Church of the East (Chaldean-Syriac Rite), Province of North and
South America, Two Coronado Avenue — Suite 21, Daly City, CA 94015.
Catholic Commission on Intellectual and Cultural Affairs, 620 Michigan
Avenue, N.E., Washington, DC 20064.
Catholic Committee of Appalachia, 31-A South Third Avenue, Prestonsburg,
KY 41653.
Catholic Committee on Scouting, (See National Catholic Committee on
Scouting).
Catholic Committee on Urban Ministry, c/o Rev. Philip J. Murnion, Chair-
man, P.O. Box 544, Notre Dame, IN 46556.
Catholic Conference on Ethnic and Neighborhood Affairs, 1521 16th Street,
N.W., Washington, DC 20036.
Catholic Congress Organization (*Episcopal*), (See The American Church Union).
Catholic Convert Club, (See National Guilds of St. Paul).
Catholic Counselors in the American Personnel and Guidance Association, (See
Association for Religious and Value Issues in Counseling).
Catholic Daughters of America, 10 West 71st Street, New York, NY 10023.
Catholic Economic Association, (See Association for Social Economics).
The Catholic Evangelical League (*Eastern Orthodox, Loyal Anglicans, Polish National
Catholic*), c/o Herbert J. Mainwaring, 13 Terrane Avenue, Natick, MA 01760.
Catholic Evidence Guild, 127 West 31st Street, New York, NY 10001.
Catholic Family Life Insurance, 1572 East Capitol Drive, Milwaukee, WI
53211.
Catholic Family Missionary Alliance, c/o Our Lady of the Angels Monastery,
5817 Old Leeds Road, Birmingham, AL 35210.
Catholic Fine Arts Society, 57 Chestnut Street, Binghamton, NY 13905.
Catholic Guardian Society, 1011 First Avenue, New York, NY 10022.
Catholic Guild for All the Blind, (See The Carroll Center for the Blind).
Catholic Home Bureau for Dependent Children, 1011 First Avenue, New York,
NY 10022.
The Catholic Hospital Association, 1438 South Grand Blvd., St. Louis, MO
63104.

Catholic Institute of the Food Industry, P.O. Box 192, Baldwin, Long Island, NY 11510.

Catholic Institute of the Press, (See Catholic Alliance for Communications).

Catholic Interracial Council of Chicago, 1307 South Wabash Avenue, Chicago, IL 60605.

Catholic Interracial Council of New York, Inc., 225 East 52nd Street, New York, NY 10022.

Catholic Knights Insurance Society, 1100 West Wells Street, Milwaukee, WI 53233.

Catholic Knights of America, 3525 Hampton Avenue, St. Louis, MO 63139.

Catholic Knights of St. George, 709 Brighton Road, Pittsburgh, PA 15233.

Catholic Kolping Society of America, 2003 Wintergreen Avenue, Mt. Prospect, IL 60056.

Catholic League, 1200 North Ashland Avenue, Chicago, IL 60622.

Catholic League for Religious and Civil Rights, 1100 West Wells Street, Milwaukee, WI 53233.

Catholic League for Religious Assistance to Poland, 1200 North Ashland Avenue, Chicago, IL 60622.

Catholic Library Association, 461 West Lancaster Avenue, Haverford, PA 19041.

Catholic Life Insurance Union, 1635 N.E. Loop — No. 410, San Antonio, TX 78209.

Catholic Medical Mission Board, 10 West 17th Street, New York, NY 10011.

Catholic Microfilm Center, c/o Graduate Theological Union Library, 2452 Virginia Street, Berkeley, CA 94709.

Catholic Mission Radio Association, (See International Mission Radio Association).

Catholic Near East Welfare Association, 1011 First Avenue, New York, NY 10022.

The Catholic Negro-American Mission Board, 335 Broadway — Room 1102, New York, NY 10013.

Catholic Order of Foresters, 305 West Madison Street, Chicago, IL 60606.

Catholic Pamphlet Society, 2171 Fillmore Avenue, Buffalo, NY 14214.

Catholic Peace Fellowship 339 Lafayette Street, New York, NY 10012.

Catholic Press Association of the U.S., Inc., 119 North Park Avenue, Rockville Centre, NY 11570.

Catholic Relief Service — U.S. Catholic Conference, 1011 First Avenue, New York, NY 10022.

Catholic Relief Services — National Catholic Welfare Conference, (See Catholic Relief Service — U.S. Catholic Conference).

Catholic Renascence Society, c/o Viterbo College, LaCrosse, WI 54601.

Catholic Scholarships for Negroes, c/o Mrs. R. L. Putnam, 73 Chestnut Street, Springfield, MA 01103.

Catholic School Press Association, c/o College of Journalism, Marquette University, 615 North 11th Street, Milwaukee, WI 53233.

Catholic Theological Society of America, c/o Edward H. Konerman, Secretary, St. Mary of the Lake Seminary, Mundelein, IL 60060.

Catholic Traditionalist Movement, c/o Fr. Gommar A. de Pauw, 210 Maple Avenue, P.O. Box 781, Westbury, L.I., NY 11590.

Catholic Truth Society, 2816 East Burnside Street, Portland, OR 97214.

Catholic Union of the Sick in America, 176 West 8th Street, Bayonne, NJ 07002.

Catholic War Veterans of the U.S.A., Two Massachusetts Avenue, N.W., Washington, DC 20001.

Catholic War Veterans of the U.S.A., Ladies Auxiliary, Two Massachusetts Avenue, N.W., Washington, DC 20001.

Catholic Women for the ERA, 2222 Kroger Bldg., 1014 Vine Street, Cincinnati, OH 45202.

Catholic Worker Movement, 36 East First Street, New York, NY 10003.

Catholic Workman, (Katolicky Delnik), P.O. Box 47, New Prague, MN 56071.

Catholic Writers' Guild of America, 65 East 89th Street, New York, NY 10028.

Catholics for Christian Political Action, 1139 National Press Bldg., Washington, DC 20045.

Catholics United for the Faith, 222 North Avenue, New Rochelle, NY 10801.

The Cauldron of Cerridwen (*Witchcraft*), 3006 Julia, Tampa, FL 33609.

CBM International, (See Christian Blind Mission International).

Center For Advanced Biblical Studies, (See Probe Ministries, International).

Center for Applied Research in the Apostoloate (*Catholic*), P.O. Box 29150, Washington, DC 20017.

The Center for Attitudinal Healing (*New Age*), 23 East Main Street, Tiburon, CA 94920.

Center for Black Church Union, c/o Dr. John H. Satterwhite, 1814 Tamarack Street, N.E., Washington, DC 20012.

Center for Contemporary Celebration, 410 South Cornell Avenue, Villa Park, IL 60181.

Center for Creative Resources, 1107 Marshall, Houston, TX 77006.

Center for Credology (*New Age*), Two Pennsylvania Plaza, New York, NY 10001.

Center for Holocaust Studies, c/o Dr. Yaffa Eliach, Director, 1609 Avenue J, Brooklyn, NY 11230.

Center for Inner Awareness (*New Age*), P.O. Box 966, Bellflower, CA 90706.

Center for Inner Motivation and Awareness (*New Age*), 3569 4th Avenue, P.O. Box 3561, San Diego, CA 92103.

Center for Law and Religious Freedom, P.O. Box 2069, 820 Ontario, Oak Park, IL 60303.

Center for Meta-Wisdom (*New Thought*), c/o Dr. Carroll Holloway, 21901 Dupont Street — No. 1, Chatsworth, CA 91311.

Center for Pastoral Liturgy, c/o The Catholic University of America, Washington, DC 20064.

Center for Reformation Research, 6477 San Bonita Avenue, St. Louis, MO 63105.

Center for Religion, Education and Society (*New Age*), 25 West 25th Avenue, San Mateo, CA 94403.

Center for Social Action, (See Office for Church in Society).

Center for Spiritual Awareness (*New Age*), Lake Rabun Road, Lakemont, GA 30552.

Center for Studies in Awareness (*New Age*), 644 South Bundy Drive, Los Angeles, CA 90049.

Center for the Healing Arts (*New Age*), 11081 Missouri Avenue, Los Angeles, CA 90025.

Center for the Study of American Catholicism, c/o Memorial Library — Room 1109, University of Notre Dame, Notre Dame, IN 46556.

The Center for the Study of Campus Ministry (*Lutheran*), c/o Rev. Phil Schroeder, Director, Valparaiso University, Valparaiso, IN 46383.

Center for the Study of Judaism, c/o Jacob Neusner, Director, Brown University, Providence, RI 02912.

The Center for the Study of Southern Culture and Religion, 236 Williams Bldg., Florida State University, Tallahassee, FL 32306.

Center for the Study of Spirituality (*Catholic*), c/o Institute of Man, Duquesne University, Pittsburgh, PA 15219.

Center for the Study of the Future (*New Age*), 4110 N.E. Alameda, Portland, OR 97212.

Center for the Study of World Religions, 42 Francis Avenue, Cambridge, MA 02138.

Center for Theological Study, c/o California Lutheran College, Thousand Oaks, CA 91360.

Center for Theology and Public Policy, 4400 Massachusetts Avenue, N.W., Washington, DC 20016.

Center for World Peace (*New Age*) 635 North Hampton Road, Dallas, TX 75208.

Center of Concern, c/o William F. Ryan, S. J. , Director, 3700 13th Street, N.E., Washington, DC 20017.

The Center of Light (*New Age*), P.O. Box 540, Great Barrington, MA 01230.

Center of Light and Truth (*New Age*), c/o Dr. Kenneth W. Turner, 3360 Fourth Street, Boulder, CO 80302.

Central Alaska Friends Conference (*Unaffiliated*), P.O. Box 252, Fairbanks, AK 99707.

Central Alaskan Missions, Inc., Glennallen, AK 99588.

Central American Mission International, (See CAM International).

Central Association of the Miraculous Medal (*Catholic*), 475 East Chelten Avenue, Philadelphia, PA 19144.

Central Baptist Association, c/o Dana M. Crawford, 726 Hollis Street, Kingsport, TN 37660.

Central Bureau for the Jewish Aged, 225 Park Avenue South, New York, NY 10003.

Central Conference of American Rabbis (*Jewish-Reform*), 790 Madison Avenue, New York, NY 10021.

Central Premonitions Registry, P.O. Box 482, Times Square Station, New York, NY 10036.

Central Rabbinical Congress (*Jewish*), 603 Bedford Avenue, Brooklyn, NY 11211.

Central Yearly Meeting of Friends (*Unaffiliated*), 302 South Black Street, Alexandria, IN 46001.

Centro Hispano Catolico (*Catholic*), 130 Northeast Second Street, Miami, FL 33132.

Centurion Door, (See Truth Station).

The Chamber of Holy Voodoo, P.O. Box 341, Lenox Hill Station, New York, NY 10021.

C.H.A.O.S. Ltd., (Research and Information Service on Cults, Heresies, and Occult Sects), P.O. Box 6224, Oakland, CA 94603.

Chaplains' Aid Association, Inc. (*Catholic*), 1011 First Avenue, New York, NY 10022.

Chaplains Association of the American Protestant Hospital Association, (See College of Chaplains).

Chaplains' Association of the Army of the United States of America, (See Military Chaplains Association of the U.S.A.).

Chardavogne Barn (*Gurdjieff*), Chardavogne Road, Warwick, NY 10990.

Charis Life Ministries (*Lutheran*), P.O. Box 12201, Portland, OR 97212.

Charismatic Communion of Presbyterian Ministers, (See Presbyterian Charismatic Communion).

Charismatic Renewal Services (*Catholic*), 237 North Michigan Street, South Bend, IN 46601.

Charismatic Singles, P.O. Box 429, Coatesville, PA 19320.

Charismatic Writers Association, 237 North Michigan Street, South Bend, IN 46601.

Charles and Els Bendheim Foundation (*Jewish*), 10 Columbus Circle, New York, NY 10019.

Charles E. Fuller Institute of Evangelism & Church Growth, P.O. Box 989, Pasadena, CA 91102.

Charles Trombley Ministries, 500 North Elm Place, Broken Arrow, OK 74012.

Chela Center (*Hindu*), 614 East Atlantic Blvd., Pompano Beach, FL 33060.

Chemdah Coven (*Witchcraft*), c/o Levanah Shell Bdolak, 556 46th Street, Oakland, CA 94609.

Chesterfield Hypnotherapy Center (*Psychic*), Woods Mill Towers — Suite N408, Chesterfield, MO 63017.

Chicago Bible Students, P.O. Box 6016, Chicago, IL 60680.

Chicago Circle of Occult Sorcery, c/o James J. Kohler, 2158 West Barry Avenue, Chicago, IL 60618.

Chicago Hebrew Mission, (See American Messianic Fellowship).

Chicago Religious Institute, c/o Prof. Philip Harley, Director, Garrett-Evangelical Theological Seminary, 2121 Sheridan Road, Evanston, IL 60201.

Chidvilas Rajneesh Meditation Center (*Hindu*), 154 Valley Road, Montclair, NJ 07042.

Child Evangelism Fellowship, P.O. Box 348, Warrenton, MO 63383.

Children of God, (also known as Family of Love), P.O. Box 704, Lynwood, CA 90262.

Children of Light, Star Route — Box 39, Dateland, AZ 85333.

Children of Light Reunion, P.O. Box 2103, San Jose, CA 95109.

The Children of the Dawn (*Neo-Paganism*), 1017 Dartmouth, N.E., Albuquerque, NM 87106.

Children of the Moon, 4611 Upshur, Bladensburg, MD 20710.

Children of the Universe, c/o Rev. David Rupp, 1118 Lonesome Road, Nokesville, VA 22123.

Children to Palestine, (See Fellowship in Israel for Arab-Jewish Youth).

Children's Haven International, c/o Lee and Shirley Mendoza, Directors, 514 South Cage Blvd., Pharr, TX 78577.

China Graduate School of Theology, Inc., 817 Silver Spring Avenue — Room 404, Silver Spring, MD 20910.

China Inland Mission, (See Overseas Missionary Fellowship).

China Inland Mission Overseas Missionary Fellowship, (See Overseas Missionary Fellowship).

Chinese-American New Testament Missionary Fellowship, 1055 Bingle Road, Houston, Tx 77055.

Chinese Buddhist Association, 42 Kawananakoa Place, Honolulu, HI 96817.

Chinese Christian Church of New England, 62 Tyler Street, Boston, MA 02111.

Chinese Christian Fellowship, Inc., 549 West 123rd Street, New York, NY 10027.

Chinese Christian Mission, c/o Rev. Mark Kor Cheng, General Secretary, 3503 Petaluma Blvd., North, Petaluma, CA 94952.

Chinese for Christ, Inc., 510 North Bunker Hill Avenue, Los Angeles, CA 90012.

Chinese Gospel Crusade, Inc., P.O. Box 420595, Miami, Fl 33142.

Chinese Outreach, 1238 North Edgemont, Los Angeles, CA 90029.

Chinmaya Mission — West (*Hindu*), P.O. Box 2753, Napa, CA 94558.

Chirothesian Church of Faith (*New Age*), 1747 North Normandie Avenue, Los Angeles, CA 90027.

Chosen Vessels, c/o Elder Anna S. Krieter, 1030 E Street, San Diego, CA 92101.

Chowado Henjo Kyo (*Buddhist*), c/o Rev. Reisai Fujita, 1757 Algaroba Street, Honolulu, HI 96826.

C.H.R.I.S.T., (Christians Helping Resist Insidious Satanic Teachings), P.O. Box 2722, Pasco, WA 99302.

Christ Brotherhood, Inc., c/o Tarna L. Halsey, P.O. Box 244, Logan, UT 84321.

Christ Catholic Church, c/o Most Rev. Karl Pruter, 1638 Granville Avenue, Chicago, IL 60660.

Christ Catholic Exarchate of Americas and Eastern Hemisphere, c/o Most Rev. Peter A. Zurawetzky, 946 Leesville Avenue, Rahway, NJ 07065.

Christ Centered Ministries, c/o Dr. David Forbes Morgan, P.O. Box 824, Denver, CO 80201.

Christ Faith Mission (*Pentecostal*), 6026 Echo, Los Angeles, CA 90042.

Christ for Everyone, Inc., c/o Paul A. Stewart, Director, P.O. Box 200, Belmont, MI 49306.

Christ for the Cults, P.O. Box 4295, Santa Clara, CA 95050.

Christ for the Nations, Inc., P.O. Box 24910, Dallas, TX 75224.

Christ Gospel Churches (*Pentecostal*), Jeffersonville, IN 47130.

Christ Light Community, c/o Dr. Gilbert N. Holloway, Star Route 2, Deming, NM 88030.

Christ Metaphysical Church, Inc., c/o Rev. William Lawson Lamb, P.O. Box 4677, Tampa, FL 33677.

Christ Ministry Foundation (*Psychic*), P.O. Box 9543, San Jose, CA 95157.

Christ Truth Foundation, 711 S.W. Alder Street, Portland, OR 97205.

Christ Truth League (*New Thought*), 2400 Canton, Fort Worth, TX 76112.

Christ Universal Temple (*New Thought*), 8601 South State Street, Chicago, IL 60619.

The Christadelphians, c/o H. P. Zilmer, 1002 Webster Lane, Des Plaines, IL 60016.

Christadelphians-Amended, P.O. Box 1066, Pasadena, CA 91102.

Christananda, 977 Asbury, San Jose, CA 95126.

Christian Action Council, 788 National Press Bldg., Washington, DC 20045.

Christian Aid Mission, 5028 Wisconsin Avenue, N.W., Washington, DC 20016.

Christian Alliance, (See The Christian and Missionary Alliance).

The Christian and Missionary Alliance (*Holiness*), 350 North Highland Avenue, Nyack, NY 10960.

Christian Answers and Information, P.O. Box 3295, Chico, CA 95927.

Christian Anti-Communism Crusade, 124 East First Street, Long Beach, CA 90802.

Christian Anti-Narcotic Association, (See Shepherds Fold Ministries).

Christian Apologetics Project, P.O. Box 105, Absecon, NJ 08201.

Christian Apologetics: Research and Information Service, P.O. Box 2067, Costa Mesa, CA 92626.

Christian Apostolic Church (Forrest, Illinois), c/o Elder Peter Schaefer, Sr., Forrest, IL 61741.

Christian Apostolic Church (Sabetha, Kansas), c/o Elder Ben Edelman, Sabetha, KS 66534.

Christian Appalachian Project, 217 Lexington Street, Lancaster, KY 40444.

Christian Artists, P.O. Box 1984, Thousand Oaks, CA 91360.

Christian Assembly (*New Thought*), 72 North Fifth Street, San Jose, CA 95112.

Christian Association for Psychological Studies, c/o University Hills Christian Center, 27000 Farmington Road, Farmington Hills, MI 48018.

Christian Believers Conference, 1828 South 47th Court, Cicero, IL 60650.

Christian Bible Society, Nashville, TN 37210.

Christian Blind Mission International, 1506 East Roosevelt Road, P.O. Box 175, Wheaton, IL 60187.

Christian Booksellers Association, 2620 Venetucci Blvd., P.O. Box 200, Colorado Springs, CO 80901.

Christian Brethren, (See Plymouth Brethren).

The Christian Broadcasting Network, Inc., CBN Center, Virginia Beach, VA 23463.

Christian Brothers Education Association (*Catholic*), (See Regional Education Council of the Christian Brothers).

Christian Business Men's Committee of U.S.A., P.O. Box 3380, Chattanooga, TN 37404.

Christian Camping International, P.O. Box 400, Somonauk, IL 60552.

Christian Catholic Church, Dowie Memorial Drive, Zion, IL 60099.

Christian Century Foundation, 407 South Dearborn Street, Chicago, IL 60605.

Christian Children's Associates, Inc., c/o Jean Donaldson, President, 820 Ocean View Drive, Toms River, NJ 08753.

Christian Children's Fund, Inc., P.O. Box 26511, Richmond, VA 23261.

Christian Church (Disciples of Christ), 222 South Downey Avenue, P.O. Box 1986, Indianapolis, IN 46206.

Christian Church of North America (*Pentecostal*), Route 18 & Rutledge Road, Box 141-A — R.D. No. 1, Transfer, PA 16154.

Christian Churches and Churches of Christ, 3533 Epley Lane, Cincinnati, OH 45239.

Christian Churches and Churches of Christ, National Missionary Convention, P.O. Box 177, Kempton, IN 46049.

Christian Communication, 150 South Los Robles — Suite 600, Pasadena, CA 91101.

Christian Communication Council of Metropolitan Detroit Churches, 1300 Mutual Bldg., 28 West Adams, Detroit, MI 48226.

Christian Communications, Inc., P.O. Box 80, Scottsdale, AZ 85252.

The Christian Community (*Anthroposophical*), (Movement for Religious Renewal), 309 West 74th Street, New York, NY 10023.

Christian Conference of Connecticut, 60 Lorraine Street, Hartford, CT 06105.
The Christian Congregation, Inc., 804 West Hemlock Street, LaFollette, TN 37766.
The Christian Coptic Fellowship, P.O. Box 25, 1174 West Grand River, Okemos, MI 48864.
Christian Counseling & Educational Foundation, 1790 East Willow Grove Avenue, Philadelphia, PA 19118.
Christian Crusade, c/o Dr. Billy James Hargis, P.O. Box 977, Tulsa, OK 74102.
Christian Culture Society, P.O. Box 325, Kokomo, IN 46901.
Christian Data Center, P.O. Box 7031, Van Nuys, CA 91409.
Christian Dental Society, c/o Dr. Everett C. Claus, Executive Secretary, 5235 Skytrail, Littleton, CO 80123.
Christian Dental Society, (See Interchurch Medical Assistance).
Christian Destiny, Inc., P.O. Box 100, Wheaton, IL 60187.
Christian Echoes National Ministry, (See Christian Crusade).
Christian Evangelizers Association, P.O. Box 747, Joplin, MO 64801.
Christian Evidence League, P.O. Box 173, Malverne, NY 11565.
Christian Family Crusades, P.O. Box 1199, Bridgeton, NJ 08302.
Christian Family Movement, 2500 New York Avenue, P.O. Box 792, Whiting, IN 46394.
Christian Family Renewal, P.O. Box 73, Clovis, CA 93612.
Christian Feminists, 11618 Gail Street, Wheaton, MD 20902.
Christian Freedom Foundation, Inc., 7960 Crescent Avenue, Buena Park, CA 90620.
Christian Government Movement, 804 Penn Avenue, Pittsburgh, PA 15221.
Christian Graduate Studies Foundation, P.O. Box 12791, Seattle, WA 98111.
Christian Growth Ministries, P.O. Box 22888, Ft. Lauderdale, FL 33335.
Christian Healing Foundation, Inc., c/o Mrs. Myrtle M. Rawlings, President, P.O. Box 384, Annapolis, MD 21404.
Christian Health Ministry, 14319 Burke Avenue North, Seattle, WA 98133.
Christian Herald Ministries, 40 Overlook Drive, Chappaqua, NY 10514.
Christian Holiness Association, Seven Lawrence Avenue, Stanhope, NJ 07874.
Christian Homesteading Movement, Oxford, NY 13830.
The Christian Information Network, Inc., P.O. Box 421, Pine Lake, GA 30072.
Christian Information Service, P.O. Box 1048, Rochester, NY 14603.
Christian Institute for Psychotherapeutic Studies, 183 Broadway, Hicksville, NY 11801.
Christian Interfaith Media Evaluation Center, Ltd., 432 Park Avenue South, New York, NY 10016.
Christian Israelite Church, 1204 North Rural Street, Indianapolis, IN 46201.
The Christian Jew Foundation, 611 Broadway, San Antonio, TX 78215.
Christian Joy Fellowship, P.O. Box 8448, Jacksonville, FL 32211.
Christian Labor Association of the U.S.A., 9820 Gordon Street, P.O. Box 65, Zeeland, MI 49464.
Christian Laity Counseling Board, 5901 Plainfield Drive, Charlotte, NC 28215.
Christian Law Association, P.O. Box 30290, Cleveland, OH 44130.
Christian Law Institute, c/o Herbert J. Porras, Jr., Secretary, 1138 First City National Bank, Southwest Center, El Paso, TX 79901.
Christian Laymans Counseling Board, 5901 Plainfield Drive, Charlotte, NC 28215.

Christian League, P.O. Box 2607, El Cajon, CA 92021.
Christian League of Southern Africa, 1012 City Avenue, Philadelphia, PA 19151.
Christian Legal Defense & Educational Foundation, Inc., P.O. Box 2771, Garland, TX 75041.
Christian Legal Society, P.O. Box 2069, 820 Ontario, Oak Park, IL 60303.
Christian Life, Inc., Gundersen Drive and Schmale Road, Wheaton, IL 60187.
Christian Literature Crusade, Inc., 701 Pennsylvania Avenue, Fort Washington, PA 19034.
Christian Literature International, P.O. Box 777, Canby, OR 97013.
Christian Media Network, P.O. Box 20121, Minneapolis, MN 55420.
Christian Medical Foundation International, Inc., 4821 Memorial Highway, Tampa, FL 33614.
Christian Medical Society, P.O. Box 689, 1616 Gateway Blvd., Richardson, TX 75080.
Christian Mental Health Society, Inc., 1038 N.E. 4th Avenue, Ft. Lauderdale, FL 33304.
Christian Methodist Episcopal Church, c/o Rev. N. Charles Thomas, Secretary, P.O. Box 74, Memphis, TN 38101.
Christian Ministries International, c/o Ron Carlson, President, 7601 Superior Terrace, Eden Prairie, MN 55344.
A Christian Ministry in the National Parks, c/o Dr. Warren Ost, Director, 222¹/₂ East 49th Street, New York, NY 10017.
Christian Ministry to Cults, P.O. Box M-507, Hoboken, NJ 07030.
Christian Missionary Fellowship, P.O. Box 26306, Indianapolis, IN 46226.
Christian Missions in Many Lands (*Plymouth Brethren*), P.O. Box 13, Spring Lake, NJ 07762.
Christian Motorcyclists Association, c/o Herb Shreve, Director, Hatfield, AR 71945.
Christian Nation Church U.S.A. (*Holiness*), c/o Rev. Clarence Ratcliff, General Secretary, P.O. Box 458, Hinton, WV 25951.
Christian Nation Evangelists (*Holiness*), (See Christian Nation Church U.S.A.).
Christian Nationalist Crusade, P.O. Box 202, Eureka Springs, AR 72632.
Christian Nationals Evangelism Commission, Inc., c/o Allen B. Finley, President, 1470 North 4th Street, San Jose, CA 95112.
Christian News Service, P.O. Box 6001, Grand Rapids, MI 49506.
Christian Pilgrim Church (*Holiness*), Coldwater, MI 49036.
Christian Pilots Association, c/o Howard Payne, President, P.O. Box 1988, West Covina, CA 91793.
Christian Prison Volunteers, c/o Duane Pederson, P.O. Box 80, San Juan Capistrano, CA 92693.
Christian Record Benevolent Association, (See Christian Record Braille Foundation).
Christian Record Braille Foundation, 4444 South 52nd Street, Lincoln, NE 68516.
Christian Reformed Church, 2850 Kalamazoo Avenue, S.E., Grand Rapids, MI 49508.
Christian Renewal Ministry, 428 N.W. 34th Street, Oklahoma City, OK 73118.
Christian Research, c/o Gerda Koch, Director, 279 Spring Street, Eureka Springs, AR 72632.

The Christian Research Alliance, P.O. Box 160165, Sacramento, CA 95816.
Christian Research Associates, P.O. Box 10,000, Denver, CO 80210.
Christian Research Institute, P.O. Box 500, San Juan Capistrano, CA 92693.
Christian Restoration Association (*Christian Churches and Churches of Christ*), 5664 Cheviot Road, Cincinnati, OH 45239.
Christian Retreat, (See Gospel Crusade, Inc.).
Christian Rose Cross Church, 5218 Rumac Street, S.E., Olympia, WA 98503.
Christian Rural Overseas Program (*National Council of Churches*), (See CROP).
Christian Salvage Mission, 200 Free Street, Fowlerville, MI 48836.
Christian School of the Arts, c/o American Baptist Assembly, Green Lake, WI 54941.
Christian Schools International, 865 28th Street, S.E., Grand Rapids, MI 49508.
Christian Science, (See Church of Christ, Scientist).
Christian Service Brigade, P.O. Box 150, Wheaton, IL 60187.
Christian Service Club, 2110 Enterprise Street, S.E., Grand Rapids, MI 49508.
Christian Service Corps, P.O. Box 56518, Washington, DC 20011.
Christian Services Fellowship, Inc., c/o Donald W. Moore, General Director, 5716 Benton Avenue, Minneapolis, MN 55436.
Christian Singles, (Pen Pal Club), P.O. Box 203, Union City, CA 94587.
Christian Society for Drama, 3041 Broadway, New York, NY 10027.
Christian Solidarity International, 12906 Matey Road, Wheaton, MD 20906.
Christian Spirit Center (*Spiritualism*), P.O. Box 114, Elon College, NC 27244.
Christian Spiritual Alliance, c/o Roy Eugene Davis, Director, P.O. Box 7, Rabun Road, Lakemont, GA 30552.
Christian Studies Center, P.O. Box 11110, Memphis, TN 38111.
Christian Success Institute, P.O. Box 25487, Cleveland, OH 44125.
Christian Theatre Artist Guild, One Groveland Terrace, Minneapolis, MN 55403.
Christian Union, P.O. Box 38, Excelsior Springs, MO 64024.
Christian Unity Baptist Association, c/o Elder Thomas T. Reynolds, Thomasville, NC 27360.
Christian Universalist Church of America, P.O. Box 323, Deerfield Beach, FL 33441.
"Christian Vedanta", (See Foundation for Inner Peace).
Christian Vegetarian Transformation Movement, P.O. Box 102, Abington, MA 02351.
Christian Voice, 413 Forest, Pacific Grove, CA 93950.
Christian Voters Victory Fund, 418 C Street, N.E., Washington, DC 20002.
Christian Women's Fellowship, P.O. Box 1986, Indianapolis, IN 46206.
The Christian Workers Foundation, 3577 Bankhead Avenue, Montgomery, AL 36111.
Christian World Liberation Front, P.O. Box 4309, Berkeley, CA 94704.
Christian Writers' Fellowship, P.O. Box 1708, Brooksville, FL 33512.
Christian Writers Grand Ole Workshop, c/o Dr. John Warren Steen, 6511 Currywood Drive, Nashville, TN 37205.
Christian Writers' Guild, c/o Norman Rohrer, Director, P.O. Box 707, La Canada, CA 91011.
Christian Writers' Institute, 396 East St. Charles Road, Wheaton, IL 60187.
Christian Writers' League of America, c/o Noel and Jean Dudley, 1604 East Taylor, Harlingen, TX 78550.

Christian Writers' Seminar, P.O. Box 8682, Waco, TX 76710.

Christian Writers' Workshop, (See Christian School of the Arts).

Christians Fellowship International, P.O. Box 10388, Bradenton, FL 33507.

Christians in Action, c/o Lee Shelley, President, P.O. Box 7271, Long Beach, CA 90807.

Christians United in Action, P.O. Box 28, Monrovia, CA 91016.

Christians United in Global Outreach, P.O. Box 71748, Los Angeles, CA 90001.

Christine Temple of Learning (*Psychic*), P.O. Box 5464, Rockford, IL 61125.

Christmount Christian Assembly, Inc. (*Disciples of Christ*), Route 1 — Box 38-E, Black Mountain, NC 28711.

Christology, (See Institute of Esoteric Transcendentalism).

Christology Church (*Psychic*), 1821 Bacon Street, San Diego, CA 92107.

Christopher Career Guidance School (*Catholic*), (See Gabriel Richard Institute).

The Christophers (*Catholic*), 12 East 48th Street, New York, NY 10017.

Christos Lavatus, P.O. Box 5806, Spartanburg, SC 29304.

Christ's Church (*Mormon*), c/o Gerald Wilbur Peterson, P.O. Box 1327, Provo, UT 84601.

Christ's Faith Mission (*Pentecostal*), P.O. Box 68, Highland Park Station, Los Angeles, CA 90042.

Christ's Love Retreat, (See The Teachings of the Angelic Host Within the Kingdom of Heaven).

Christ's Mission, P.O. Box 176, Hackensack, NJ 07602.

Christ's Sanctified Holy Church (*Holiness*), South Cutting Avenue & East Spencer Street, Jennings, LA 70546.

Christ's Sanctified Holy Church (West Columbia, S.C.) (*Holiness*), c/o CSHC Campground, Perry, GA 31069.

Christ's Truth Church and School of Wisdom (*New Age*), P.O. Box 356, Columbus, NM 88029.

Chung Fu Kuan, (See Taoist Sanctuary).

Church and School of Christian Philosophy (*New Thought*), 6017 East Hollyhock, Phoenix, AZ 85018.

Church and Society (*Episcopal*), P.O. Box 359, Ambler, PA 19002.

Church and Synagogue Library Association, P.O. Box 1130, Bryn Mawr, PA 19010.

Church Architectural Guild of America, (See Interfaith Forum on Religion, Art and Architecture).

Church Army in the U.S.A., (See National Institute for Lay Training).

Church Army Society (*Episcopal*), Eight Beach Street, Brockton, MA 02402.

Church Association for Seamen's Work, (See Seamen's Church Institute of New York).

Church by Christ Jesus Fellowship, P.O. Box 41, Brenham, TX 77833.

The Church Center for the United Nations, 777 United Nations Plaza, New York, NY 10017.

The Church Federation of Greater Chicago, 111 East Wacker Drive — Suite 510, Chicago, IL 60601.

Church for Positive Directions (*New Age*), c/o Dr. Gene Steele, P.O. Box 4336, Valley Village Station, North Hollywood, CA 91607.

Church for the Fellowship of All People, 2041 Larkin Street, San Francisco, CA 94109.

Church Historical Society (*Episcopal*), (See Historical Society of the Episcopal Church).

Church Leadership Resources (*United Church of Christ*), P.O. Box 179, St. Louis, MO 63166.

Church League of America, 422 North Prospect Street, Wheaton, IL 60187.

Church Literature Foundation (*Episcopal*), (See Living Church Foundation).

Church Men of the United Evangelical Lutheran Church, (See American Lutheran Church Men).

Church Music Association of America (*Catholic*), 548 Lafond Avenue, St. Paul, MN 55103.

Church Music Publishers Association, P.O. Box 4239, Washington, DC 20012.

Church of Ageless Wisdom (*Psychic*), (See The International Church of Ageless Wisdom).

Church of All Christian Faiths, 4222 East Lincoln Drive, Paradise Valley, AZ 85253.

Church of All Religions, (See Self-Realization Fellowship).

Church of All Worlds (*Neo-Paganism*), c/o Forever Forests, P.O. Box 212, Redwood Valley, CA 95470.

Church of All Worlds Atlanta Nest (*Neo-Paganism*), P.O. Box 9721, Atlanta, GA 30319.

Church of Antioch (Ashram West), P.O. Box 5A, Orcas, WA 98280.

Church of Antioch, Malabar Rite (*Liberal Catholic*), c/o Most Rev. H. Adrian Spruit, P.O. Box 1015, Mountain View, CA 94042.

Church of Armageddon (*Communal*), c/o Love Israel, 617 West McGraw Street, Seattle, WA 98119.

Church of Awareness, 920 Annette, Socorro, NM 87801.

Church of Basic Truth (*Psychic*), P.O. Box 6084, Phoenix AZ 85005.

Church of Bible Understanding, 607 West 51st Street, P.O. Box 841, Radio City Station, New York, NY 10019.

Church of Christ (Bronson) (*Mormon*), P.O. Box 146, Independence, MO 64051.

Church of Christ (Burt) (*Mormon*), P.O. Box 1165, Colorado Springs, CO 80901.

Church of Christ (Fetting) (*Mormon*), c/o Holland J. Davis, Route 2 — Box 94, Morton, MS 39117.

Church of Christ (Holden, Missouri) (*Mormon*), Route 1 — Box 37, Holden, MO 64040.

Church of Christ (Holiness) U.S.A., 329 East Monument Street, Jackson, MS 39202.

Church of Christ (Lukeite) (*Mormon*), 723 South Crysler, Independence, MO 64052.

Church of Christ (Morton, Mississippi) (*Mormon*), Route 1 — Box 160, Morton, MS 39117.

Church of Christ (Temple Lot) (*Mormon*), River & Lexington Blvd., P.O. Box 472, Independence, MO 64051.

Church of Christ at Zion's Retreat (*Mormon*), c/o Gerald A. Hall, Schell City, MO 64783.

Church of Christ in God, (See Church of the Living God).

Church of Christ, Scientist (*New Thought*), c/o Christian Science Church Center, 107 Falmouth Street, Boston, MA 02115.

Church of Christ with the Elijah Message (*Mormon*), c/o Rev. James W. Savage, 608 Lacy, Independence, MO 64050.

Church of Christian Liberty, 203 East McDonald Road, Prospect Heights, IL 60070.

Church of Circle Wicca (*Witchcraft*), P.O. Box 9013, Madison, WI 53715.

Church of Cosmic Light, Inc., c/o Rev. Elizabeth J. Fifield, Secretary, 1101 Bay Street, Santa Monica, CA 90405.

Church of Cosmic Origin & School of Thought (*Psychic*), P.O. Box 257, June Lake, CA 93529.

The Church of Cosmic Power (*New Age*), P.O. Box 75175, Los Angeles, CA 90075.

Church of Daniel's Band (*Holiness*), c/o Rev. Wesley Hoggard, President, R.F.D. 2, Midland, MI 48640.

The Church of Divine Knowledge (*New Age*), 659 South St. Andrews Place, Los Angeles, CA 90005.

The Church of Eductivism, (See Eductivism).

Church of Essential Science (*Spiritualist*), P.O. Box 4055, Scottsdale, AZ 85258.

Church of General Psionics (*Psychic*), 204 North Catalina Avenue, Redondo Beach, CA 90277.

Church of Gentle Brothers and Sisters (*New Age*), 486 Clipper Street, San Francisco, CA 94114.

Church of God and Saints of Christ (*Black Jews*), c/o Bishop Howard Z. Plummer, P.O. Box 187, Portsmouth, VA 23705.

Church of God (Anderson, Indiana) (*Holiness*), P.O. Box 2420, Anderson, IN 46011.

Church of God (Apostolic) (*Holiness*), c/o St. Peter's Church of God — Apostolic, 11th Street and Highland Avenue, Winston-Salem, NC 27101.

Church of God at Cleveland, Ohio (*Adventist*), P.O. Box 02026, Cleveland, OH 44102.

Church of God — Bible Beacon (*Adventist*), 430 Live Oak Street, Edgewater, FL 32032.

Church of God, Body of Christ (*Adventist*), c/o Elder Ivan W. Igames, Route 1 — Box 86, Mocksville, NC 27028.

Church of God by Faith (*Pentecostal*), 3220 Haines Street, Jacksonville, FL 32206.

Church of God (Cleveland, Tennessee) (*Pentecostal*), Keith at 25th Street, N.W., Cleveland, TN 37311.

Church of God For Answered Prayer, Inc., c/o Rev. Peter E. Ione, P.O. Box 50, Carmichael, CA 95608.

Church of God General Conference (Oregon, Illinois), P.O. Box 100, Oregon, IL 61061.

Church of God (Guthrie, Oklahoma) (*Holiness*), c/o Faith Publishing House, 920 West Mansur Avenue, Guthrie, OK 73044.

Church of God (Holiness), 7415 Metcalf Avenue, Overland Park, KS 66204.

The Church of God House of Prayer (*Pentecostal*), c/o Rev. Charles MacNevin, Markleysburg, PA 15459.

The Church of God in Christ (*Pentecostal*), 938 Mason Street, Memphis, TN 38126.

Church of God in Christ, Congregational (*Pentecostal*), 918 Bond Avenue, East St. Louis, IL 62201.

The Church of God in Christ, International (*Pentecostal*), 170 Adelphi Street, Brooklyn, NY 11205.

Church of God in Christ, Mennonite, 420 North Wedel Street, Moundridge, KS 67107.

Church of God in the Lord Jesus Christ, 810 East Walnut Street, Pasadena, CA 91101.

Church of God Incarnate (Ramnian), 1642 North Wilcox Avenue, Hollywood, CA 90028.

The Church of God, International (*Adventist*), P.O. Box 2525, Tyler, TX 75710.

Church of God (Jerusalem Acres) (*Pentecostal*), P.O. Box 1207, Jerusalem Acres, Cleveland, TN 37311.

The Church of God of Prophecy (*Pentecostal*), Bible Place, Cleveland, TN 37311.

Church of God of the Abrahamic Faith, (See Church of God General Conference — Oregon, Illinois).

Church of God of the Apostolic Faith (*Pentecostal*), 13334 East 14th Street, Tulsa, OK 74108.

Church of God of the Mountain Assembly (*Pentecostal*), Florence Avenue, Jellico, TN 37762.

Church of God of the Union Assembly, Inc. (*Pentecostal*), P.O. Box 1323, Dalton, GA 30720.

Church of God, Sabbatarian (*Adventist*), P.O. Box 1134, Hawthorne, CA 90250.

Church of God (Sanctified Church) (*Holiness*), 1037 Jefferson Street, Nashville, TN 37208.

The Church of God (7th Day) (*Adventist*), 79 Water Street, P.O. Box 328, Salem, WV 26426.

Church of God (Seventh Day) (*Adventist*), P.O. Box 33677, Denver, CO 80233.

Church of God Seventh Era (*Adventist*), c/o Larry Gilbert Johnson, P.O. Box A-1, Cabot, AR 72023.

Church of God, The Eternal (*Adventist*), P.O. Box 775, Eugene, OR 97440.

Church of God, The House of Prayer (*Pentecostal*), Cleveland, TN 37311.

The Church of God (U.S. Headquarters) (*Pentecostal*), 2504 Arrow Wood Drive, Huntsville, AL 35803.

Church of God (Which He Purchased with His Own Blood), 1628 N.E. 50th, Oklahoma City, OK 73111.

Church of Gospel Ministry, 486 Skyhill Court, Chula Vista, CA 92012.

Church of Health, 3308 Midway Drive — Suite 267, San Diego, CA 92110.

The Church of Holistic Gardeners (*New Age*), P.O. Box 636, Ramona, CA 92065.

The Church of Holy Light, P.O. Box 4478, Pittsburgh, PA 15205.

Church of Illumination (*Psychic*), Beverly Hall, Clymer Road, Quakertown, PA 18951.

The Church of Inner Light (*Psychic*), c/o Rev. Trudy Jarno, 1557 South Barrington Avenue, West Los Angeles, CA 90025.

Church of Inner Wisdom (*New Thought*), c/o Joan Gibson, P.O. Box 4765, San Jose, CA 95159.

Church of Jesus (*Pentecostal*), (See Jesus Church).

The Church of Jesus Christ (*Pentecostal*), 5336 Orebank Road, Kingsport, TN 37664.

The Church of Jesus Christ (Bickertonites) (*Mormon*) P.O. Box 72, Sixth & Lincoln Streets, Monongahela, PA 15063.

Church of Jesus Christ, Christian, c/o Rev. John Hendrixson, P.O. Box 68, Rabun Gap, GA 30568.

Church of Jesus Christ Christian (Aryan Nations), P.O. Box 362, Hayden Lake, ID 83835.

Church of Jesus Christ (Cutlerite) (*Mormon*), c/o Rupert J. Fletcher, 819 South Cottage, Independence, MO 64050.

The Church of Jesus Christ Ministerial Alliance (*Pentecostal*), 2797 Bryant Street, Portage, IN 46368.

Church of Jesus Christ of Erie (*Mormon*), 616 Tyndall Avenue, Laurence Park, Erie, PA 16511.

Church of Jesus Christ of Georgia, c/o Elder Wilbur Childress, Route 1, Ranger, GA 30734.

The Church of Jesus Christ of Latter-day Saints (*Mormon*), 50 East North Temple Street, Salt Lake City, UT 84103.

Church of Jesus Christ of Latter-Day Saints (Kingston) (*Mormon*), Bountiful, UT 84010.

Church of Jesus Christ of Latter-Day Saints (Leroy Johnson) (*Mormon*), Colorado City, AZ 86021.

Church of Jesus Christ of Latter-Day Saints (Strangites) (*Mormon*), c/o Stanley Johnston, 828 Hickory Street, Lansing, MI 48912.

Church of Jesus Christ Restored (*Mormon*), P.O. Box 551, Owen Sound, Ontario, Canada.

Church of Light (*Occult*), 657 St. Andrews Place South, Los Angeles, CA 90005.

The Church of Man, (See The Phoenix Institute).

Church of Metaphysical Christianity (*Spiritualist*), 2717 Browning Street, Sarasota, FL 33577.

Church of One Sermon (*Buddhist*), 8135 Lincoln Street, Lemon Grove, CA 92045.

Church of Our Lord Jesus Christ of the Apostolic Faith, Inc. (*Pentecostal*), 2081 7th Avenue, New York, NY 10027.

Church of Psychonomy, 2116 Monroe Avenue, San Diego, CA 92116.

Church of Religious Dynamics, 4029 Baywood Street, Los Angeles, CA 90039.

The Church of Revelation, P.O. Box 574, Lakewood, CA 90714.

The Church of Revelation and Astral Physics (*Psychic*), P.O. Box 88231, Honolulu, HI 96815.

Church of Scientology, 2125 S Street, N.W., Washington, DC 20008.

Church of Scientology Advanced Organization, 1306 North Berendo Street, Los Angeles, CA 90027.

Church of Scientology of California, c/o New American Saint Hill, 1413 North Berendo Street, Los Angeles, CA 90027.

Church of Seven Arrows (*Neo-Paganism*), c/o George Dew, 4385 Hoyt Street — No. 103, Wheat Ridge, CO 80033.

Church of Spiritual Advisory Council, c/o Rev. Paul V. Johnson, 112 Shadow Lake Drive, Longwood, FL 32750.

Church of Spiritual Freedom, (See Eductivism).

Church of the Awakening (*Psychic*), c/o John Aiken, P.O. Box 1097, Socorro, NM 87801.

Church of the Bible Covenant (*Holiness*), c/o The Covenanter, 2127 South Delaware Court, Tulsa, OK 74114.

The Church of the Blessed Hope, 7450 Wilson Mills Road, Chesterland, OH 44026.

Church of the Body of the Spirit of Christ (*Mormon*), c/o Max E. Powers, P.O. Box 712, Kansas City, MO 64141.

Church of the Brethren, 1451 Dundee Avenue, Elgin, IL 60120.

Church of the Brethren in Christ (Independent), (See Brethren in Christ Fellowship).

Church of the Burning Bush (*Holiness*), (See Metropolitan Church Association).

Church of the Children of the Desert, P.O. Box 528, Pittman, NV 89044.

Church of the Christian Spiritual Alliance (CSA) (*New Age*), Lakemont, GA 30552.

Church of the Covenanters, (See Reformed Presbyterian Church of North America).

Church of the Creator, P.O. Box 5908, Lighthouse Point, FL 33064.

Church of the Essence, P.O. Box 36, Niwot, CO 80544.

The Church of the Eternal Light (*Neo-Paganism*), 909 Reinli — No. 115, Austin, TX 78751.

Church of the Eternal Source (*Neo-Paganism*), P.O. Box 7091, Burbank, CA 91510.

Church of the Full Gospel, Inc., (See General Conference of the Evangelical Baptist Church, Inc.).

Church of the God Within, Inc., P.O. Box 9097, West Palm Beach, FL 33404.

Church of the Gospel (*Holiness*), c/o Marion E. Green, 20¹/₂ Walnut Street, Hudson Falls, NY 12839.

Church of Hermetic Sciences, P.O. Box 3341, Pasadena, CA 91103.

Church of the Holy Brotherhood, P.O. Box 929, San Francisco, CA 94101.

Church of the Holy Monarch, c/o Robert Walker, P.O. Box 1116, Port Orange, FL 32019.

Church of the Humanitarian God, c/o Ron Libert, P.O. Box 13236, St. Petersburg, FL 33733.

Church of the Jesus Ethic, 336 West Colorado Street, Glendale, CA 91204.

Church of the Larger Fellowship (*Unitarian Universalist*), 25 Beacon Street, Boston, MA 02108.

Church of the Little Children (*Pentecostal*), c/o Mrs. Edgar C. Wenzlaff, Route 1, Black Rock, AR 72415.

Church of the Living Christ / Order of Melchizedek, 355 Serrano Drive — No. 122, San Francisco, CA 94132.

Church of the Living Earth (*Neo-Paganism*), P.O. Box 5041, Esmond, RI 02917.

Church of the Living God (*Pentecostal*), c/o Chief Bishop F. C. Scott, 801 N.E. 17th Street, Oklahoma City, OK 73105.

Church of the Living God (Apostolic Faith), (See Church of the Living God).

Church of the Living God, General Assembly, (See Church of the Living God).

The Church of the Living Word, (also known as "The Walk"), 8855 Haskell Avenue, Sepulveda, CA 91343.

Church of the Lord Jesus Christ (*Pentecostal*), (See Assemblies of the Lord Jesus Christ).

Church of the Lord Jesus Christ of the Apostolic Faith (*Pentecostal*), 22nd & Bainbridge Streets, Philadelphia, PA 19146.

Church of the Lutheran Brethren, 704 Vernon Avenue West, Fergus Falls, MN 56537.

Church of the Lutheran Confession, c/o Rev. Egbert Albrecht, President, Markesan, WI 53946.

Church of the Mother (*Witchcraft*), P.O. Box 1544, Iowa City, IA 52241.

Church of the Nazarene (*Holiness*), 6401 The Paseo, Kansas City, MO 64131.

Church of the New Essenes (*Witchcraft*), P.O. Box 933, Pascagoula, MS 39567.

Church of the New Testament, 1602 Harvey Street, Austin, TX 78702.

Church of the Open Door, 550 South Hope Street, Los Angeles, CA 90071.

Church of the Palma Christi (*New Age*), c/o Dr. Robert Danner, 8624 Balcom Avenue, Northridge, CA 91325.

Church of the Saviour (*Communal*), 2025 Massachusetts Avenue, N.W., Washington, DC 20036.

Church of the Supreme Presence, Cudahy, WI 53110.

Church of the Tolerants, (See Association of Churches of The Tolerants).

Church of the Tree of Life (*Neo-Paganism*), 405 Columbus Avenue, San Francisco, CA 94133.

Church of the Trinity (Invisible Ministry) (*New Thought*), P.O. Box 37, San Marcos, CA 92069.

Church of the Truth (*New Thought*) c/o Dr. Ervin Seale, New York Church of the Truth, 154 West 57th Street, New York, NY 10019.

Church of the United Brethren in Christ, (See The United Methodist Church).

Church of the United Brethren in Christ (Old Constitution), 302 Lake Street, P.O. Box 650, Huntington, IN 46750.

Church of the Word (Seth), c/o Guy Gipson, P.O. Box 742, West Chester, PA 19380.

Church of Transition, c/o Bruce Cole, 210 N.E. 48 Terrace, Miami, FL 33137.

Church of Tzaddi (*New Age*), 11236 Dale Street, Garden Grove, CA 92641.

Church of Universal Brotherhood, 6311 Yucca Street, Hollywood, CA 90028.

The Church of Universal Healing Arts and Research (*New Age*), P.O. Box 793, Roundup, MT 59072.

Church of Universal Love (*New Age*), 8034 Lowd Avenue, El Paso, TX 79907.

Church of Universal Triumph / The Dominion of God (*Holiness*), c/o Rev. Lord James Shaffer, 8317 LaSalle Blvd., Detroit, MI 48206.

Church of Universology, 3519 Thom Blvd., Las Vegas, NV 89106.

Church of Voodoo, Ltd., P.O. Box 5718, Pikesville, MD 21208.

Church of What's Happening Now, c/o Imagene W. Stewart, 214 P Street, N.W., Washington, DC 20001.

Church of Wicca (*Witchcraft*), c/o Rev. Wayne Anderson, 196 West End Avenue, Toms River, NJ 08753.

Church of Wicca of Bakersfield, (See Georgian Church).

Church of World Messianity, 3068 San Marino Street, Los Angeles, CA 90006.

Church of World Peace, c/o Rev. Willie Conklin, P.O. Box 12514, Denver, CO 80212.

Church of Y Tylwyth Teg (*Witchcraft*), P.O. Box 4152, Athens, GA 30602.

The Church on the Way (*Pentecostal*), 14344 Sherman Way, Van Nuys, CA 91405.

Church Peace Union, (See Council on Religion and International Affairs).

Church Pensions Conference, c/o Huggins & Company, Inc., 229 South 18th Street, Philadelphia, PA 19103.

Church Project on United States Investments in Southern Africa, (See Interfaith Center on Corporate Responsibility).

Church Research & Information Projects, P.O. Box 223, Cathedral Station, New York, NY 10025.

Church Truth Universal — Aum, (See AUM Temple of Universal Truth).

Church Universal and Triumphant, Inc., (See The Summit Lighthouse).

Church Women United in the U.S.A., 475 Riverside Drive — Room 806, New York, NY 10115.

Church World Service Community Appeal (*National Council of Churches*), (See CROP).

Church World Service, (*National Council of Churches*), 475 Riverside Drive, New York, NY 10115.

The Churches' Center for Theology and Public Policy, 4400 Massachusetts Avenue, N.W., Washington, DC 20016.

Churches of Christ in Christian Union (*Holiness*), P.O. Box 30, Circleville, OH 43113.

Churches of Christ (Non-instrumental), c/o J. Roy Vaughan, 1006 Elm Hill Road, Nashville, TN 37210.

Churches of Christ (Non-instrumental-Charismatic) (*Pentecostal*), c/o Elder Dan Peters, Hillcrest Church of Christ, 2420 Hillcrest Drive, Thousand Oaks, CA 91360.

Churches of Christ (Non-instrumental-Conservative), c/o Elder William E. Wallace, Affton Church of Christ, 6939 Weber Road, St. Louis, MO 63213.

Churches of Christ (Non-instrumental-Open), P.O. Box 15024, Austin, TX 78761.

Churches of Christ (Non-instrumental-Premillennial), c/o Elder H. E. Schreiner, Highview Church of Christ, 6105 East Manslick Road, Louisville, KY 40219.

Churches of God, General Conference, 700 East Melrose Avenue, P.O Box 926, Findlay, OH 45840.

Churches of God, Holiness, 170 Ashby Street, N.W., Atlanta, GA 30314.

Churches of God in North America (General Eldership), (See Churches of God, General Conference).

Churches of God (Independent Holiness People), 1225 East First Street, Fort Scott, KS 66701.

Churches of God of the Original Mountain Assembly (*Pentecostal*), Williamsburg, KY 40769.

Churches of the New Jerusalem (*Swedenborgian*), (See General Church of the New Jerusalem; see also General Convention of the New Jerusalem in the U.S.A.).

The Churchman Associates, Inc. (*Religious Humanism*), 1074 23rd Avenue North, St. Petersburg, FL 33704.

Churchpeople for Change and Reconciliation, c/o Rev. Leonard Stark, Executive Director, 221 West North Street, Lima, OH 45801.

Cimarron Zen Center (*Buddhist*), 2505 Cimarron Street, Los Angeles, CA 90018.

Circle (*Witchcraft*), c/o Selena Fox, P.O. Box 9013, Madison, WI 53715.

Circle in the Greenwood (*Witchcraft*), R.D. 1 — Box 28, Niverville, NY 12130.

Circle of the Mystic and Occult Arts, P.O. Box 42, West Nyack, NY 10995.

Citizens Engaged in Freeing Minds, P.O. Box 82664, Atlanta, GA 30354.

Citizens Freedom Foundation, P.O. Box 7000-89, 1719 Via El Prado, Redondo Beach, CA 90277.

Citizens Organized for Public Awareness of Cults, P.O. Box 3194, Greensboro, NC 27402.

City-Of-The-Sun Foundation (Christ's Truth Church and School of Wisdom) (*New Age*), P.O. Box 356, Columbus, NM 88029.

The Claymont Society (*New Age*), P.O. Box 112, Charles Town, WV 25414.
"Clean Up TV" Campaign, c/o Rev. John Hurt, P.O. Box 218, Joelton, TN 37080.
The Clear Light Society (*New Age*), P.O. Box 219, Boston, MA 02123.
Clergy and Laity Concerned, 198 Broadway — Room 302, New York, NY 10038.
Clergy and Laymen Concerned, (See Clergy and Laity Concerned).
Clergy and Laymen Concerned About Vietnam, (See Clergy and Laity Concerned).
Clergy Economic Education Foundation, (See Economic Education Foundation for Clergy).
Coalition for Human Needs (*Episcopal*), 815 Second Avenue, New York, NY 10017.
Coalition 14 (*Episcopal*), 815 Second Avenue, New York, NY 10017.
Coalition of Black Members in The American Lutheran Church, c/o Ms. Vivian Merriweather, 917 Prichard Avenue, Prichard, AL 33610.
Colel Hibath Jerusalem (*Jewish*), (See Society of the Devotees of Jerusalem).
Collectors of Religion on Stamps, c/o Mrs. Viola Esau, 600 West Orange Grove Road — G-184, Tucson, AZ 85704.
College of Chaplains (*American Protestant Hospital Association*), 840 North Lake Shore Drive — Room 607, Chicago, IL 60611.
College of Occult Sciences, (See Temple of Kriya Yoga).
College Theology Society, c/o Dolores Greeley, Secretary, Department of Theological Studies, St. Louis University, St. Louis, MO 63103.
Collegiate Association for the Research of Principles, (See The Unification Church).
The Colony (*Communal*), Burnt Ranch, CA 95527.
Colorado Council of Churches, 5209 Montview Blvd., Denver, CO 80207.
Colored Cumberland Presbyterian Church, (See Second Cumberland Presbyterian Church in the United States).
Colored Fire-Baptized Holiness Church, (See Fire Baptized Holiness Church of God in the Americas).
Colored Methodist Episcopal Church, (See Christian Methodist Episcopal Church).
Columbian Squires (*Catholic*), P.O. Drawer 1670, New Haven, CT 06507.
Combined Campaign for American Reform Judaism, (See Reform Jewish Appeal).
Comenius World Council, 247 South Street, Hartford, CT 06114.
Commandment Keepers Congregation of the Living God (*Black Jews*), c/o Rabbi Wentworth A. Matthews, One West 123rd Street, New York, NY 10027.
Commandment Keepers, Holy Church of the Living God, Pillar and Ground of the Truth, (See Commandment Keepers Congregation of the Living God).
Commission for Catholic Missions Among the Colored People and the Indians, 2021 H Street, N.W., Washington, DC 20006.
Commission of the Churches on International Affairs (*World Council of Churches*), UN Headquarters Liaison Office, 777 U.N. Plaza, New York, NY 10017.
Commission of World Service of the Evangelical and Reformed Church, (See United Church Board for World Ministries).
Commission on Archives and History of the United Methodist Church, P.O. Box 488, Lake Junaluska, NC 28745.

49

Commission on Education for Mission (*National Council of Churches*), 475 River-side Drive — Room 772, New York, NY 10115.

Commission on History of the Reformed Church in America, c/o New Bruns-wick Theological Seminary, New Brunswick, NJ 08901.

Commission on Missionary Education (*National Council of Churches*), (See Com-mission on Education for Mission).

Commission on Regional and Local Ecumenism (*National Council of Churches*), 475 Riverside Drive, New York, NY 10115.

Commission on Religion in Appalachia, Inc., c/o Bishop D. Frederick Wertz, Chairman, 864 Weisgarber Road, N.W., Knoxville, TN 37919.

Commission on Social Action of Reform Judaism, 838 5th Avenue, New York, NY 10021.

The Committee for Continuing Christian Universalist Churches, (See Christian Universalist Church of America).

Committee for Lutheran Cooperation, c/o Rev. Duane Lindberg, Coordinator, 605 West Fourth Street, Waterloo, IA 50702.

Committee for Public Education and Religious Liberty, c/o UPA, 95 Madison Avenue, New York, NY 10016.

Committee for Southern Africa Theological College for Independent Churches, 1012 City Avenue, Philadelphia, PA 19151.

Committee for the Furtherance of Torah Observance (*Jewish*), 1430 57th Street, Brooklyn, NY 11219.

Committee for the Restoration of the Permanent Diaconate in the United States, 1312 Massachusetts Avenue, N.W., Washington, DC 20005.

Committee of Concerned Citizens, P.O. Box 113, Kensington, MD 20795.

Committee of Friends on Bisexuality, 723 Hastings Hall, Union Theological Seminary, 600 West 122nd Street, New York, NY 10027.

Committee of Southern Churchmen, c/o Gideon Fryer, President, P.O. Box 2215, Nashville, TN 37214.

Committee on Army and Navy Chaplains, (See National Conference on Ministry to the Armed Forces).

Committee on Christian Literature for Women and Children in Mission Fields, 475 Riverside Drive — Room 670, New York, NY 10115.

Committee on Missionary Evangelism, P.O. Box 46492, 688 Broadway, Bedford, OH 44146.

Committee Opposing Congregational Political Action, (See League to Uphold Congregational Principles, Inc.).

Communication Commission (*National Council of Churches*), 475 Riverside Drive — Room 856, New York, NY 10115.

Community Churches, (See American Evangelical Christian Churches; see also National Council of Community Churches).

Community for Religious Research and Education, P.O. Box 9164, Berkeley, CA 94709.

Community Ministries, P.O. Box 1245, Tempe, AZ 85281.

Community of Micah (*Jewish*), 1808 Wyoming Avenue, N.W., Washington, DC 20009.

The Community of St. John Baptist (*Episcopal*), P.O. Box 42, Mendham, NJ 07945.

Community of the Transfiguration (*Episcopal*), 495 Albion Avenue, Cincinnati, OH 45246.

Community of True Inspiration, (See Amana Church Society).

Community Services (*Seventh-day Adventist*), c/o General Conference of Seventh-day Adventists, 6840 Eastern Avenue, N.W., Washington, DC 20012.

Company of the Paraclete, P.O. Box 16, Milburn, NJ 07041.

Compassion International, 3955 Cragwood Drive, P.O. Box 7000, Colorado Springs, CO 80933.

Composers' Forum for Catholic Worship, Inc., c/o Robert Igoe Blanchard, Executive Director, 100 North Sterling Avenue, Sugar Creek, MO 64054.

Compost Coven (*Witchcraft*), c/o Valerie Walker, 731 5th Avenue, San Francisco, CA 94118.

Concerned Christians, (See Fellowship of Conservative Southern Baptists).

Concerned Christians for Good Government, P.O. Box 266, Stone Mountain, GA 30086.

Concerned Presbyterians, Inc., (See Presbyterian Church in the United States).

Concilio Olazabal de Iglesias Latino-Americano, Inc. (*Pentecostal*), c/o Tabernaculo Bethesda, 1925 East First Street, Los Angeles, CA 90033.

Concordia Historical Institute (*Lutheran*), 801 De Mun Avenue, St. Louis, MO 63105.

Concordia Historical Society (*Lutheran*), (See Concordia Historical Institute).

Concordia Lutheran Conference, c/o Rev. O.W. Schaeffer, 8630 West 163rd Street, Orland Park, IL 60462.

Concordia Mutual Life (*Lutheran*), 20 North Wacker Drive, Chicago, IL 60606.

Concordia Tract Mission (*Lutheran*), c/o Emil W. Benz, Director, P.O. Box 201, St. Louis, MO 63166.

Conference of Authentic Lutherans, c/o Rev. Robert E. Yount, Christ the King Lutheran Church, 6541 Eastern Avenue, Bell Gardens, CA 90201.

Conference of Church Workers Among the Deaf (*Episcopal*), (See Episcopal Conference of the Deaf).

Conference of Ecclesiastical Endorsing Agents for the Armed Forces, (See National Conference on Ministry to the Armed Forces).

Conference of Jewish Communal Service, 15 East 26th Street, New York, NY 10010.

Conference of Major Religious Superiors of Women's Institutes of the United States of America (*Catholic*), (See Leadership Conference of Women Religious of the U.S.A.).

Conference of Major Superiors of Men's Institutes (*Catholic*), 1302 18th Street, N.W. — Suite 601, Washington, DC 20036.

Conference of Presidents of Major American Jewish Organizations, 515 Park Avenue, New York, NY 10022.

Conference of Theological Seminaries of the United States and Canada, (See Association of Theological Schools in the United States and Canada).

Conference on Christianity and Literature, c/o Prof. Roy Battenhouse, Department of English, Indiana University, Bloomington, IN 47401.

Conference on Faith and History, Department of History, Indiana State University, Terre Haute, IN 47809.

Conference on Jewish Material Claims Against Germany, 15 East 26th Street — Room 1901, New York, NY 10010.

Conference on Jewish Relations, (See Conference on Jewish Social Studies).

Conference on Jewish Social Studies, 250 West 57th Street — Room 904, New York, NY 10019.

Conference on Science, Philosophy and Religion, 3080 Broadway, New York, NY 10027.

Conference on the Religious Life in the Anglican Communion of the United States and Canada (*Episcopal*), c/o Rev. Mother Mary Grace, Chairman, St. Mary's Convent, John Street, Peekskill, NY 10566.

Confraternity Home Study Service (*Catholic*), 3473 South Grand Blvd., St. Louis, MO 63118.

Confraternity of Christian Doctrine Correspondence Courses (*Catholic*), 424 North Broadway, Wichita, KS 67202.

Confraternity of Deists, Inc., P.O. Box 179, Homosassa Springs, FL 32647.

The Confraternity of the Blessed Sacrament (*Episcopal*), 438 Valley Street, Orange, NJ 07050.

Confraternity of the Immaculate Conception of Our Lady of Lourdes (*Catholic*), P.O. Box 561, Notre Dame, IN 46556.

Confraternity of the Most Holy Rosary (*Catholic*), (See Rosary Altar Society).

Congregation of Aten (*Neo-Paganism*), 2809 South Trumbull Avenue, Chicago, IL 60623.

The Congregation of Saint Augustine (*Episcopal*), P.O. Drawer 640, Picayune, MS 39466.

The Congregation of the Servants of Christ (*Lutheran*), c/o St. Augustine's House, Oxford, MI 48051.

Congregational Bible Church (*Mennonite*), Marietta, PA 17547.

Congregational Christian Churches, (See United Church of Christ).

Congregational Christian Historical Society, 14 Beacon Street, Boston, MA 02108.

Congregational Christian Service Committee, (See United Church Board for World Ministries).

Congregational Church of Practical Theology (*Psychic*), c/o Dr. E. Arthur Winkler, 211 North Pine Street, Valley, NE 68064.

Congregational Holiness Church (*Pentecostal*), 3888 Fayetteville Highway, Griffin, GA 30223.

Congregational Methodist Church (*Holiness*), c/o Rev. A. F. O'Connor, P.O. Box 555, Florence, MS 39073.

Congress for Jewish Culture, 25 East 78th Street, New York, NY 10021.

Conscious Development, c/o Terri L. Johnson, P.O. Drawer 20295, Dallas, TX 75220.

Conservative Amish Mennonite Conference, (See Conservative Mennonite Conference).

Conservative Baptist Association of America, P.O. Box 66, Wheaton, IL 60187.

Conservative Baptist Fellowship of Northern Baptists, (See Conservative Baptist Association of America).

Conservative Baptist Foreign Mission Society, P.O. Box 5, Wheaton, IL 60187.

Conservative Baptist Home Mission Society, P.O. Box 828, Wheaton, IL 60187.

Conservative Congregational Christian Conference, 2489 North Rice Street — Suite No. 204, St. Paul, MN 55113.

Conservative Congregational Christian Fellowship, (See Conservative Congregational Christian Conference).

Conservative Dunkers, (See Church of the Brethren).

Conservative Mennonite Conference, c/o Rosedale Mennonite Missions, Route 1, 9920 Rosedale — Milford Center Road, Irwin, OH 43029.

Conservative Mennonite Fellowship, P.O. Box 36, Hartville, OH 44632.

Conservative Mennonite Fellowship (Nonconference), c/o Levi Schrock, 705 Jersey Ridge Road, Zanesville, OH 43701.

Consortium Perfectae Caritatis (*Catholic*), 13000 Auburn Road, Chardon, OH 44024.

Consultation of Cooperating Churches in Kansas, 4125 Gage Center Drive, Topeka, KS 66604.

"Consultation of Presbyterian Evangelicals", (See Evangelical Presbyterian Church — Trenton, MI).

Consultation on Church Union, 228 Alexander Street, Princeton, NJ 08540.

Consultative Council of Jewish Organizations, 61 Broadway, New York, NY 10006.

Contact Teleministries USA, 900 South Arlington Avenue — Room 125, Harrisburg, PA 17109.

The Conversion Center, Inc., 18 West Eagle Road, Drawer V, Havertown, PA 19083.

Convert Makers of America (*Catholic*), (See Convert Movement Our Apostolate).

Convert Movement Our Apostolate (*Catholic*), c/o Our Lady of Grace Rectory, 430 Avenue W, Brooklyn, NY 11223.

Coordinating Board of Jewish Organizations, c/o Dr. Daniel Thrusz, Executive Director, 1640 Rhode Island Avenue, N.W., Washington, DC 20036.

Coptic Fellowship International (*New Age*), 1223 Arbor Vitae Road, Deerfield, IL 60015.

Coptic Orthodox Church, Diocese of North America, c/o Archpriest Fr. Gabriel Abdelsayed, 427 West Side Avenue, Jersey City, NJ 07304.

Coral Ridge Ministries (*Presbyterian*), P.O. Box 5555, Ft. Lauderdale, FL 33310.

Cord of St. Thomas Confraternity (*Catholic*), (See Angelic Warfare Confraternity).

Cornerstone Ministry, P.O. Box 43189, Birmingham, AL 35243.

CORPUS — National Association Resigned/Married Priests (*Catholic*), P.O. Box 2649, Chicago, IL 60690.

Cosmic Awareness Communications (*Psychic*), P.O. Box 115, Olympia, WA 98507.

Cosmic Church of Life and Spiritual Science, Inc. (*Spiritualist*), c/o Rev. Michelina Russo, 2885 Homestead Road — Suite No. 1, Santa Clara, CA 95051.

Cosmic Circle of Fellowship (*Psychic*), P.O. Box A3179, Chicago, IL 60690.

Cosmic Communication Communes (*Psychic*), 100 Elm Court, Decorah, IA 52101.

Cosmic Energy and Man Association (*Psychic*), 827 Montline Lane, Los Angeles, CA 90024.

Cosmic Joy Fellowship, P.O. Box 621, Larkspur, CA 94939.

Cosmic Science Research Center (*Psychic*), c/o Edward M. Palmer, 1646 S. E. Elliott, Portland, OR 97214.

Cosmic Sources (*Psychic*), 5300 Wasson, Austin, TX 78745.

Cosmic Study Center (*Psychic*), 7405 Masters Drive, Potomac MD 20854.

Council for American Judaism, 309 Fifth Avenue, New York, NY 10016.

Council for Christian Medical Work (*Lutheran*), 1333 South Kirkwood Road, St. Lous, MO 63122.

Council for Christian Social Action, (See Office for Church in Society).

Council for Clinical Training, (See Association for Clinical Pastoral Education).
Council for Democratic and Secular Humanism, P.O. Box 5, Central Park Station, Buffalo, NY 14215.
Council For Evangelical Baptist Churches For the Soviet Union, 300 East Jackson Blvd., Elkhart, IN 46514.
Council for Religion in Independent Schools, 107 South Broad Street, Kennett Square, PA 19348.
Council for the Clinical Training of Theological Students, (See Association for Clinical Pastoral Education).
Council of American Witches, 476 Summit Avenue, St. Paul, MN 55102.
The Council of Churches of Greater Washington, 1401 Massachusetts Avenue, N.W., Washington, DC 20005.
The Council of Churches of the City of New York, 475 Riverside Drive — Suite 456, New York, NY 10115.
The Council of Community Churches, Chittenden Hotel, 18 West Spring Street, Columbus, OH 43215.
Council of Eastern Orthodox Youth Leaders of the Americas, c/o Michael Herzak, 20783 Sandalwood Lane, Strongsville, OH 44136.
Council of Imams in North America (*Muslim*), 1214 Cambridge Crescent, Sarnia, Ontario N7S 3W4, Canada.
Council of Isis (*Witchcraft*), c/o Laurie Cabot, 125 Essex Street, Salem, MA 01970.
The Council of Islamic Organizations of America, 676 St. Marks Avenue, Brooklyn, NY 11216.
Council of Jewish Federations, Inc., 575 Lexington Avenue, New York, NY 10022.
Council of Jewish Federations and Welfare Funds, (See Council of Jewish Federations, Inc.).
Council of Liberal Churches, (See Unitarian Universalist Association).
Council of Mennonite Colleges, Eastern Mennonite College, Harrisonburg, VA 22801.
Council of Protestant Colleges and Universities, 1818 R Street, N.W., Washington, DC 20009.
Council of the Mystic Arts (*Neo-Paganism*), 11701 Quartz Circle, Austin, TX 78750.
Council of the Sacred Earth (*Neo-Paganism*), P.O. Box 60151, Chicago, IL 60660.
Council of Theological Seminaries (*United Presbyterian Church in the U.S.A.*), 475 Riverside Drive, New York, NY 10115.
Council of Young Israel Rabbis (*Jewish*), Three West 16th Street, New York, NY 10011.
Council on Christian Union, (See Council on Christian Unity).
Council on Christian Unity, P.O. Box 1986, 222 South Downey Avenue, Indianapolis, IN 46206.
Council on Earth Religions, c/o Stephen Bell, 4445 36th Street, San Diego, CA 92116.
Council on Graduate Studies in Religion, c/o Kenneth Kuntz, Secretary-Treasurer, 313 Gilmore Hall, University of Iowa, Iowa City, IA 52242.
Council on Jewish Federations and Welfare Funds, 575 Lexington Avenue, New York, NY 10022.

Council on Religion and International Affairs, 170 East 64th Street, New York, NY 10021.

Council on Religion and Law, c/o Thomas Porter, One Beacon Street — Suite 1910, Boston, MA 02108.

Council on Religion and the Homosexual, P.O. Box 42010, San Francisco, CA 94101.

Council on the Study of Religion, c/o Winton U. Solberg, Secretary, 309 Gregory Hall, University of Illinois, Urbana, IL 61801.

Council on Women and the Church (*United Presbyterian Church in the U.S.A.*), 475 Riverside Drive — Room 1149, New York, NY 10115.

Counselor Enterprises (*New Age*), c/o Janet Redding, Administrator, 766 East Howard Street, Pasadena, CA 91104.

Coven of Ankhfrost (*Witchcraft*), c/o Dellanna Gordon, 12069 Gist Park Drive, Bridgeton, MO 63044.

The Coven of Boskednan (*Witchcraft*), (See National Church and School of Wicca).

Coven of Lothlorien (*Witchcraft*), P.O. Box 1615, Buffalo, NY 14216.

Coven of Sothistar (*Witchcraft*), P.O. Box 9513, North Hollywood, CA 91609.

The Coven of the Mirror (*Witchcraft*), c/o Bob Clark, 1728 East 12th Street, Des Moines, IA 50316.

Coven of Trer Dryw Religion (*Witchcraft*), P.O. Box 1064, Boulder, CO 80306.

The Covenant Fellowship (*Presbyterian*), (See Presbyterian Church in the United States).

Covenant of the Ancient Way (*Witchcraft*), 1907 P Street, Sacramento, CA 95814.

Covenant Presbytery, c/o Ralph J. Schuler, Faith Bible Presbyterian Church, 6901 Haycock Road, Falls Church, VA 22043.

Covens One (*Neo-Paganism*), P.O. Box 664, Chicago Heights, IL 60411.

Cowboy Camp Meeting, Inc., c/o Evangelist George Havens, 1243 South Waverly Drive, Dallas, TX 75208.

The Co-Workers of Mother Teresa in America, Inc. (*Catholic*), c/o Mrs. Warren L. Kump, Chairman, 4243 Glenwood Avenue, Minneapolis, MN 55422.

Creating Our Life (*New Age*), c/o Charlotte Colorado, Director, P.O. Box 374, Venice, CA 90291.

Creation Research Society, 2717 Cranbrook Road, Ann Arbor, MI 48104.

Creation-Science Research Center, (See Institute for Creation Research).

Creative Initiative Foundation, 222 High Street, Palo Alto, CA 94301.

Creative Programs of Denver (*Psychic*), 50 Ogden Street, Denver, CO 80218.

CRISTA Ministries, 19303 Fremont Avenue North, Seattle, WA 98133.

Criswell Center for Biblical Studies, 525 North Ervay, Dallas, TX 75201.

Croation Catholic Union of the U.S.A., One West Old Ridge Road, Hobart, IN 46342.

The Croation Fraternal Union of America, 100 Delaney Drive, Pittsburgh, PA 15235.

CROP (*National Council of Churches*), 28606 Phillips Street, Elkhart, IN 46514.

Crown of Life Fellowship, Route 2 — Box 190, Albany, OR 97321.

Crusade for a More Fruitful Preaching and Hearing of the Word of God, Inc. (*Catholic*), Allendale, NJ 07401.

Crusade for Family Prayer, Inc. (*Catholic*), c/o Rev. Patrick Peyton, 773 Madison Avenue, Albany, NY 12208.

Crusade for Life, Inc., P.O. Box 1433, Whittier, CA 90609.

Crusade for Morality, c/o Bob Green, 925 Arthur Godfrey Road, Miami Beach, FL 33140.

The Crusaders (*Catholic*), (See Crusade for a More Fruitful Preaching and Hearing of the Word of God, Inc.).

Cult and Occult Unification Program, P.O. Box 80, Scottsdale, AZ 85252.

Cult Exodus for Christ, P.O. Box 4033, Covina, CA 91723.

Cultural Integration Fellowship (*Hindu*), 3494 21st Street, San Francisco, CA 94110.

Cumberland Presbyterian Church, c/o Cumberland Presbyterian Center, 1978 Union Avenue, Memphis, TN 38104.

Cumberland Valley Mennonite Church, c/o Amos E. Martin, Moderator, Route 3 — Box 191, Shippensburg, PA 17257.

Cymry ab Prydian (*Witchcraft*), (See Church of Y Tylwyth Teg).

Cyril and Marie O'Neil Foundation (*Catholic*), c/o Richards & O'Neil, 645 Madison Avenue, New York, NY 10022.

Czech Catholic Union, 5349 Dolloff Road, Cleveland, OH 44127.

Czech Catholic Union of Texas, 214 Colorado Street, P.O. Box 297, La Grange, TX 78945.

Dames of Malta, 4127 Brownsville Road, Pittsburgh, PA 15227.

Damien-Dutton Society (*Catholic*), (See Damien-Dutton Society for Leprosy Aid, Inc.).

Damien-Dutton Society for Leprosy Aid, Inc. (*Catholic*), 616 Bedford Avenue, Bellmore, NY 11710.

Daniel Prayer Fellowship, P.O. Box 6072, Bend, OR 97701.

Danish Evangelical Lutheran Church Association in America, (See The American Lutheran Church).

Danish Evangelical Lutheran Church in North America, (See The American Lutheran Church).

Danish Evangelical Lutheran Church of America, (See Lutheran Church in America).

The Danish Interest Conference of the Lutheran Church in America, c/o Rev. Willard R. Garred, 2824 East 16th Street, Des Moines, IA 50316.

Daughters of Columbus (*Catholic*), (See Catholic Workman).

Daughters of Isabella (*Catholic*), 375 Whitney Avenue, New Haven, CT 06511.

Daughters of Sarah, 2716 West Cortland, Chicago, IL 60647.

Daughters of the King (*Episcopal*), 815 Second Avenue — Room 518, New York, NY 10017.

David Barnard Ministries, P.O. Box 1127, San Francisco, CA 94101.

David Wilkerson Youth Crusades, Route 1 — Box 80, Lindale, TX 75771.

Davidian SDA Association (*Adventist*), Bashan Hill, Exeter, MO 65647.

Davis County Cooperative Society (*Mormon*), c/o Ortell Kingston, 53 West Angelo Avenue, Salt Lake City, UT 84115.

Dawn Bible Students Association, 199 Railroad Avenue, East Rutherford, NJ 07073.

The Dawn Horse Communion, (See The Free Primitive Church of Divine Communion).

Dawn of Enlightenment Church, c/o Rev. James E. Osborne, 627 Hardin Drive — No. 5, Inglewood, CA 90302.

Dawn Research Institute (*New Thought*), c/o Aurora Nordhausen, President, 4143 Via Marina — No. 814, Marina Del Rey, CA 90291.

De Rance, Inc. (*Catholic*), 7700 West Blue Mound Road, Milwaukee, WI 53213.

Decision Magazine's School of Christian Writing, P.O. Box 779, Minneapolis, MN 55440.

Defenders of the Christian Faith (*Pentecostal*), P.O. Box 886, Wichita, KS 67201.

Defenseless Mennonite Brethren in Christ of North America, (See Evangelical Mennonite Brethren Conference).

Delaware Institute for the Science of Being, 2321 Fells Lane, Wilmington, DE 19808.

Delmarva Ecumenical Agency, 1626 North Union Street, Wilmington, DE 19806.

Delta Epsilon Sigma (*Catholic*), Loyola University, New Orleans, LA 70118.

Delta Resources Committee, Inc., c/o Ms. E. Jean Phillips, Director, 300 North Edison Street, P.O. Box 584, Greenville, MS 38701.

The Dena Foundation, c/o Merta Mary Parkinson, 4117 N.W. Willow Drive, Kansas City, MO 64116.

Denominational Executives of Christian Education, c/o Frances D. Decker, 5101 North Francisco Avenue, Chicago, IL 60625.

Denominational Sunday School Secretaries, (See Denominational Executives of Christian Education).

Department of Education for Mission (*National Council of Churches*), (See Commission on Education for Mission).

Department of United Church Women of the National Council of Churches, (See Church Women United).

Derek Prince Ministries, P.O. Box 300, Ft. Lauderdale, FL 33302.

Descendants of Schwenkfeldian Exiles, c/o Sherman L. Gerhard, 1525 Wassergass Road, Hellertown, PA 18055.

Desert Center for Psychic Research, P.O. Box 787, Mojave, CA 93501.

The Desert Community (*New Age*), c/o Diana Spencer, 388 Freeman, Long Beach, CA 90814.

Dharma Realm Buddhist University, City of Ten Thousand Buddhas, P.O. Box 271, Talmage, CA 95481.

Dharmadhatu (*Buddhist*), 2853 West 7th Street, Los Angeles, CA 90005.

Dharmadhatu Meditation Center (*Buddhist*), 640 North State Street, Chicago, IL 60610.

Dialogue Foundation (*Mormon*), P.O. Box 1387, Arlington, VA 22210.

Dialogue House, 80 East 11th Street, New York, NY 10003.

Diamond Christian Mission, c/o Dr. John R. Andrew, Route 5 — Box 230, Ellijay, GA 30540.

Diamond Sangha (*Buddhist*), Maui Zendo, Route 1 — Box 702, Kaupakalua Street, Haiku, HI 96708.

Diet, Discipline and Discipleship, Inc., 2710 Chili Avenue, Rochester, NY 14624.

Dignity (*Catholic*), 755 Boylston Street — Room 413, Boston, MA 02116.

The Diocese of Brooklyn and New Jersey of the Autocephalous Greek Orthodox Church of America, 141 West Market Street, Newark, NJ 07103.

"Disciples of Christ" (See Christian Church).

Disciples of Christ Church for All People (*Pentecostal*), P.O. Box 2156, Austin, TX 78768.

Disciples of Christ Historical Society (*Christian Church*), 1101 19th Avenue South, Nashville, TN 37212.

Disciples Peace Fellowship (*Christian Church*), 222 South Downey Avenue, P.O. Box 1986, Indianapolis, IN 46206.

The Disciplined Order of Christ, c/o Dr. Lloyd M. Bertholf, President, 307 Phoenix Avenue, Bloomington, IL 61701.

Divine Immortality Church, P.O. Drawer 4000, Dayton, WA 99328.

Divine Light Mission (*Hindu*), 511 16th Avenue East, Denver, CO 80203.

Divine Science Church and College, Inc. (*New Thought*), (See Divine Science Federation International).

Divine Science Federation International (*New Thought*), 1819 East 14th Avenue, Denver, CO 80218.

Divine Word Foundation, Inc. (*Psychic*), Warner Springs, CA 92086.

Divine Word Funds, Inc. (*Catholic*), c/o Rev. Francis Kamp, Techny, IL 60082.

Division of Health and Welfare Ministries of the United Methodist Church, (See National Association of Health and Welfare Ministries of the United Methodist Church).

Doctrine of Truth Foundation, Inc., P.O. Box 787, Oceanside, CA 92054.

The Domestic and Foreign Missionary Society of the Protestant Episcopal Church in the U.S.A., The Episcopal Church Center, 815 Second Avenue, New York, NY 10017.

Dominican Educational Association (*Catholic*), 1101 Aline Street, New Orleans, LA 70115.

Don Gossett Ministries, P.O. Box 2, Blaine, WA 98230.

Don Hughes Evangelistic Association, P.O. Box 840, Broken Arrow, OK 74012.

Don Loving Ministries, P.O. Box 5698, Cleveland, OH 44101.

Don Stewart Evangelistic Association, P.O. Box 2960, Phoenix, AZ 85062.

Door of Faith Churches of Hawaii (*Pentecostal*), 1161 Young Street, P.O. Box 5362, Honolulu, HI 96814.

Dorcas Welfare Society (*Seventh-day Adventist*), (See Community Services).

Dream Dynamics Institute (*New Age*), 22270 Main Street, Hayward, CA 94541.

Dror Young Zionist Organization (*Jewish*), 215 Park Avenue South, New York, NY 10003.

Duck River (and Kindred) Associations of Baptists, c/o Marvin Davenport, Auburntown, TN 37016.

Duck River Association of Missionary Baptists, c/o J. C. Carpenter, P.O. Box 820, Tullahoma, TN 37388, (See also Southern Baptist Convention).

The Duda Foundation (*Lutheran*), P.O. Box 257, Oviedo, FL 32765.

The Duke Endowment (*United Methodist*), 30 Rockefeller Plaza, New York, NY 10020.

Dunkard Brethren Church, c/o Harley Rush, Secretary, General Mission Board, Route 1, Converse, IN 46919.

Dutch Reformed Church, (See Reformed Church in America).

Dyad School of Enlightenment (*New Age*), 3100 White Sulphur Springs Road, St. Helena, CA 94574.

Dynamic Judaism, Inc., Two Pennsylvania Plaza, New York, NY 10001.

Earth Church of Amargi (*Neo-Paganism*), c/o Don Wildgrube, Route 3 — Box 596, Bonne Terre, MO 63628.

The Earth Light Program (*New Age*), P.O. Box 1798, La Jolla, CA 92038.

Earth Rites (*Neo-Paganism*), c/o Sherry Mestel, 398 8th Street, Brooklyn, NY 11215.

Earthstar Temple (*Witchcraft*), c/o The Magickal Childe, Inc., 35 West 19th Street, New York, NY 10011.

East Coast Durga Puja Association (*Hindu*) 79-30 268th Street, Floral Park, NY 11004.

East Syrian Church, (See Holy Apostolic and Catholic Church of the East-Assyrian).

The East/West Center for Holistic Health, Inc. (*New Age*), c/o Marie Valenta, Director, 141 Fifth Avenue, New York, NY 10010.

East West Christian Organization, c/o Connie Cole, 6127 S.E. 85th Avenue, Portland, OR 97266.

East-West Cultural Center (*Hindu*), 2865 West 9th Street, Los Angeles, CA 90006.

East West Foundation (*New Thought*), 359 Boylston Street, Boston, MA 02116.

East/West News Service, (A Division of Evangelism Center International), North American Communication Center, P.O. Box 57, Pasadena, CA 91109.

Eastern Catholic Church, Syro-Chaldean Archdiocese of North America, c/o Archbishop Elijah Coady, 921 West 8th Street, Davis, CA 95616.

Eastern Conference of the Methodist Protestant Church, (See The Bible Protestant Church).

Eastern Crescent Pagan Council, P.O. Box 1615, Buffalo, NY 14216.

Eastern European Mission, 232 North Lake Avenue, Pasadena, CA 91101.

"Eastern Mysticism Project", Campus Crusade for Christ, Arrowhead Springs, San Bernardino, CA 92414.

Eastern Orthodox Catholic Church in America, c/o Rev. Gregory R.P. Adair, 1914 Highway 17-92, Maitland, FL 32751.

Eastern Religious Vocation Directors' Assocation (*Catholic*), c/o Brother Philip Ouellette, Chairman, 1241 Kennedy Blvd., Bayonne, NJ 07002.

Eastern States Buddhist Temple of America, 64 Mott Street, New York, NY 10013.

Ecclesia Cantans (*Lutheran*), c/o Prof. Philip Gehring, Music Department, Valparaiso University, Valparaiso, IN 46383.

Eckankar (*Psychic*), P.O. Box 3100, Menlo Park, CA 94025.

Economic Education Foundation for Clergy, 1000 16th Street, N.W., Washington, DC 20036.

Ecuador Concerns Committee, 475 Riverside Drive — 16th Floor, New York, NY 10115.

Ecumedia News Service, 475 Riverside Drive — Suite 850, New York, NY 10115.

Ecumenical Association of Churches in Idaho, 2308 North Cole Road, Boise, ID 83704.

Ecumenical Clergy Association, c/o Graymoor Ecumenical Institute, Garrison, NY 10524.

Ecumenical Institute, 4750 North Sheridan Road, Chicago, IL 60640.

Ecumenical Media Resource Center, c/o First Baptist Church — Room 214, 8th South 13th East, Salt Lake City, UT 84102.

Ecumenical Methodist Conference, (See World Methodist Council).

Ecumenical Ministries of Oregon, 0245 S.W. Bancroft Street — Suite B, Portland, OR 97201.

Ecumenical Research Academy, c/o Rev. J. Rodman Williams, Director, 10 Freedman Way, Anaheim, CA 92802.

The Edelstan Foundation, P.O. Box 184, Ashland, OR 97520.

The Edith Stein Guild (*Catholic*), c/o Our Lady of Victory Church, 60 William Street, New York, NY 10005.

Editorial Communications, Inc. (*New Age*), c/o Roland Gammon, Executive Director, 575 Madison Avenue, New York, NY 10022.

Editorial Council of the Religious Press, (See The Associated Church Press).

Edmundite Seminary Guild (*Catholic*), 15 Allen Street, Mystic, CT 06355.

Education for Christian Life and Mission, National Council of Churches, 475 Riverside Drive, New York, NY 10115.

Education in the Society (*National Council of Churches*), 475 Riverside Drive — Room 710, New York, NY 10115.

The Educational Center (*Episcopal*), 6357 Clayton Road, St. Louis, MO 63117.

Educational Foundation for Jewish Girls, (See Jewish Foundation for Education of Women).

Eductivism (*Psychic*), 1335 Lincoln Blvd. — Suite 203, Santa Monica, CA 90401.

Egyptian Holy Church, (See Pristine Egyptian Orthodox Church).

Eighth Day Center for Justice (*Catholic*), 22 East Van Buren, Chicago, IL 60605.

ELIM, (See Evangelical Lutherans in Mission).

Elim Ministerial Fellowship (*Pentecostal*), (See Elim Missionary Assemblies).

Elim Missionary Assemblies (*Pentecostal*), Elim Bible Institute, Lima, NY 14485.

Embassy of the Gheez-Americans (*Psychic*), Mt. Helion Sanctuary, Rock Valley Road — Box 53, Long Eddy, NY 12760.

EMFJ Ministries, (Ex-Mormons for Jesus), P.O. Box 1076, Issaquah, WA 98027.

Emissary Communities, (See Ontological Society).

Emissary Society, (See Ontological Society).

Emmanuel Association (*Holiness*), West Cucharras and 27th Street, Colorado Springs, CO 80904.

Emmanuel Holiness Church (*Pentecostal*), P.O. Box 818, Bladenboro, NC 28320.

Emunah Women of America (*Jewish*), 370 Seventh Avenue — Suite 11 N, New York, NY 10001.

Encounter Ministries, Inc., c/o Dr. Stephen F. Olford, President, P.O. Box 1366, Holmes Beach, FL 33509.

End Time Body-Christian Ministries, c/o Christian Ministries Day School, 1305 State Street, Lake Township, Canton, OH 44720.

"Enlightenment Intensives", (See Dyad School of Enlightenment).

Enthronement of the Sacred Heart in the Home (*Catholic*), Three Adams Street, Fairhaven, MA 02719.

Entibond (*New Age*), c/o Rev. Frank L. Ziegler, Director, 3807 West 119th Place, Hawthorne, CA 90250.

Epiphanes Pantheist Communion (*Neo-Paganism*), P.O. Box 25129, Chicago, IL 60625.

Epiphany Bible Students Association, 1507 North Donnelly Avenue, Mt. Dora, FL 32757.

Episcopal Actor's Guild of America, One East 29th Street, New York, NY 10016.

Episcopal Charismatic Fellowship, (See Episcopal Renewal Ministries).

The Episcopal Church, (See Protestant Episcopal Church).

Episcopal Church Committee on Social Responsibility in Investments, 815 Second Avenue, New York, NY 10017.

Episcopal Church, Evangelical, (See Evangelical Episcopal Church).

Episcopal Churchmen for South Africa, 853 Broadway, New York, NY 10003.

Episcopal Commission for Black Ministries, 815 Second Avenue, New York, NY 10017.

Episcopal Communicators, c/o Rev. David G. Pritchard, Episcopal Diocese Office, 1335 Asylum Avenue, Hartford, CT 06105.

Episcopal Conference of the Deaf, 504 West Hanover Street, Hanover, PA 17331.

Episcopal Foundation for Drama, P.O. Box 8934, Universal City, CA 91602.

Episcopal Guild for the Blind, 157 Montague Street, Brooklyn, NY 11201.

Episcopal Laymen's Mission Society, c/o William Temple House, 615 N.W. 20th Avenue, Portland, OR 97209.

Episcopal Peace Fellowship, 61 Gramercy Park North, New York, NY 10010.

Episcopal Radio-TV Foundation, 3376 Peachtree Road, N.E., Atlanta, GA 30326.

Episcopal Renewal Ministries, 769 Wye Road, Bath, OH 44210.

Episcopal School Association, (See National Association of Episcopal Schools).

Episcopal Young Adult Ministry Network, c/o Episcopal Church Center, 815 Second Avenue, New York, NY 10017.

The Epsilon Society (*Swedenborgian*), 74 Park Drive, Glenview, IL 60025.

Ernest Angley Ministries, Akron, OH 44309.

Ernest Holmes Research Foundation, (See The Holmes Center for Research in Holistic Healing).

Ernesto A. Montgomery Crusades, P.O. Box 19549, Los Angeles, CA 90019.

Esoteric Fraternity (*Communal*), P.O. Box 37, Applegate, CA 95703.

The Esoteric Philosophy Center, 523 Lovett Blvd., Houston, TX 77006.

Esoteric Traditions Research Society, (See Neo-Pythagorean Gnostic Church).

ESP Laboratory (*Psychic*), 7559 Santa Monica Blvd., Los Angeles, CA 90046.

ESP Research Associates Foundation, 1630 Union National Plaza, Little Rock, AR 72201.

Essene School of Thought (*Psychic*), 831 West Fir, San Diego, CA 92101.

The Essene Teachings, Inc. (*Psychic*), c/o Dr. Mary L. Myers, Executive Secretary, 3427 Denson Place, Charlotte, NC 28215.

Essene Universe Foundation (*Psychic*), 405 West Coso, P.O. Box 421, Ridgecrest, CA 93555.

The Estonian Evangelical Lutheran Church, c/o Dr. Arthur Voobus, 230 South Euclid Avenue, Oak Park, IL 60302.

Ethel Tulloch Banks Memorial Healing Prayer Fellowship, 2243 Front Street, San Diego, CA 92101.

Etherian Religious Society of Universal Brotherhood (*Psychic*), P.O. Box 446, San Marcos, CA 92069.

Ethiopian Hebrew Culture Center, (See United Hebrew Congregation).

Ethiopian Orthodox Church of the Western Hemisphere, 140-142 West 176th Street, P.O. Box 292, Bronx, NY 10451.

Ethiopian Orthodox Coptic Church, Diocese of North and South America, c/o Most Rev. Abune Gabre Kristos Mikael, 1255 Bedford Avenue, Brooklyn, NY 11216.

Ethiopian Overcoming Holy Church of God (*Pentecostal*), (See Apostolic Overcoming Holy Church of God).

Ethnic Ministry Program (*Episcopal*), 815 Second Avenue, New York, NY 10017.

Eucharistic Catholic Church, c/o Church of the Beloved Disciple, 348 West 14th Street, New York, NY 10014.

Eucharistic Guard for Nocturnal Adoration (*Catholic*), 800 North Country Club Road, Tucson, AZ 85716.

European Evangelistic Society (*Christian Church*), P.O. Box 268, Aurora, IL 60507.

The Eurythmy Association of North America (*Anthroposophical Society*), c/o Mrs. Ruth Pusch, 224 Hungry Hollow Road, Spring Valley, NY 10977.

Evangel Missionary Fellowship, P.O. Box 25, Largo, FL 33540.

The Evangelical Alliance Mission, P.O. Box 969, Wheaton, IL 60187.

Evangelical and Catholic Mission (*Episcopal*), 133 West 46th Street, New York, NY 10036.

Evangelical and Reformed Church, (See United Church of Christ).

Evangelical and Reformed Historical Society, c/o Philip Schaff Library, Lancaster Theological Seminary, 555 West James Street, Lancaster, PA 17603.

Evangelical Association of Adventists, (See Advent Christian Church).

Evangelical Baptist Missions, Inc., c/o David L. Marshall, General Director, P.O. Box 2225, Kokomo, IN 46901.

Evangelical Bible Church (*Pentecostal*), (Evangelical Church of God), 2444 Washington Blvd., Baltimore, MD 21230.

Evangelical Catholic Communion, c/o Bishop John Andrew, Community of Saint Francis, South Newbury, VT 05066.

Evangelical Christian Churches, (See American Evangelical Christian Churches).

Evangelical Christian Publishers Association, P.O. Box 35, La Habra, CA 90631.

The Evangelical Church, (See The United Methodist Church).

The Evangelical Church Alliance, P.O. Box 9, Bradley, IL 60915.

Evangelical Church Library Association, P.O. Box 353, Glen Ellyn, IL 60137.

Evangelical Church of Christ (Holiness), 1938 Savannah Place, S.E., Washington, DC 20020.

Evangelical Church of North America (*Holiness*), c/o Dr. V. A. Ballantyne, Superintendent, 8719 Johns Drive, Indianapolis, IN 46234.

Evangelical Communication Research Foundation, 2848 West Kingsley, Garland, TX 75041.

Evangelical Congregational Church, 100 West Park Avenue, Myerstown, PA 17067.

Evangelical Council for Financial Accountability, P.O. Box 1750, Pasadena, CA 91109.

The Evangelical Covenant Church of America, 5101 North Francisco Avenue, Chicago, IL 60625.

Evangelical Education Society (*Episcopal*), 251 South Broad Street — Room 301, Philadelphia, PA 19107.

Evangelical Enterprises, Inc., c/o Rev. Willis Stitt, Director, P.O. Box 1555, Topeka, KS 66601.

Evangelical Episcopal Church, c/o Rt. Rev. Dean Stephens, 4602 Lanier Drive, Savannah, GA 31405.

Evangelical Fellowship Chapels, (See Fellowship Deaconry, Inc.).

Evangelical Foreign Missions Association, 1430 K Street, N.W., Washington, DC 20005.

Evangelical Free Baptist Church, Inc., P.O. Box 529, Addison, IL 60101.

The Evangelical Free Church Association, (See The Evangelical Free Church of America).

The Evangelical Free Church of America, 1515 East 66th Street, Minneapolis, MN 55423.

Evangelical Friends Alliance, c/o Galen Weingart, 2462 Easton Street, N.E., North Canton, OH 44721.

Evangelical Friends Church, Eastern Region c/o Galen Weingart, 2462 Easton Street, N.E., North Canton, OH 44721.

Evangelical Literature Overseas, P.O. Box 725, Wheaton, IL 60187.

The Evangelical Lutheran Church, (See The American Lutheran Church).

Evangelical Lutheran Church in America (Eielsen Synod), c/o Rev. Thore Larson, Jackson, MN 56143.

The Evangelical Lutheran Federation, c/o Rev. E. C. Dobberstein, P.O. Box 477, Kingston, WA 98346.

Evangelical Lutheran Fellowship, P.O. Box 8, Cannon Falls, MN 55009.

The Evangelical Lutheran Joint Synod of Ohio and Other States, (See The American Lutheran Church).

Evangelical Lutheran Joint Synod of Wisconsin and Other States, (See Wisconsin Evangelical Lutheran Synod).

Evangelical Lutheran Sanatorium Association, (See Wheat Ridge Foundation).

Evangelical Lutheran Synod, c/o Bethany Lutheran College, 734 Marsh Street, Mankato, MN 56001.

Evangelical Lutheran Synod of Iowa and Other States, (See The American Lutheran Church).

The Evangelical Lutheran Synod of Missouri, Ohio, and Other States, (See The Lutheran Church-Missouri Synod).

Evangelical Lutherans in Mission, 539 North Grand, St. Louis, MO 63103.

Evangelical Mennonite Brethren Conference, 5800 South 14th Street, Omaha, NE 68107.

Evangelical Mennonite Church, Inc., 1420 Kerrway Court, Fort Wayne, IN 46805.

Evangelical Mennonites, (See The Missionary Church).

Evangelical Methodist Church, 3000 West Kellogg Drive, Wichita, KS 67213.

The Evangelical Methodist Church of America, P.O. Box 751, Kingsport, TN 37662.

Evangelical Ministers & Churches International, 105 Madison Street, Chicago, IL 60602.

Evangelical Ministries, Inc., 1716 Spruce Street, Philadelphia, PA 19103.

Evangelical Mission Covenant Church of America, (See The Evangelical Covenant Church of America).

Evangelical Missionary Alliance, (See The Christian and Missionary Alliance).

Evangelical Missions Information Service, P.O. Box 794, Wheaton, IL 60187.

The Evangelical Orthodox Church, P.O. Box 1325, Isla Vista, CA 93017.

Evangelical Orthodox Church in America (Non-Papal Catholic), c/o Most Rev. Frederick L. Pyman, P.O. Box 982, San Jose, CA 95108.

Evangelical Philosophical Society, c/o Stephen Clinton, International Christian Graduate University, San Bernardino, CA 92414.

Evangelical Presbyterian Church, (See Reformed Presbyterian Church, Evangelical Synod).

Evangelical Presbyterian Church, c/o Rev. Calvin Gray, First Presbyterian Church, 2799 West Road, Trenton, MI 48183.

Evangelical Press Association, c/o Gary Warner, Director, P.O. Box 4550, Overland Park, KS 66204.

Evangelical Scripture Mission, 134 South Ferry Street, Monroe, WA 98272.

Evangelical Sisterhood of Mary, c/o Canaan in the Desert, 9849 North 40th Street, Phoenix, AZ 85028.

Evangelical Slovak Women's Union, (See United Lutheran Society).

Evangelical Student News Service, c/o Biola College, La Mirada, CA 90639.

Evangelical Teacher Training Association, P.O. Box 327, Wheaton, IL 60187.

Evangelical Theological Society, 5422 Clinton Blvd., Jackson, MS 39209.

The Evangelical United Brethren Church, (See The United Methodist Church).

Evangelical Unity of the Czech-Moravian Brethren in North America, (See Unity of the Brethren).

Evangelical Wesleyan Church (*Holiness*), 2400 Avenue East, Kearney, NE 68847.

Evangelical Wesleyan Church of North America (*Holiness*), (See Evangelical Wesleyan Church).

Evangelicals Concerned, c/o Dr. Ralph Blair, 30 East 60th Street — Suite 803, New York, NY 10022.

Evangelicals for Social Action, c/o Ronald J. Sider, President, 300 West Apsley Street, Philadelphia, PA 19144.

Evangelism in Music Ministries, Inc. (*Pentecostal*), P.O. Box 2114, Melbourne, FL 32901.

Evangelism to Communist Lands, P.O. Box 303, Glendale, CA 91209.

Evangelistic Faith Missions, c/o Victor Glenn, P.O. Box 609, Bedford, IN 47421.

Evangelistic Ministerial Alliance, (See Bethel Ministerial Association, Inc.).

Evangelistic Outreach, Inc., P.O. Box 56, Pedro, OH 45659.

Evangelize China Fellowship, P.O. Box 550, Los Angeles, CA 90053.

Evolutionist Society, P.O. Box 246, Stamford, CT 06904.

Ewan Chowden Tibetan Buddhist Center, 254 Cambridge Street, Kensington, CA 94707.

"Ex-Christian Scientists for Jesus", (See New Beginnings).

Ex-Jehovah's Witnesses for Jesus, c/o William I. Cetnar, Route 2, Weir Lake Road, Kunkletown, PA 18058.

The Ex-members Against Moon, P.O. Box 62, Brookline, MA 02146.

Ex-Mormons for ERA, c/o Equal Rights Coalition of Utah, P.O. Box 1533, Salt Lake City, UT 84110.

Ex-Mormons for Jesus, (See EMFJ Ministries).

Eymard League (*Catholic*), 194 East 76th Street, New York, NY 10021.

Ezrat Nashim (*Jewish*), 81 Columbia Heights, Brooklyn, NY 11201.

F.A.C.T. (*New Age*), (Foundation for Alternative Cancer Therapies), P.O. Box 48, Wynnewood, PA 19096.

Faith Alive (*Episcopal*), c/o Fred C. Gore, President, 373 West Market Street, P.O. Box 21, York, PA 17405.

Faith Bible and Tract Society, 61 Oak Street, Salem, WV 26426.

Faith Broadcasting Network, Inc., P.O. Box 32147, Minneapolis, MN 55432.

Faith City, Inc., 415 East 5th Street, Amarillo, TX 79101.

Faith Communion Free Spiritual Community and Church (*New Age*), 1604 West 11th Avenue, Spokane, WA 99204.

Faith Ministries and Publications, P.O. Box 904, Warsaw, IN 46580.

Faith Ministries, Inc., 22 Gallivan, Greenville, SC 29609.

Faith Mission Church (*Holiness*), c/o Rev. Ray Snow, 1318 26th Street, Bedford, IN 47421.

Faith Mission Society (*Lutheran*), c/o Bethany Lutheran College, 734 Marsh Street, Mankato, MN 56001.

Faith Outreach Ministries (*Pentecostal*), P.O. Box 844, Canyon, TX 79015.

Faith Prison Ministries (*Pentecostal*), P.O. Box 18702, Tampa, FL 33679.

Faith Women of America (*Pentecostal*), P.O. Box 433, Pine Lake, GA 30072.

Families for Christ (*Catholic*), 6026 West Harwood Avenue, Orlando, FL 32811.

Family Communion Crusade, Inc. (*Catholic*), c/o Rev. Hector C. Lemieux, Executive Director, 194 East 76th Street, New York, NY 10021.

Family Crusades, 2209 Windsor, Waco, TX 76708.

Family Henge (*Witchcraft*), c/o Ron Genzoli, 451 Valle Vista, Hayward, CA 94544.

Family Location and Legal Services (*Jewish*), (See Jewish Family Service).

Family of Love, (See Children of God).

Family Rosary Crusade (*Catholic*), 773 Madison Avenue, Albany, NY 12208.

Family Rosary, Inc. (*Catholic*), (See Family Rosary Crusade).

Far East Broadcasting Company, P.O. Box 1, La Mirada, CA 90637.

Far Eastern Gospel Crusade, c/o Philip E. Armstrong, General Director, P.O. Box 513, Farmington, MI 48024.

Far Eastern Literature Fellowship, P.O. Box 8161, Chattanooga, TN 37411.

Far Eastern Refugee Service, (See American Mission to the Chinese and Asian).

Far Horizons Theosophical Sierra Camp, 125 Conifer Lane, Walnut Creek, CA 94598.

The Farm (*Communal*), RFD 1 — Box 197, Summertown, TN 38483.

FARMS, Inc., 123 West 57th Street, New York, NY 10019.

The Father's House (*New Age*), 2656 Newhall Street — No. 43, Santa Clara, CA 95050.

Fathers of the Good Shepherd, 3585 Fourth Avenue, San Diego, CA 92103.

The Federal Council of the Churches of Christ in America, (See the National Council of Churches of Christ in the U.S.A.).

Federated Council of Beth Jacob Schools (*Jewish*), 142 Broome Street, New York, NY 10002.

Federated Norwegian Lutheran Young People's Societies of America, (See Lutheran Mission Societies).

Federated Russian Orthodox Clubs, 10 Downs Drive, Wilkes-Barre, PA 18705.

Federation for Authentic Lutheranism, (See Conference of Authentic Lutherans).

Federation of Diocesan Liturgical Commissions (*Catholic*), 1307 South Wabash, Chicago, IL 60605.

The Federation of Islamic Associations in the United States and Canada, 300 East 44th Street — 2nd Floor, New York, NY 10017.

Federation of Jewish Philanthropies of New York, 130 East 59th Street, New York, NY 10022.

Federation of Jewish Women's Organizations, 55 West 42nd Street, New York, NY 10036.

Federation of Latvian Evangelical Lutheran Churches in America, (See The Latvian Evangelical Lutheran Church in America)

Federation of Protestant Welfare Agencies, 281 Park Avenue South, New York, NY 10010.

Federation of Reconstructionist Congregations and Fellowships (*Jewish*), (See Reconstructionist Federation of Congregations and Fellowships).

The Fellowship (*Episcopal*), P.O. Box 6, Howard University, Washington, DC 20059.

Fellowship Deaconry, Inc., P.O. Box 204, Liberty Corner, NJ 07938.

Fellowship for a Biblical Church (*Lutheran*), c/o Rev. Marvin Huggins, 1110 Nixon Drive, Norton, KS 67654.

Fellowship for Original Free-Will Baptists, (See General Conference of Original Free Will Baptists).

The Fellowship for Spiritual Understanding (*New Age*), c/o Dr. Marcus Bach, Director, P.O. Box 816, Palos Verdes Estates, CA 90274.

Fellowship Foundational Teachings (*Pentecostal*), P.O. Box 6598, Silver Spring, MD 20906.

Fellowship in Israel for Arab-Jewish Youth, c/o Mrs. Krister Stendahl, 45 Francis Avenue, Cambridge, MA 02138.

Fellowship in Prayer, 20 Nassau Street — Suite 250 E, Princeton, NJ 08540.

Fellowship of Campus Ministry, (See National Campus Ministry Association).

Fellowship of Catholic Scholars, c/o St. John's University, Jamaica, NY 11439.

Fellowship of Charismatic Christians in the United Church of Christ, P.O. Box 12, Sassamansville, PA 19472.

The Fellowship of Christian Assemblies (*Pentecostal*), c/o Fellowship Press, 657 West 18th Street, Los Angeles, CA 90015.

Fellowship of Christian Athletes, 8701 Leeds Road, Kansas City, MO 64129.

Fellowship of Christian Magicians, 1705 Barbara Lane, Connersville, IN 47331.

Fellowship of Christian Men, c/o Julius Rose, P.O. Box 188, Richland, NJ 08350.

Fellowship of Christian Peace Officers, P.O. Box 30179, Los Angeles, CA 90030.

Fellowship of Christian Pilgrims (*Pentecostal*), 133 Hualalai, Kailua Kona, HI 96740.

Fellowship of Christian Policemen, (See Fellowship of Christian Peace Officers).

Fellowship of Christian Racers, P.O. Box 363, Jonesboro, LA 71251.

The Fellowship of Concerned Churchmen (*Anglican Catholic Church*), P.O. Box 252, Eureka Springs, AR 72632.

Fellowship of Conservative Southern Baptists, P.O. Box 1184, Naples, FL 33939.

Fellowship of Contemplative Prayer (*Anglican*), P.O. Box 75, Mount Vernon, VA 22121.

Fellowship of Fundamental Baptist Churches, c/o Rev. Paul Brewer, R.R. 2, Lepreau, New Brunswick, Canada.

Fellowship of Gospel Churches, (See The Evangelical Free Church of America).

Fellowship of Grace Brethren Churches, c/o Clyde K. Landrum, Secretary, 1180 Chestnut Avenue, Winona Lake, IN 46590.

Fellowship of Hesperides (*Neo-Paganism*), (See Fereferia).

Fellowship of Independent Evangelical Churches, c/o Howard Boyll, Secretary, 2311 Anderson Street, Bristol, TN 37620.

Fellowship of Independent Methodists, Inc., P.O. Box 361, Macon, MS 39341.

Fellowship of Independent Missions (*Independent Fundamental Church of America*), c/o Rev. Philip Weiss, P.O. Box 72, Fairless Hills, PA 19030.

Fellowship of Methodist Pacifists, (See Methodist Peace Fellowship).

The Fellowship of Missions, c/o William J. Hopewell, Jr., D. D., President, 4205 Chester Avenue, Cleveland, OH 44103.

Fellowship of Pan (*Witchcraft*), P.O. Box 58024, Houston, TX 77058.

Fellowship of Reconciliation, P.O. Box 271, Nyack, NY 10960.

Fellowship of Religious Humanists, 105 West North College Street, Yellow Springs, OH 45387.

The Fellowship of St. Gregory and St. Augustine (*Anglican and Roman Catholic*), c/o Holy Cross Monastery, West Park, NY 12493.

Fellowship of Saint James of Jerusalem, P.O. Box 2693, Terminal Annex, Los Angeles, CA 90051.

Fellowship of Southern Churchmen, (See Committee of Southern Churchmen).

Fellowship of the Awakening, 1701 Spruce Street, Berkeley, CA 94709.

Fellowship of the Body of Christ (*Pentecostal*), 210 Third Avenue, N.E., Grand Rapids, MN 55744.

The Fellowship of the Inner Light (*Psychic*), 620 14th Street, Virginia Beach, VA 23451.

Fellowship of United Methodist Musicians, P.O. Box 840, Nashville, TN 37202.

Fellowship of Universal Guidance (*New Age*), c/o Dr. Wayne A. Guthrie, 1524 West Glenoaks Blvd., Glendale, CA 91201.

Fellowship of World Christians, c/o David B. Graham, Director, 1605 East Elizabeth, Pasadena, CA 91104.

Fereferia (*Neo-Paganism*), P.O. Box 41363, Eagle Rock, CA 90041.

Filipino Assemblies of the First Born, Inc. (*Pentecostal*), 1229 Glenwood, Delano, CA 93215.

Filipino Community Churches in Hawaii, 838 Kanoa Street, Honolulu, HI 96817.

Finnish-American Historical Archives (*Lutheran*), c/o Suomi College, Hancock, MI 49930.

Finnish Apostolic Lutheran Church of America, (See Apostolic Lutheran Church of America).

Finnish Evangelical Lutheran Church of America (Suomi Synod), (See Lutheran Church in America).

The Finnish Interest Conference of the Lutheran Church in America, c/o Rev. E. Olaf Rankinen, Suomi College, Hancock, MI 49930.

Fire-Baptized Holiness Association, (See Pentecostal Holiness Church, Inc.; see also Fire Baptized Holiness Church of God in the Americas).

Fire Baptized Holiness Association of Southeastern Kansas, (See Fire Baptized Holiness Church — Wesleyan).

Fire-Baptized Holiness Church, (See Pentecostal Holiness Church, Inc.).

Fire Baptized Holiness Church of God, (See Fire Baptized Holiness Church of God in the Americas).

Fire Baptized Holiness Church of God in the Americas (*Pentecostal*), 130 Jackson Street, N.E., Atlanta, GA 30312.

Fire Baptized Holiness Church (Wesleyan) (*Holiness*), 600 College Avenue, Independence, KS 67301.

First Catholic Slovak Ladies' Association, U.S.A., 24950 Chagrin Blvd., Beachwood, OH 44122.

First Catholic Slovak Ladies Union, (See First Catholic Slovak Ladies' Association, U.S.A.).

First Catholic Slovak Union (Jednota), 3289 East 55th Street, Cleveland, OH 44127.

First Century Christian Fellowship, (See Moral Re-Armament).

First Century Church (*Psychic*), c/o Rev. David Buber, P.O. Box 4300, Memphis, TN 38104.

The First Church in Community of the Cosmic Christ (*New Age*), P.O. Box 1059, Ojai, CA 93023.

First Church of Jesus Christ (*Pentecostal*), 1100 East Lincoln Street, Tullahoma, TN 37388.

First Church of Spiritual Vision, (See Universal Brotherhood).

First Church of Wicca of Marin (*Witchcraft*), P.O. Box 126, Mill Valley, CA 94941.

First Congregational Methodist Church of the U.S.A., c/o Rev. Austin Watson, P.O. Box 67, Florence, MS 39073.

First Deliverance Church (*Pentecostal*), 65 Hardwick Street, S.E., Atlanta, GA 30315.

First Fellowship of Neo-Pagans, P.O. Box 12415, San Francisco, CA 94112.

First Interdenominational Christian Association (*Pentecostal*), Calvary Temple Holiness Church, 1061 Memorial Drive, S.E., Atlanta, GA 30316.

First Samoan Full Gospel Pentecostal Church, 522 Carter Street, San Francisco, CA 94134.

First Temple of Astrology, c/o Harriet K. Banes, 733 South Burlington Avenue, Los Angeles, CA 90057.

First Temple of Universal Law, 5030 North Drake, Chicago, IL 60625.

First Wiccan Church of Minnesota (*Witchcraft*), 476 Summit Avenue, St. Paul, MN 55102.

First Zen Institute of America, Inc. (*Buddhist*), 113 East 30th Street, New York, NY 10016.

Fischel Foundation (*Jewish*), (See Harry and Jane Fischel Foundation).

Fishers of Men Opportunities, Inc., (See Fishers of Men Theatrical Agency).

Fishers of Men Theatrical Agency, c/o Bob Green, 925 Arthur Godfrey Road, Miami Beach, FL 33140.

Fishnet Ministries, Inc. (*Pentecostal*), P.O. Box 29889, Richmond, VA 23229.

Five Years Meeting of Friends, (See Friends United Meeting).

Fivefold Path, Inc. (*Hindu*), c/o Parama Dham, RFD 1 — Box 121, Madison, VA 22727.

Florida Council of Churches, 122 East Colonial Drive, Orlando, FL 32801.

Florida Society for Psychical Research, c/o Laura Langan, 4312 South 46th Avenue, St. Petersburg, FL 33711.

Focolare Movement (*Catholic*), P.O. Box 496, New York, NY 10021.

The Fold, Inc., RFD 2, Lyndonville, VT 05851.

Followers of Christ, c/o Elder Marion Morris, Route 2, Ringwood, OK 73768.

Food for the Hungry International, 7729 East Greenway Road, Scottsdale, AZ 85260.

The Foreign Missions Conference of North America, (See the National Council of Churches of Christ in the U.S.A.).

Forest Home Christian Conference Center, Forest Falls, CA 92339.

The Forever Family, (See Church of Bible Understanding).

Forever Forests (*Neo-Paganism*), P.O. Box 212, Redwood Valley, CA 95470.

Fort Worth Area Council of Churches, 1000 Macon Street, Fort Worth, TX 76102.

The FORUM (*New Age*), c/o Carol Bell, Director, 25166 Southport, Laguna Hills, CA 92653.

The Forum for Scriptural Christianity, Inc. (*United Methodist Church*), 308 East Main Street, Wilmore, KY 40390.

The Foundation Church, (See Foundation Faith of God).

Foundation Church of the Millennium, (See Foundation Faith of God).

Foundation Church of the New Birth (*Spiritualist*), P.O. Box 996, Benjamin Franklin Station, Washington, DC 20044.

The Foundation Faith, (See Foundation Faith of God).

Foundation Faith of God (*Psychic*), P.O. Box 5424, Phoenix, AZ 85010.

The Foundation Faith of the Millenium, (See Foundation Faith of God).

Foundation for a Christian Civilization, Estate of Our Lady of Good Success, Bedford Hills, NY 10507.

Foundation for American Christian Education, 2946 25th Avenue, San Francisco, CA 94132.

Foundation for Better Living, 225 East 63rd Street — Lobby H, New York, NY 10021.

Foundation for Biblical Research (*Adventist*), P.O. Box 928, Pasadena, CA 91102.

The Foundation for Biblical Research and Preservation of Primitive Christianity (*Church of Christ, Scientist*), P.O. Box 373, Charlestown, NH 03603.

Foundation for Christian Living, c/o Ruth Stafford Peale, Pawling, NY 12564.

Foundation for Christian Theology (*Episcopal/Anglican*), 403 North Main, P.O. Box 2624, Victoria, TX 77901.

Foundation for Episcopal Colleges, (See Association of Episcopal Colleges).

Foundation for Inner Peace, c/o Judith R. Skutch, President, P.O. Box 635, Tiburon, CA 94920.

Foundation for Religion and Mental Health, 30 South State Road, Briarcliff Manor, NY 10510.

Foundation for Spiritual Understanding, (See The Fellowship for Spiritual Understanding).

Foundation for the Arts, Religion and Culture, (See Society for the Arts, Religion and Contemporary Culture).

Foundation for the Jewish National Fund, 42 East 69th Street, New York, NY 10021.

Foundation for the Science of Spiritual Law, c/o Dr. Alfred Holmer, Tonopah, AZ 85354.

Foundation for TOWARD THE LIGHT, 16645 Bosque Drive, Encino, CA 91436.

Foundation for Universal Understanding (*New Age*), 8623 Holloway Drive, Los Angeles, CA 90069.

Foundation of Human Understanding (*New Age*), P.O. Box 34036, 8780 Venice Blvd., Los Angeles, CA 90034.

Foundation of Infinite Metaphysics (*New Age*), P.O. Box 9821, North Hollywood, CA 91609.

Foundation of Religious Transition, (See The Love Project).

Foundation of Revelation (*Hindu*), 59 Scott Street, San Francisco, CA 94117.

Foundation of Scientific Spiritual Understanding, P.O. Box 93, Redondo Beach, CA 90277.

Foundation of Truth (*New Age*), 270 15th Street, N.E., P.O. Box 7133, Atlanta, GA 30309.

Foundation of Universal Truth (*New Age*), 1015 South Manhattan Place, Los Angeles, CA 90019.

The Foundation of Your Life (*New Age*), c/o Ron Podrow, Director, P.O. Box 9176, San Diego, CA 92109.

Foundation of Life Fellowship (*Adventist*), c/o James L. Porter, Valley Center, KS 67147.

Foursquare Worldwide Missions (*Pentecostal*), 1100 Glendale Blvd., Los Angeles, CA 90026.

"Fourth Way Conventions" (*Sufism*), (See Second Foundation).

Franciscan Communications Center (*Catholic*), c/o Fr. Anthony Scannell, 1229 South Santee Street, Los Angeles, CA 90015.

Franciscan Education Center (*Catholic*), 774 South Lake Shore Drive, Lake Geneva, WI 53147.

Franciscan Educational Conference (*Catholic*), c/o Capuchin Seminary of St. Mary, Crown Point, IN 46307.

The Franciscan Institute (*Catholic*), c/o St. Bonaventure University, St. Bonaventure, NY 14778.

Franciscan Missionary Union (*Catholic*), 135 West 31st Street, New York, NY 10001.

Franciscan Vocation Conference (*Catholic*), 3320 St. Paschal Drive, Oak Brook, IL 60521.

The Frank Gavin Liturgical Foundation, Inc., P.O. Box 25, Mount Sinai, L.I., NY 11766.

Frank J. Lewis Foundation (*Catholic*), P.O. Box 9726, Riviera Beach, FL 33404.

Fransisters and Brothers, 2168 South Lafayette Street, Denver, CO 80210.

Fraternitas Rosae Crucis, (See Rosicrucian Fraternity).

The Fraternity of Jesus, c/o Rev. Royce Hughes, Director, P.O. Box 214, Houston, TX 77001.

Fred B. Snite Foundation (*Catholic*), 4800 North Western, Chicago, IL 60625.

Free and Old Christian Reformed Churches in Canada, (See Free Reformed Churches of North America).

The Free Bible Literature Society, P.O. Box 201, Hawthorne, NJ 07507.

Free Christian Zion Church of Christ, 1315 Hutchinson Street, Nashville, AR 71852.

The Free Church of Berkeley, 2200 Parker Street, Berkeley, CA 94704.

Free Gospel Church (*Pentecostal*), c/o Rev. Chester H. Heath, P.O. Box 477, Export, PA 15632.

Free Magyar Reformed Church in America, (See Hungarian Reformed Church in America).

Free Methodist Church of North America (*Holiness*), 901 College Avenue, Winona Lake, IN 46590.

Free Methodist World Fellowship, 9th and College, Winona Lake, IN 46590.

Free Minds, Inc., P.O. Box 4216, Minneapolis, MN 55414.

The Free Primitive Church of Divine Communion (*Hindu*), P.O. Box 3680, Clearlake Highlands, CA 95422.

Free Reformed Church, (See Free Reformed Churches of North America).

Free Reformed Churches of North America, 950 Ball Avenue, N.E., Grand Rapids, MI 49503.

Free Sons of Israel (*Jewish*), 932 Broadway, New York, NY 10010.

Free Thinkers of America, Inc., c/o Martin J. Martin, G.P.O. Box 1654, New York, NY 10001.

Free Will Baptist Church of the Pentecostal Faith, P.O. Box 278, Elgin, SC 29045.

Free Will Baptist Press Foundation, Inc., 811 North Lee Street, Ayden, NC 28513.

Free Will Baptists, (See National Association of Free Will Baptists).

Freedom From Religion Foundation, 30 West Mifflin Street — Suite 312, Madison, WI 53703.

Freedom of Faith, (A Christian Committee of Religious Rights), 106 West 56th Street, New York, NY 10019.

Freeland League (*Jewish*), (See League for Yiddish).

Freeland League for Jewish Territorial Colonization, (See League for Yiddish).

Freeman Memorial Anticult Foundation, c/o Robert Felton, P.O. Box 3598, Akron, OH 44310.

Friedland Family Foundation (*Jewish*), (See Samuel Friedland Family Foundation).

Friendly Hills Fellowship (*New Age*), 26126 Fairview Avenue, Hemet, CA 92343.

Friends Africa Gospel Mission, c/o Dr. John L. Robinson, General Superintendent, 2018 Maple, Wichita, KS 67213.

The Friends' Committee for Gay Concerns, P.O. Box 222, Sumneytown, PA 18084.

Friends Committee on National Legislation, 245 Second Street, N.E., Washington, DC 20002.

Friends Coordinating Committee on Peace, c/o Robert Rumsey, Friends World Committee, P.O. Box 235, Plainfield, IN 46168.

Friends Council on Education, 1507 Cherry Street, Philadelphia, PA 19102.

Friends General Meeting, (See Philadelphia Yearly Meeting of the Religious Society of Friends).

Friends Historical Association, Haverford College Library, Haverford, PA 19041.

Friends Historical Society of Philadelphia, (See Friends Historical Association).

Friends of Buddhism, c/o Frank Baker, 211 Ward Avenue, Staten Island, NY 10304.

Friends of Buddhism, Inc., 306 Caroline Street, Fredericksburg, VA 22401.

The Friends of Israel Gospel Ministry, 475 White Horse Pike, West Collingswood, NJ 08107.

Friends of Israel Missionary and Relief Society, Inc., (See The Friends of Israel Gospel Ministry).

Friends of Meher Baba (*Sufism*), P.O. Box 50481, Nashville, TN 37205.

Friends of the Jewish Book, (See Society of Jewish Bibliophiles).

Friends of the Lusitanian Church (*Episcopal*), c/o Rev. Canon Edmund W. Olifiers, Jr., P.O. Box 165, Lindenhurst, NY 11757.

Friends of the World Council of Churches, 475 Riverside Drive — Room 1062, New York, NY 10115.

Friends of Turkey and Postal Evangelism, Inc., c/o Roy L. Marler, Sr., Chairman, Route 4 — Box 197, Rogersville, TN 37857.

Friends Peace Committee, 1515 Cherry Street, Philadelphia, PA 19102.

Friends Religious Conference, (See General Conference of the Religious Society of Friends).

Friends Union for Philanthropic Labor, (See General Conference of the Religious Society of Friends).

Friends United Meeting, 101 Quaker Hill Drive, Richmond, IN 47374.

Friends World Committee for Consultation, American Section, 1506 Race Street, Philadelphia, PA 19102.

Friendship House (*Catholic*), 343 South Dearborn — Room 317, Chicago, IL 60604.

The Friendship Ministry, c/o Dorothy C. Haskin, President, 2218 West Burbank Blvd., Burbank, CA 91506.

Front Line Evangelism, P.O. Box 1501, Tulsa, OK 74101.

Frontline Fellowship, P.O. Box 14407, Louisville, KY 40214.

Full Gospel Assemblies International (*Pentecostal*), c/o Dr. C. E. Strauser, 75 West 5th Avenue, P.O. Box 429, Coatesville, PA 19320.

Full Gospel Business Men's Fellowship International, P.O. Box 5050, Costa Mesa, CA 92626.

Full Gospel Church Association, Inc. (*Pentecostal*), P.O. Box 265, Amarillo, TX 79105.

Full Gospel Defenders Conference of America (*Pentecostal*), 3311 Hartel Avenue, Philadelphia, PA 19136.

Full Gospel Evangelistic Association (*Pentecostal*), 5828 Chippewa Blvd., Houston, TX 77086.

Full Gospel Fellowship of Churches and Ministers, International (*Pentecostal*), 1545 West Mockingbird Lane — Suite 1012, P.O. Box 209, Dallas, TX 75235.

Full Gospel Native Missionary Association (*Pentecostal*), 1605 Wall Street, Joplin, MO 64801.

Full Gospel of Christ Fellowship, 11610 Durant Road, Raleigh, NC 27614.

Full Gospel Pentecostal Association, 1032 North Sumner, Portland, OR 97217.

Full Moon Meditation Groups of Southern California (*New Age*), c/o Intergroup Committee for the Three Linked Festivals, P.O. Box 5105, Beverly Hills, CA 90210.

Full Salvation Union, 51630 West Eight Mile Road, Northville, MI 48167.

Fuller Evangelistic Association, P.O. Box 989, Pasadena, CA 91102.

Fund for Episcopal Colleges, (See Association of Episcopal Colleges).

Fund for Theological Education, 909 State Road, Princeton, NJ 08540.

Fundamental Baptist Congress of North America, 23800 West Chicago, Detroit, MI 48239.

Fundamental Baptist Fellowship, c/o Tabernacle Baptist Church, 717 North Whitehurst Landing Road, Virginia Beach, VA 23464.

Fundamental Brethren Church, c/o Rev. Calvin Barnett, Route 1 Box 304, Greenmountain, NC 28740.

Fundamental Evangelistic Association, P.O. Box 6278, Los Osos, CA 93402.

Fundamental Methodist Church, Inc., 1034 North Broadway, Springfield, MO 65802.

The Fundamental Ministerial Association, (See The Evangelical Church Alliance).

Future Foundation (*Psychic*), P.O. Box 26, Steinauer, NE 68441.

Future Life Church, P.O. Box 43, Leavittsburg, OH 44430.

Gabriel Richard Institute (*Catholic*), 2315 Orleans Street, Detroit, MI 48207.

Gabriel Society of Divine Metaphysics, P.O. Box 105, La Grange, IL 60525.

Gamma Delta, International Association of Lutheran Students, (See Lutheran Student Movement — USA).

Ganden Mahayana Center (*Buddhist*), 5127 Lake Mendota Drive, Madison, WI 53705.

The Garden of Eden Spiritual Society (*New Age*), c/o Russ Sandy, 34 Scenic Road, Fairfax, CA 94930.

The Garden of Sanjivani, P.O. Box 712, Santa Cruz, CA 95060.

Garden State Sikh Association, Inc., c/o Mr. A. S. Mahal, P.O. Box 118, Fords, NJ 08863.

Gardnerian Wicca (*Witchcraft*), P.O. Box 56, Commack, NY 11725.

The Garner Ted Armstrong Evangelistic Association, P.O. Box 2530, Tyler, TX 75710.

Garr Memorial Church (*Pentecostal*), (See Carolina Evangelistic Association).

Gedatsu Church of America (*Buddhist*), 401 Baker, San Francisco, CA 94117.

Geeta Temple Ashram, Inc. (*Hindu*), c/o Swami Jagdishwaranand, 89-14 48th Avenue, Elmhurst, NY 11373.

Gelasian Guild (*Catholic*), c/o James A. Serritella, P.O. Box 4993, Chicago, IL 60680.

Genealogical Society of The Church of Jesus Christ of Latter-day Saints, c/o J. Thomas Fyans, President, 50 East North Temple Street, Salt Lake City, UT 84103.

General Assembly and Church of the First Born (*Pentecostal*), 2719 Tindall Avenue, Indianapolis, IN 46203.

"General Assembly of God (which is God's organism)" (*Pentecostal*), (See Assemblies of God).

General Assembly of the Apostolic Assemblies (*Pentecostal*), (See Pentecostal Assemblies of the World, Inc.).

General Association of Baptist Churches, (See American Baptist Association).

General Association of Baptists, (See Duck River — and Kindred — Associations of Baptists).

General Association of General Baptists, c/o Rev. Glen O. Spence, Executive Secretary, 100 Stinson Drive, Poplar Bluff, MO 63901.

General Association of Regular Baptist Churches, 1300 North Meacham Road, Schaumburg, IL 60195.

General Christian Apostolic Mission, (See New Apostolic Church of North America).

General Church of the New Jerusalem (*Swedenborgian*), Bryn Athyn, PA 19009.

General Commission on Chaplains, (See National Conference on Ministry to the Armed Forces).

General Commission on Chaplains and Armed Forces Personnel, (See National Conference on Ministry to the Armed Forces).

General Conference Mennonite Church, 722 Main Street, Newton, KS 67114.

The General Conference of Brethren Churches, (See Brethren Church — Ashland, Ohio).

General Conference of German Baptist Churches in North America, (See North American Baptist Conference).

General Conference of Original Free Will Baptists, Ayden, NC 28513.

General Conference of the Evangelical Baptist Church, Inc. (*Pentecostal*), Kevetter Bldg., 2400 East Ash Street, Goldsboro, NC 27530.

General Conference of the Religious Society of Friends, 1520-B Race Street, Philadelphia, PA 19102.

General Convention of the New Jerusalem in the U.S.A. (*Swedenborgian*), c/o Mrs. Wilfred Rice, Secretary, 48 Sargent Street, Newton, MA 02158.

General Council of Cooperating Baptist Missions of North America, Inc., (See Baptist Mid-Missions).

General Council of the Churches of God (Seventh Day) (*Adventist*), 302 East Gruber, Meridian, ID 83642.

General Council of the Evangelical Lutheran Church in North America, (See Lutheran Church in America).

General Council on Ministries (*United Methodist Church*), c/o Norman E. Dewire, General Secretary, 601 West Riverview Avenue, Dayton, OH 45406.

General Six-Principle Baptists, c/o Pauline C. Josefson, Clerk, 146 Brunswick Drive, Warwick, RI 02886.

General Synod of the Evangelical Lutheran Church in the U.S.A., (See Lutheran Church in America).

The General Yearly Meeting for Friends of Pennsylvania, East and West Jersey and of the Adjacent Provinces, (See Philadelphia Yearly Meeting of the Religious Society of Friends).

Genesis Fellowship (*Pentecostal*), 2110 N.W. Circle Blvd., Corvallis, OR 97330.

Geneva Point Center (*National Council of Churches*), Star Route 62 — Box 469, Center Harbor, NH 03226.

George Ohsawa Macrobiotic Foundation (*Taoism*), 1544 Oak Street, Oroville, CA 95965.

Georgia Christian Council, 848 Peachtree Street, N.E., Atlanta, GA 30308.

Georgian Church (*Witchcraft*), c/o George Patterson, 1908 Verde Street, Bakersfield, CA 93304.

German Apostolic Christian Church, c/o Elder George Ift, Route 3, Fairbury, IL 61739.

The German Interest Conference of the Lutheran Church in America, c/o Rev. Wolf D. Knappe, Tabor Lutheran Church, 4860 North Howard Street, Philadelphia, PA 19120.

Gideons International, 2900 Lebanon Road, Nashville, TN 37214.

Glastonbury Society (*Anglican*), P.O. Box 4066, Tyler, TX 75712.

Global Congress of the World's Religions, c/o Prof. Warren Lewis, Unification Theological Seminary, Barrytown, NY 12507.

The Global Meditation Committee, 4280A Army Street, San Francisco, CA 94131.

Global Outreach, Inc., P.O. Box 711, Buffalo, NY 14240.

Global Press International, Inc., 203 East McDonald Road, Prospect Heights, IL 60070.

Gnostic Association, 3760 West Lawrence Avenue, Chicago, IL 60625.

God Unlimited (*New Age*), Campo, CA 92006.

God's House of Prayer for All Nations (*Pentecostal*), 1801 Northeast Madison Street, Peoria, IL 61603.

God's Missionary Church, Inc. (*Holiness*), Penns Creek, PA 17862.

The Gold Key Foundation (*New Age*), 1112 Carlisle Blvd., S.E., Albuquerque, NM 87106.

The Golden Key Ministry (*New Age*), P.O. Box 1463, Mesa, AZ 85201.

Good News (*United Methodist Church*), (See The Forum for Scriptural Christianity, Inc.).

The Good News Broadcasting Association, Inc., P.O. Box 82808, Lincoln, NE 68501.

Good News Mission, c/o Rev. Dave Duley, 1036 South Highland Street, Arlington, VA 22204.

Goreichi Spiritual Sanctuary (*Buddhist*), (See Gedatsu Church of America).

Gospel Assembly (*Pentecostal*), c/o Rev. Tom M. Jolly, 500 Kingshighway Blvd., North, St. Louis, MO 63108.

Gospel Assembly Churches (*Pentecostal*), c/o Gospel Assembly Ministers Fund, 100 North Military Highway, Norfolk, VA 23502.

Gospel Association for the Blind, 4705 North Federal Highway, Boca Raton, FL 33431.

Gospel Crusade, Inc., c/o Gerald Derstine, Director, Route 2 — Box 279, Bradenton, FL 33508.

Gospel Furthering Fellowship, Malvern Courts — Lot C II, Malvern, PA 19355.

Gospel Harvester Evangelistic Association (*Pentecostal*), 836 Euclid Avenue, N.E., Atlanta, GA 30307.

Gospel Harvesters Evangelistic Association, Inc. (*Pentecostal*), 1159 Seneca Street, Buffalo, NY 14210.

Gospel Light International, (See Gospel Literature International).

Gospel Literature International, P.O. Box 6688, Ventura, CA 93003.

Gospel Mission Corps (*Holiness*), P.O. Box 175, Hightstown, NJ 08520.

Gospel Missionary Union, 10,000 North Oak, Kansas City, MO 64155.

Gospel Music Association, 38 Music Square West, P.O. Box 23201, Nashville, TN 37203.

The Gospel of Regeneration, c/o Joseph Aidones, Route 1 — Box 34, Hope, AR 71801.

Gospel Outreach, 1300 California Street, P.O. Box 973, Eureka, CA 95501.

Gospel Trail Ministry, c/o Rev. Art Mueller, Director, P.O. Box 411, Fergus Falls, MN 56537.

Gospel Truth Association, c/o Dr. James E. Kurtz, P.O. Box 3563, Bloomington, IL 61701.

Gospel Workers Church of Canada (*Holiness*), (See Church of the Nazarene).

Grace and Hope Mission (*Holiness*), Four South Gay Street, Baltimore, MD 21202.

Grace Gospel Evangelistic Association International, Inc. (*Pentecostal*), c/o Rev. John D. Kennington, 909 N.E. 30th Avenue, Portland, OR 97232.

Grace Gospel Fellowship, 1011 Aldon Street, S.W., Grand Rapids, MI 49509.

Grace Mission, Inc. (*Grace Gospel Fellowship*), c/o Daniel C. Bultema, Executive Director, 2125 Martindale Avenue, S.W., Grand Rapids, MI 49509.

Grace of God Movement for the Women of America, (See Grace of God Movement for the Women of the World).

Grace of God Movement for the Women of the World, c/o 3HO Foundation, 1620 Preuss Road, Los Angeles, CA 90035.

The Grail (*Catholic*), (See International Grail Movement).

Grand Teton Meditation Retreat, Inc. (*New Thought*), P.O. Box 6282, Salt Lake City, UT 84106.

The Graymoor Ecumenical Institute, Graymoor/Garrison, NY 10524.

Great Commission Crusades, Inc., P.O. Box 55, Intercession City, FL 33848.

Great Commission International (*Pentecostal*), P.O. Box 1249, Hanford, CA 93230.

Great I Am Movement, 176 West Washington Street, Chicago, IL 60602.

Great White Brotherhood, 130 Southern, P.O. Box 3274, Corpus Christi, TX 78404.

Greater Cleveland Interchurch Council, 2230 Euclid Avenue, Cleveland, OH 44115.

Greater Dallas Community of Churches, 901 Ross Avenue, Dallas, TX 75202.

Greater Europe Mission, P.O. Box 668, Wheaton, IL 60187.

Greek Catholic Union of the U.S.A., 502 East 8th Avenue, Munhall, PA 15120.

Greek Orthodox Archdiocese of North and South America, 8-10 East 79th Street, New York, NY 10021.

Greek Orthodox Ladies Philoptochos of the Greek Archdiocese of North and South America, 8 East 79th Street, New York, NY 10021.

Greek Orthodox Youth of America, 10 East 79th Street, New York, NY 10021.

"Green Lake Center", (See American Baptist Assembly).

Gregorian Institute of America (*Catholic*), 7404 South Mason Avenue, Chicago, IL 60638.

Group Seven (*Catholic*), P.O. Box 1376, Wise, VA 24293.

Grove of the Unicorn (*Witchcraft*), P.O. Box 9865, Atlanta, GA 30319.

"Grundtvigians", (See Lutheran Church in America).

Guard of Honor of the Immaculate Heart of Mary (*Catholic*), 135 West 31st Street, New York, NY 10001.

Guardians of the Holy City (*Jewish*), (See Neturei Karta of U.S.A.).

Guideposts Outreach Ministries, c/o Norman Vincent Peale, Carmel, NY 10512.

Guild for Religious Architecture, (See Interfaith Forum on Religion, Art and Architecture).

The Guild of All Souls (*Episcopal*), 233 Grove Road, South Orange, NJ 07079.

Guild of Catholic Lawyers, Empire State Bldg. — Room 316, 350 Fifth Avenue, New York, NY 10001.

Guild of Catholic Psychiatrists, (See National Guild of Catholic Psychiatrists).

Guild of Our Lady of Ransom (*Catholic*), c/o St. Timothy's Rectory, 650 Nichols Street, Norwood, MA 02062.

Guild of St. Ives (*Episcopal*), 1047 Amsterdam Avenue, New York, NY 10025.

Guild of St. John Vianney (*Episcopal*), c/o Fr. George E. Hoffman, 117 South Hyer Avenue, Orlando, FL 32801.

Guild of St. Paul (*Catholic*), 601 Hill'n Dale, Lexington, KY 40503.

Gurdjieff Foundation (*Sufism*), 123 East 63rd Street, New York, NY 10021.

Gurdjieff Foundation of California (*Sufism*), P.O. Box 549, San Francisco, CA 94101.

Guru Bawa Fellowship, U.S.A. (*Sufism*), 5820 Overbrook Avenue, Philadelphia, PA 19131.

The Gustav Wurzweiler Foundation, Inc. (*Jewish*), 129 East 73rd Street, New York, NY 10021.

Gustave Weigel Society, c/o Rev. Elwyn D. Brown, 109 South Washington Street, Rockville, MD 20850.

Gwynvyd Church of Wicca (*Witchcraft*), P.O. Box 35204, Edina, MN 55435.

Habibiyya-Shadhiliyya Sufic Order, 3029 Benvenue, Berkeley, CA 94705.

Habonim Labor Zionist Youth (*Jewish*), (See Ichud Habonim Labor Zionist Youth).

Hadassah Medical Relief Association (*Jewish*), 50 West 58th Street, New York, NY 10019.

Hadassah, The Women's Zionist Organization of America, Inc. (*Jewish*), 50 West 58th Street, New York, NY 10019.

Hadassah Zionist Youth Commission (*Jewish*), 50 West 58th Street, New York, NY 10019.

Hagdud Haivri League (*Jewish*), c/o Jewish Community Council, 1776 Broadway — Suite 506, New York, NY 10019.

Haggai Institute for Advanced Leadership Training, P.O. Box 13, Atlanta, GA 30301.

Haiku Zendo (*Buddhist*), 746 University Avenue, Los Altos, CA 94022.

The Haitian Independent Baptist Mission, Inc., P.O. Box 155, Paris, IL 61944.

Hall Deliverance Foundation, Inc. (*Pentecostal*), 9840 North 15th Street, P.O. Box 9910, Phoenix, AZ 85068.

Hall of the True Gods (*Norse Paganism*), c/o Greg Canter, 8-B Plateau Place, Greenbelt, MD 20770.

Hallowed Grounds Fellowship of Spiritual Healing and Prayer (*Spiritualist*), c/o Rev. George Daisley, 629 San Ysidro Road, Santa Barbara, CA 93108.

The Hallowed House of God, the King of Kings and Lord of Lords, (See Ka Hale Hoano Hou O Ke Akua).

Hamilton Roddis Foundation, Inc. (*Episcopal*), 1108 East 4th Street, Marshfield, WI 54449.

Hanafi Madh-Hab Center (*Black Muslims*), 7700 16th Street, N.W., Washington, DC 20012.

Handclasp International, Inc., P.O. Box 1496, Santa Ana, CA 92702.

Hanuman Fellowship (*Hindu*), 2083 Ocean Street, P.O. Box 712, Santa Cruz, CA 95060.

Hanuman Foundation (*Hindu*), P.O. Box 1558, Boulder, CO 80306.

Hanuman Foundation (*Hindu*), Prison-Ashram Project, P.O. Box 39, Nederland, CO 80466.

Hapoel Hamizrachi Women's Organization (*Jewish*), (See Emunah Women of America).

Hare Krishna, (See International Society for Krishna Consciousness).

Harmony Buddhist Mission, c/o Rev. Frank Newton, Clarksville, AR 72830.

Harmony of Life Fellowship, 1434 Fremont Avenue, Los Altos, CA 94022.

Harold Institute (*New Age*), P.O. Box 11024, Winston-Salem, NC 27106.

Harry and Jane Fischel Foundation (*Jewish*), 276 Fifth Avenue, New York, NY 10001.

Hashachar (*Jewish*), 50 West 58th Street, New York, NY 10019.

Hashomer Hadati, Bnei Akiva (*Jewish*), (See Bnei Akiva of North America).

Hashomer Hatzair Socialist Zionist Youth Movement (*Jewish*), 150 Fifth Avenue — No. 710, New York, NY 10011.

Hashomer Hatzair Zionist Youth Organization (*Jewish*), (See Hashomer Hatzair Socialist Zionist Youth Movement).

Hassidism-Bobov (*Jewish*), c/o Rabbi Halberstam, Yeshiva B'nai Zion, 1533 48th Street, Brooklyn, NY 11219.

Hassidism-Boston (*Jewish*), c/o Rabbi Moshe L. Horowitz, 983 48th Street, Brooklyn, NY 11219.

Hassidism-Cernobyl (*Jewish*), c/o Rabbi Israel Jacob Twersky, 1520 49th Street, Brooklyn, NY 11219.

Hassidism-Lubavitch (*Jewish*), 770 Eastern Parkway, Brooklyn, NY 11213.

Hassidism-Novominsk (*Jewish*), c/o Rabbi Nahum Mordecai Perlow, 1620 46th Street, Brooklyn, NY 11204.

Hassidism-Satmar (*Jewish*), c/o Congregation Yetew Lew D'Satmar, 152 Rodney, Brooklyn, NY 11211.

Hassidism-Stolin (*Jewish*), c/o Yeshiva Karlin Stolin, 1818 54th Street, Brooklyn, NY 11204.

Hassidism-Ziditshoiv (*Jewish*), c/o Chassidic Center of Ziditshoiv, 1519 57th Street, Brooklyn, NY 11219.

Hauge Lutheran Innermission Federation, c/o Arnold E. Windahl, 327 West Spruce, Fergue Falls, MN 56537.

Hauge Synod, (See The American Lutheran Church).

Haunt Hunters, 215 North Meramec, Clayton, MO 63105.

Havurat Shalom (*Jewish*), 113 College Avenue, Boston, MA 02144.

Hawaii Chinese Buddhist Society, 1614 Nuuanu Avenue, Honolulu, HI 96817.

Hawaii Council of Churches, 200 North Vineyard Blvd. — Room 403, Honolulu, HI 96817.

Hawaii Ichizuchi Jinga (*Shinto*), 2020 South King Street, Honolulu, HI 96826.

HCJB Missionary Radio, P.O. Box 3000, Opa Locka, FL 33055.

He is Able Ministry (*Pentecostal*), Jonesboro, AR 72401.

The Healing Light Center (*New Age*), 138 North Maryland Avenue, Glendale, CA 91206.

Healing Light Foundation (*New Age*), P.O. Box 355, Yampa, CO 80483.

Healthy, Happy, Holy Organization (3HO Foundation) (*Sikhism*), 1620 Preuss Road, P.O. Box 35906, Los Angeles, CA 90035.

Heart Consciousness Church, P.O. Box 82, Middletown, CA 95461.

Heart of Africa Mission, (See Worldwide Evangelization Crusade).

Heartspring Creative Awareness Center (*New Age*), c/o Gretchen Alim, Route 1 — Box 68, Central City, PA 15926.

Heaven on Earth Religion, c/o Rev. Cyrill A. Kolocotronis, P.O. Box 94999, Fort Steilacoom, WA 98494.

Hebrew Actors Union, 31 East Seventh Street, New York, NY 10003.

Hebrew Christian Alliance of America, (See Messianic Jewish Alliance of America).

Hebrew Christian Fellowship, c/o William J. Randolph, 1033 Twining Road, P.O. Box 777, Dresher, PA 19025.

Hebrew Christians of Bridgeport, Inc., P.O. Box 1257, Merritt Island, FL 32952.

Hebrew Culture Foundation, c/o Milton Konvitz, Chairman, 515 Park Avenue, New York, NY 10022.

Hebrew Culture Service Committee for American High Schools and Colleges (*Jewish*), (See National Hebrew Culture Council).

Hebrew Free Burial Association (*Jewish*) c/o Harry Moskowitz, Secretary, 1170 Broadway, New York, NY 10001.

Hebrew Language and Culture Association (*Jewish*), (See Histadruth Ivrith of America).

Hebrew Messianic Center, P.O. Box 46040, Los Angeles, CA 90046.

"Hebrew Mormonism", (See The True Church of Jesus Christ Restored, Inc.).

Hebrew Sheltering and Immigrant Aid Society (*Jewish*), (See HIAS).

Hebrew Veterans of the War with Spain, 87-71 94th Street, Wood Haven, NY 11421.

Hechalutz Hatzair (*Jewish*), (See Dror Young Zionist Organization).

Heimholungswerk Jesu Christi (*Psychic*), (See The Homebringing Mission of Jesus Christ).

The Helis Foundation (*Greek Orthodox*), 912 Whitney Bldg., New Orleans, LA 70130.

Hellenic Orthodox Church in America, c/o Most Rev. Petros, Bishop of Astoria, 22-68 26th Street, Astoria, L.I., NY 11105.

Help Jesus Ministry, (See Christian Apologetics: Research and Information Service).

Helpers of the Holy Souls Society (*Catholic*), (See Society of Helpers).

Hephzibah Faith Missionary Association of Iowa (*Holiness*) (See Church of the Nazarene).

Heralds of Hope, Route 1 — Box 126-B, Wills Point, TX 75169.

Heralds of Hope, Inc., c/o Otis Yoder, President, P.O. Box 66, Lancaster, PA 17604.

Heritage Village Church and Missionary Fellowship, Inc., (See PTL Club).

Hermetic Brotherhood of Luxor, (See Church of Light).

Herondia Coven (*Witchcraft*), c/o Rev. Terry Boblet, 253 Arriba — Apt. 7, Sunnyvale, CA 94086.

Herut-USA (*Jewish*), 41 East 42nd Street, New York, NY 10017.

HIAS (*Jewish*), 200 Park Avenue South, New York, NY 10003.

"Hicksite" Yearly Meetings, (See General Conference of the Religious Society of Friends).

Hidden Children of Long Island (*Witchcraft*), 366 Neighborhood Road, Mastic Beach, NY 11951.

Higashi Hongwangi Buddhist Church, 118 North Mott Street, Los Angeles, CA 90033.

High Adventure Ministries (*Pentecostal*), P.O. Box 7466, Van Nuys, CA 91409.

High Flight Foundation, 202 East Cheyenne Mt. Blvd., Colorado Springs, CO 80906.

High School Evangelism Fellowship, P.O. Box 780, Tenafly, NJ 07670.

High School Young Christian Students (*Catholic*), 7436 West Harrison Street, Forest Park, IL 60130.

Higher Dimensions, Inc. (*Pentecostal*), P.O. Box 7322, 2705 East Skelly Drive — Suite 307, Tulsa, OK 74105.

Hightstown Gospel Mission Society (*Holiness*), (See Gospel Mission Corps).

Hill Country Pagan Grove (*Witchcraft*), 11701 Quartz Circle, Austin, TX 78750.

Hillside International Truth Center, Inc. (*New Thought*), c/o Barbara King-Blake, 2450 Cascade Road, S.W., Atlanta, GA 30311.

Himalayan Academy (*Hindu*), 3575 Sacramento Street, San Francisco, CA 94118.

Himalayan International Institute of Yoga Science and Philosophy (*Hindu*), RFD 1 — Box 88, Honesdale, PA 18431.

Hindu American Religious Institute, 17 Faye Road, Middletown, PA 17057.

Hindu Center, Inc., 2309 143rd Street, Whitestone, NY 11357.

Hindu Church of America, c/o Markandeya Peruman, P.O. Box 4603, Kailua, HI 96740.

The Hindu Community and Cultural Center, Inc., P.O. Box 4414, Walnut Creek, CA 94596.

Hindu Cultural Society of New Jersey, 66 Barkley Avenue, Clifton, NJ 07011.

Hindu Society, Inc., c/o Dr. Satish Saxena, 8321 Kilbourn Avenue, Skokie, IL 60076.

Hindu Temple Committee, (See Vedic Cultural Society, Inc.).

Hindu Temple Society of North America, 45-57 Bowne Street, Flushing, NY 11355.

Hindu Temple Society of Southern California, P.O. Box 3021, Fullerton, CA 92634.

Hindustan Bible Institute, 800 West Carson — Suite 22, Torrance, CA 90502.

Hineni (*Jewish*), 440 Hungry Harbor Road, North Woodmere, NY 11581.

His Way Ministries, P.O. Box 27247, San Francisco, CA 94127.

Hispanic Pentecostal Church of Jesus Christ, c/o Rev. Kittim Silva, 128 Liberty Avenue, Richmond Hill, Queens, NY 11419.

Histadruth Ivrith of America (*Jewish*), 1841 Broadway, New York, NY 10023.

Historical Commission, Southern Baptist Convention, 127 Ninth Avenue North, Nashville, TN 37234.

Historical Committee of the Mennonite Church, 1700 South Main Street, Goshen, IN 46526.

The Historical Foundation of the Presbyterian and Reformed Churches in the United States, P.O. Box 847R, Montreat, NC 28757.

Historical Society of the Episcopal Church, P.O. Box 2247, Austin, TX 78768.

Historical Society of the Evangelical and Reformed Church, (See Evangelical and Reformed Historical Society).

Historical Society of the Evangelical Congregational Church, 121 South College Street, Myerstown, PA 17067.

Historical Society of the Evangelical United Brethren Church, (See Commission on Archives and History of the United Methodist Church).

Historical Society of the Reformed Church in the United States, (See Evangelical and Reformed Historical Society).

Hohm Community (*New Age*), P.O. Box 75, Tabor, NJ 07878.

Holiness Christian Church, (See the Wesleyan Church).

Holiness Christian Church of the United States of America, Inc., Gibraltar, PA 19524.

The Holiness Church of God, Inc. (*Pentecostal*), c/o Bishop B. McKinney, 602 East Elm Street, Graham, NC 27253.

Holiness Gospel Mission, Route 2 — Box 13, Etters, PA 17319.

Holiness Methodist Church, (See Evangelical Church of North America).

The Holistic Center (*New Age*), P.O. Box 893, San Rafael, CA 94901.

Holistic Childbirth Institute (*New Age*), 1627 10th Avenue, San Francisco, CA 94122.

Holistic Healing Arts Clinic (*New Age*), 312 South Cedros, Solana Beach, CA 92075.

Holistic Health Organizing Committee (*New Age*), P.O. Box 166, Berkeley, CA 94701.

Holistic Health Practitioners' Association (*New Age*), 1030 Merced Street, Berkeley, CA 94707.

Holistic Life Foundation (*New Age*), 1627 Tenth Avenue, San Francisco, CA 94122.

The Hollywood Coven (*Witchcraft*), c/o Ms. Kitty Lessing, P.O. Box 1179, Hollywood, FL 33020.

The Holmes Center for Research in Holistic Healing, P.O. Box 75127, Los Angeles, CA 90075.

Holy Apostolic and Catholic Church of the East (Assyrian), Diocese of the U.S. and Canada, 7444 North Kildare, Skokie, IL 60076.

Holy Apostolic Orthodox Catholic Church, c/o Fr. Mark C. Evans, P.O. Box 4173, Louisville, KY 40204.

Holy Bible Mission Workers (*Pentecostal*), (See Pentecostal Church of Zion, Inc.).

Holy Childhood Association (*Catholic*), 1234 Massachusetts Avenue, N.W., Washington, DC 20005.

Holy Church of North Carolina (*Pentecostal*), (See United Holy Church of America, Inc.).

Holy Coptic Orthodox Archdiocese, 240 Palmetto Street, Brooklyn, NY 11221.

Holy Cross Foreign Mission Society (*Catholic*), 4301 Harewood Road, N.E., Washington, DC 20017.

Holy Grail Foundation (*Spiritualist*), c/o Rev. Leona Richards, 1344 Pacific Avenue — No. 100, Santa Cruz, CA 95060.

Holy Greek Orthodox Church of America, c/o Most Rev. Theoklitos Heliopolis, St. Athanasios Greek Orthodox Cathedral, 6557 S.W. 33rd Street, Miami, FL 33155.

Holy Land Christian Mission International, 2000 East Red Bridge Road, P.O. Box 55, Kansas City, MO 64141.

Holy Land Conservation Fund, 150 East 58th Street, New York, NY 10022.

Holy Name Society (*Catholic*), 141 East 65th Street, New York, NY 10021.

Holy Order of Mans (*Occult*), 20 Steiner Street, San Francisco, CA 94117.

Holy Order of Mother Earth (*Neo-Paganism*), P.O. Box 982, Ukiah, CA 95482.

Holy Orthodox Church, American Jurisdiction, c/o Most Rev. Walter B. Conway, Archbishop, P.O. Box 94022, Houston, TX 77018.

Holy Orthodox Church in America (Eastern Catholic and Apostolic), 321 West 101st Street, New York, NY 10025.

The Holy Shankaracharya Order (*Hindu*), Route 3 — Box 3430, Stroudsburg, PA 18360.

Holy Shroud Guild, P.O. Box 336, Ephrata, PA 17522.

Holy Spirit Association for the Unification of World Christianity, (See The Unification Church).

Holy Spirit Center, (See David Barnard Ministries).

Holy Spirit Research Center, c/o Oral Roberts University, 7777 South Lewis, Tulsa, OK 74102.

Holy Synod of the Orthodox Catholic Churches in America, (See The Orthodox Catholic Patriarchate of America).

Holy Ukrainian Autocephalic Orthodox Church in Exile, 103 Evergreen Street, West Babylon, NY 11704.

Home Bible Study, c/o Leo V. Bartsch, 744 South Fourth Street, Coos Bay, OR 97420.

The Home Missions Council of North America, (See the National Council of Churches of Christ in the U.S.A.).

Home of Onesiphorus, 3939 North Hamlin Avenue, Chicago, IL 60618.

Home of the Dharma (*Buddhist*), c/o Rev. Iru Price, 1450 Monterey Blvd., San Francisco, CA 94127.

Home Study Institute (*Seventh-day Adventist*), 6840 Eastern Avenue, N.W., Takoma Park, Washington, DC 20012.

The Homebringing Mission of Jesus Christ (*Psychic*), c/o Peter Vogt, 822 South Main Street, Spring Valley, NY 10977.

Homeland Foundation (*Catholic*), c/o Kelley, Drye and Warren, 350 Park Avenue, New York, NY 10022.

Honkyoku-Daijingu Temple (*Shinto*), 61 Puiwa Road, Honolulu, HI 96817.

Hoomana Naauoa O Hawaii (The Enlightened Worship of Hawaii), 910 Cooke Street, Honolulu, HI 96813.

Hope Aglow Ministries, Inc., P.O. Box 3057, Lynchburg, VA 24503.

Hospital Christian Fellowship, 34692 Calle Los Robles, Capistrano Beach, CA 92624.

Hospitaller Order of St. John of Jerusalem, 21435 Amulet Drive, Cupertino, CA 95014.

House of David, P.O. Box 1067, Benton Harbor, MI 49022.

House of God, Inc. (Keith Dominion) (*Pentecostal*), (See The House of God, Which Is the Church of the Living God, the Pillar and Ground of the Truth Without Controversy, Inc.).

House of God, Which Is the Church of the Living God, the Pillar and Ground of the Truth, Inc. (*Pentecostal*), c/o Bishop A. H. White, 6107 Cobbs Creek Parkway, Philadelphia, PA 19143.

The House of God, Which Is the Church of the Living God, the Pillar and Ground of the Truth Without Controversy, Inc. (*Pentecostal*), c/o Bishop J. W. Jenkins, Chief Overseer, P.O. Box 9113, Montgomery, AL 36108.

House of Prayer for All People, Inc., P.O. Box 837, Denver, CO 80201.

House of Prayer World Wide Ministries (*Pentecostal*), P.O. Box 777, Waterford, CT 06385.

Hsien Tzu Kuan, (See Taoist Sanctuary).

Huguenot Historical Society, P.O. Box 339, New Paltz, NY 12561.

Hui Neng Zen Center (*Buddhist*), (See Kwan Yin Zen Temple).

Human Dimensions Center for Spiritual Living, c/o Tim Geoghegan, 105 State Street, Black Mountain, NC 28711.

The Human Dimensions Institute, Inc. (*New Age*), 4620 West Lake Road, Canandaigua, NY 14424.

Humanist Society of Friends, c/o Dr, Maxine Negri, President, 1533 North Hayworth Avenue — No. 201, Los Angeles, CA 90046.

Humanite Society of America, P.O. Box 52200, Houston, TX 77052.

Humanity Foundation, 350 South Oxford, Los Angeles, CA 90020.

Huna International (*Psychic*), 30725 Manzano Drive, Malibu, CA 90265.

Huna Research Associates, Inc. (*Psychic*), 126 Camelia Drive, Cape Girardeau, MO 63701.

Hungarian Catholic League of America, Inc., 30 East 30th Street, New York, NY 10016.

The Hungarian Interest Conference of the Lutheran Church in America, c/o Rev. Gabor Brachna, 3411 West 122nd Street, Cleveland, OH 44111.

Hungarian Reformed Church in America, c/o Rt. Rev. Dezso Abraham, Bishop, 18700 Midway, Allen Park, MI 48101.

Hungarian Reformed Federation of America, 5360 Broadview Road, Parma, OH 44134.

Hutterian Brethren (*Communal*), c/o Joseph J. Waldner, P.O. Box 628, Havre, MT 59501.

Hutterian Brethren — Dariusleut (*Communal*), c/o Rev. Elias Walter, Surprise Creek Colony, Stanford, MT 59479.

Hutterian Brethren — Lehrerleut (*Communal*), c/o Rev. Joseph Kleinsasser, Milford Colony, Wolf Creek, MT 59648.

Hutterian Brethren — Schmiedeleut (*Communal*), c/o Rev. David D. Decker, Tschetter Colony, Olivet, SD 57052.

Hutterian Society of Brothers (*Communal*), Rifton, NY 12471.

Hymn Society of America, Wittenberg University, Springfield, OH 45501.

I Ching Institute of Los Angeles, 3605 Sunset Blvd., Los Angeles, CA 90026.

I Have Lived Before Club, 434 Avenue of the Americas — 2nd Floor, New York, NY 10011.

I.A. O'Shaughnessy Foundation, Inc. (*Catholic*), W-1271 First National Bank Bldg., St. Paul, MN 55101.

Ichud Habonim Labor Zionist Youth (*Jewish*), 575 6th Avenue, New York, NY 10009.

I.C.S.A. Centers (*Hindu*), 102 David Drive, North Syracuse, NY 13212.

I.D.H.H.B., Inc. (*Sufism*), P.O. Box 370, Nevada City, CA 95959.

IDOC/North America, 145 East 49th Street, New York, NY 10017.

Iglesia Bando Evangelical Gedeon/Gilgal Evangelical International Church (*Pentecostal*), 636 N.W. Second Street, Miami, FL 33128.

Illinois Club for Catholic Women, 820 North Michigan Avenue, Chicago, IL 60611.

Illinois Conference of Churches, 615 South 5th Street, Springfield, IL 62703.

Illinois Society for Psychic Research, c/o Randall Kryn, President, P.O. Box 1002, Oak Park, IL 60304.

Immaculate Heart Hermitage (*Catholic*), New Camaldoli, Big Sur, CA 93920.

Immanuel Bible Foundation, c/o H. W. Studer, Director, 1301 South Fell Avenue, Normal, IL 61761.

IMPACT, 100 Maryland Avenue, N.E., Washington, DC 20002.

Impact For Today's World, (See Association for Christian Development).

Independent Assemblies of God International (*Pentecostal*), c/o Rev. A. W. Rasmussen, 3840 Fifth Avenue, San Diego, CA 92103.

Independent Assemblies of God (Unincorporated) (*Pentecostal*), (See The Fellowship of Christian Assemblies).

Independent Baptist Church of America, c/o Edith Erickson, P.O. Box 164, Alma Center, WI 54611.

Independent Bible Baptist Missions, P.O. Box 90, Englewood, CO 80151.

Independent Board for Presbyterian Foreign Missions, 246 West Walnut Lane, Philadelphia, PA 19144.

Independent Catholic Church, c/o Most Rev. Edward C. Payne, P.O. Box 261, Wethersfield, CT 06109.

Independent Churches Affiliated, c/o Rev. Robert Mayer, 317 East Chestnut, Lebanon, PA 17042.

Independent Ecumenical Catholic Church International, Inc., c/o St. Jude Abbey, Route 3 — Box 155, Delmar, DE 19940.

Independent Fundamental Bible Churches, c/o Rev. Kenneth L. Barth, Secretary, 2400 Cleveland Avenue, N.W., Canton, OH 44709.

Independent Fundamental Churches of America, 1860 Mannheim Road, P.O. Box 250, Westchester, IL 60153.

Independent Fundamental Ministers Meeting, (See Fellowship of Independent Evangelical Churches).

Independent Holiness Churches, 815 Princess Street, Kingston, Ontario, Canada.

Independent Militant Fundamental Churches of America, c/o Rev. John O'Dell, Dexter Gospel Church, P.O. Box 194, Dexter, MI 48130.

Independent Order of B'nai B'rith (*Jewish*), (See B'nai B'rith International).

Independent Spiritualist Association of America, 5639 West Huron Street, Chicago, IL 60644.

India Christian Mission, Inc., 67 Glenlawn Avenue, Sea Cliff, NJ 11579.

India House of Worship, Inc., 1428 Chilton Drive, Silver Spring, MD 20904.

The India Mission (*Interdenominational Foreign Mission Association of North America*), (See International Missions).

Indian Christian Association, c/o D. M. Joseph, 8452 West Normal, Niles, IL 60648.
Indiana Council of Churches, 1100 West 42nd Street, Indianapolis, IN 46208.
Indo-Burma Pioneer Mission, (See Bibles for the World).
Infinite Way (*New Thought*), c/o Infinite Way Study Center, 157 First Avenue North, St. Petersburg, FL 33701.
Inner Awareness Movement (*New Age*), 555 South Wilton Place, Los Angeles, CA 90020.
The Inner Circle (*Witchcraft*), 149 Pennington Avenue, Passaic Park, NJ 07055.
Inner Circle Kethra E'Da Foundation, Inc. (*Psychic*), 931 26th Street, San Diego, CA 92102.
Inner Light Consciousness Institute (*New Age*), P.O. Box 206, Virginia Beach, VA 23458.
Inner Light Foundation (*Psychic*), c/o Ms. Betty Bethards, P.O. Box 761, Novato, CA 94947.
Inner Peace Movement (*Psychic*), 5103 Connecticut Avenue, N.W., Washington, DC 20008.
Inner Research Institute (*New Age*), 1135 Mission Street, San Francisco, CA 94103.
Inner Sense Scientist Association (*New Age*), c/o Dr. V. E. Vandertuin, P.O. Box 3086, Huntington Park, CA 90255.
The Inner Voice Foundation (*New Age*), P.O. Box 3675, Granada Hills, CA 91344.
Insight Meditation Society (*Buddhist*), Pleasant Street, Barre, MA 01005.
Insight Ministries (*Pentecostal*), 9809 East 37th Court, Tulsa, OK 74145.
Institute for Advanced Pastoral Studies, 380 Lone Pine Road, Bloomfield Hills, MI 48013.
Institute for Advanced Perception (*Psychic*), 719 South Clarence Avenue, Oak Park, IL 60304.
The Institute for American Church Growth, 150 South Los Robles — Suite 600, Pasadena, CA 91101.
The Institute for Antiquity and Christianity, 831 Dartmouth Avenue, Claremont, CA 91711.
Institute for Biblical Preaching, P.O. Box 567, Wheaton, IL 60187.
Institute for Biblical Renewal, Inc., c/o Dr. Roger N. Carstensen, 337 South Milledge Avenue, Athens, GA 30605.
Institute for Biblical Research, c/o Prof. E. Earle Ellis, New Brunswick Theological Seminary, 17 Seminary Place, New Brunswick, NJ 08901.
Institute for Christian Resources, Inc., P.O. Box 18006, San Jose, CA 95158.
Institute for Christian Studies (*Episcopal*), 130 North Magnolia Avenue, Orlando, FL 32801.
The Institute for Conscious Life (*New Age*), P.O. Box 76025, Los Angeles, CA 90076.
Institute for Creation Research, 2100 Greenfield Drive, P.O. Box 2666, El Cajon, CA 92021.
Institute for Democratic Education, (See Anti-Defamation League of B'nai B'rith).
Institute for Ecumenical and Cultural Research, P.O. Box 6188, Collegeville, MN 56321.
Institute for Humanistic and Transpersonal Education, P.O. Box 575, Amherst, MA 01002.

Institute for Jewish Policy Planning and Research of Synagogue Council of America, 1776 Massachusetts Avenue, N.W., Washington, DC 20036.

Institute for Justice and Peace, c/o Dr. Marc H. Ellis, Director, Maryknoll School of Theology, Maryknoll, NY 10545.

Institute for Past Life Studies (*Psychic*), c/o Dr. Frederick Lenz, San Diego Sri Chinmoy Centre, 9514 La Jolla Farms Road, La Jolla, CA 92037.

The Institute for Positive Living (*New Thought*), 3368 Peachtree Road, N.E., Atlanta, GA 30326.

Institute for Practical Idealism, Route 4 — Box 265, Bedford, VA 24523.

Institute for Religious and Social Studies, 3080 Broadway, New York, NY 10027.

Institute for Religious Development (*Sufism*), (Gurdjieff Students of William Nyland), Chardavogne Barn, Chardavogne Road, Warwick, NY 10990.

Institute for Ritual, Symbol and World Religions, c/o John Kaserow, Director, Maryknoll School of Theology, Maryknoll, NY 10545.

Institute for the Development of the Harmonious Human Being (*Sufism*), P.O. Box 370, Nevada City, CA 95959.

The Institute for the New Age, 45 East 78th Street, New York, NY 10021.

Institute for the Study of American Religion, c/o Dr. J. Gordon Melton, Director, P.O. Box 1311, Evanston, IL 60201.

Institute for the Study of Mind Control, c/o Hillel Zeitlin, 1442A Walnut Street — Suite 250, Berkeley, CA 94709.

Institute for Theological Encounter with Science and Technology, 221 North Grand Blvd., St. Louis, MO 63103.

Institute for Yoga and Esoteric Sciences (*Psychic*), c/o Celia M. Hansen, Director, 1213 Vinewood Drive, Columbus, OH 43229.

Institute in Basic Youth Conflicts, P.O. Box 1, Oak Brook, IL 60521.

Institute of Ability (*Psychic*), P.O. Box 798, Lucerne Valley, CA 92356.

Institute of Advanced Thinking (*New Age*), 845 Via LaPaz, Pacific Palisades, CA 90272.

Institute of Applied Metaphysics (*New Age*), P.O. Box 392, Weston, MA 02193.

Institute of Biblical Counseling, 301 Crawford Bldg. — Suite 101, Boca Raton, FL 33432.

Institute of Carmelite Studies (*Catholic*), 2131 Lincoln Road, Northeast, Washington, DC 20002.

The Institute of Christian Resources, Inc., P.O. Box 18006, San Jose, CA 95158.

Institute of Christian Spirituality, c/o Dr. Frederick J. Parrella, Director, 261 Bannan Hall, University of Santa Clara, Santa Clara, CA 95053.

Institute of Church Renewal, 1870 Tucker Industrial Road, Tucker, GA 30084.

Institute of Contemporary Christianity, P.O. Box A, Oakland, NJ 07436.

Institute of Cosmic Wisdom (*Psychic*), c/o Clark Wilkerson, 5797 Kalanianaole Highway, Honolulu, HI 96821.

The Institute of Divine Metaphysical Research, Inc., P.O. Box 1014, Binghamton, NY 13902.

The Institute of Eschatological Research, P.O. Box 414, Brandon, WI 53919.

The Institute of Esoteric Sciences (*New Age*), 746 East 79th Street, P.O. Box 278, Chicago, IL 60619.

Institute of Esoteric Transcendentalism (*New Thought*), c/o Robert W. C. Burke, 3278 Wilshire Blvd., Los Angeles, CA 90010.

The Institute of General Psionics (*New Age*), 204 North Catalina Avenue, Redondo Beach, CA 90277.

The Institute of Jesuit Sources (*Catholic*), c/o St. Louis University, 3700 West Pine Blvd., St. Louis, MO 63108.

The Institute of Judaeo-Christian Studies, Seton Hall University, South Orange, NJ 07079.

Institute of Man (*Catholic*), Duquesne University, Pittsburgh, PA 15219.

Institute of Mentalphysics (*New Age*), P.O. Box 640, Yucca Valley, CA 92284.

The Institute of Metaphysical Science of Apostolic Baptist Mission, Inc., 802 Judson Street, Evansville, IN 47713.

Institute of Metaphysics, 7624 Flight Avenue, Los Angeles, CA 90045.

Institute of New Thought Studies, P.O. Box 15005, San Francisco, CA 94115.

Institute of Noetic Sciences (*New Age*), c/o Barbara McNeill, 600 Stockton Street, San Francisco, CA 94108.

Institute of Parapsychology, (See The Universe Society).

Institute of Psychic Science, Inc., 2015 South Broadway, Little Rock, AR 72206.

Institute of Reality Awareness (*New Age*), 8217 Beverly Blvd. — Suite 7, Los Angeles, CA 90048.

The Institute of Religion, P.O. Box 20569, Houston, TX 77025.

Institute of Religious Studies, c/o Prof. Walter H. Capps, Director, University of California, Santa Barbara, CA 93106.

Institute of Slavic Studies, (See Slavic Gospel Association, Inc.).

Institute of Social Order of the Society of Jesus (*Catholic*), (See Jesuit Center for Social Studies).

Institute of Society, Ethics and the Life Sciences, 360 Broadway, Hastings-on-Hudson, NY 10706.

Institute of Spiritual Discovery, P.O. Box 39436, Los Angeles, CA 90039.

Institute of Women Today, c/o Sister Margaret Ellen Traxler, Director, 1340 East 72nd Street, Chicago, IL 60619.

Institute on Healing of the Whole Person, 1910 Asbury Avenue, St. Paul, MN 55113.

Institute on Interdenominational Studies, (See Institute for Religious and Social Studies).

Institute on Religion in an Age of Science, c/o Weiant Wathen-Dunn, Secretary, 44 Maple Street, Lexington, MA 02173.

Institute on Religious Life (*Catholic*), 4200 North Austin Avenue, Chicago, IL 60634.

Institutes of Religion and Health, Three West 29th Street, New York, NY 10001.

Integral Center of Self-Abidance (*Hindu*), 102 David Drive, North Syracuse, NY 13212.

Integral Life Center (*New Age*), 1002 East Florida Street, Hemet, CA 92343.

Integral Yoga Institute (*Hindu*), c/o Satchidananda Ashram, P.O. Box 108, Pomfret Center, CT 06259.

Integrated Healing Research Foundation (*New Age*), P.O. Box 66457, Los Angeles, CA 90066.

Integrity (*Episcopal*), 5014 Willows Avenue, Philadelphia, PA 19143.

Interboard Committee for Christian Work in Japan, (See Japan North American Commission on Cooperative Mission).

Intercessors For America, P.O. Box D, Elyria, OH 44036.

Interchurch Center, 475 Riverside Drive, New York, NY 10115.

Inter-Church Holiness Convention, P.O. Box 3583, Salem, OH 44460.
Interchurch Medical Assistance, 475 Riverside Drive — Room 246, New York, NY 10115.
Interchurch Ministries of Nebraska, 215 Centennial Mall South — Room 303, Lincoln, NE 68508.
Inter-Collegiate Fellowship Retreats (*Lutheran*), c/o Greg Olson, P.O. Box 8025, St. Paul, MN 55113.
Intercosmic Cultural and Spiritual Association (*Hindu*), c/o Brahmananda Ashram, 2872 Folsom Street, San Francisco, CA 94110.
Intercristo, P.O. Box 9323, Seattle, WA 98109.
Interdenominational Divine Order (*Psychic*), P.O. Box W, Twin Falls, ID 83301.
Interdenominational Foreign Mission Association of North America, P.O. Box 395, Wheaton, IL 60187.
Inter-denominational Holiness Convention, 375 West State Street, Salem, OR 44460.
Interdenominational Ministerial Alliance, c/o Rev. Lonnie Simon, 21 South Jackson Street, Youngstown, OH 44506.
Interface (*New Age*), 63 Chapel Street, Newton, MA 02158.
Interfaith Center on Corporate Responsibility, 475 Riverside Drive — Room 566, New York, NY 10115.
Interfaith Center to Reverse the Arms Race, c/o All Saints Church, 132 North Euclid Avenue, Pasadena, CA 91101.
Interfaith Christian Church (*New Age*), Route 2 — Box 67, Blue Ridge, GA 30513.
Inter-Faith Committee Against Blasphemy, P.O. Box 90, Glendale, CA 91209.
Interfaith Conference of Metropolitan Washington, 1419 V Street, N.W., Washington, DC 20009.
Interfaith Forum on Religion, Art and Architecture, 1913 Architects Bldg., Philadelphia, PA 19103.
Interfaith Hunger Coalition, 5539 West Pico Blvd., Los Angeles, CA 90019.
Interfaith Movement, c/o Melvin Prescott, Executive Secretary, Maurice Blond Agency, 45 East 33rd Street, New York, NY 10016.
Inter-Faith Task Force, 3370 South Irving, Englewood, CO 80110.
Intergroup Committee for Three Linked Festivals (*New Age*), P.O. Box 5105, Beverly Hills, CA 90210.
Intermedia, c/o Vern Rossman, Director, 475 Riverside Drive, New York, NY 10115.
Intermountain Yearly Meeting of Friends (*Unaffiliated*), c/o Gilbert F. White, Sunshine Canyon Drive, Boulder, CO 80302.
International Apostolic Evangelistic & Missionary Association (*Pentecostal*), P.O. Box 459, Lakeland, FL 33802.
International Apostolic Holiness Church, (See The Wesleyan Church).
International Association for Religious Freedom, American Chapter, c/o Rev. Polly Laughland, President, Follen Community Church, 755 Massachusetts Avenue, Lexington, MA 02173.
International Association of Hillel Directors (*Jewish*), Hofstra University, 1000 Fulton Avenue, Hempstead, NY 11550.
International Association of Religious Science Churches, (See Religious Science International).

International Association of Women Ministers, c/o Rev. Pamela Webb, P.O. Box 263, Hedrick, IA 52563.

International Association of Y's Men's Clubs, 291 Broadway, New York, NY 10007.

International Babaji Kriya Yoga Sangam (*Hindu*), 11305 Alondra Blvd., Norwalk, CA 90650.

International Bible Institute of North America, P.O. Box 2473, Santa Fe Springs, CA 90670.

International Bible Students Association, (See Jehovah's Witnesses).

International Board of Jewish Missions, 1805 Bailey Avenue, Chattanooga, TN 37404.

International Buddhist Meditation Center, 928 South New Hampshire Avenue, Los Angeles, CA 90006.

International Catholic Deaf Association, 814 Thayer Avenue, Silver Spring, MD 20910.

International Catholic Esperanto Association, 7605 Winona Lane, Sebastopol, CA 95472.

International Catholic Esperanto Union, (See International Catholic Esperanto Association).

International Catholic Truth Society, 407 Bergen Street, Brooklyn, NY 11217.

International Center of Religion and Culture, 1546 South Jersey, Denver, CO 80224.

International Center of Self-Analysis (*Hindu*), c/o Ananda Ashram, P.O. Box 805, Monroe, NY 10950.

International Christian Aid, P.O. Box 250, Glendale, CA 91209.

International Christian Churches (*Pentecostal*), 2322-26 Kanealii Avenue, Honolulu, HI 96813.

International Christian Esperanto Association, c/o Edwin C. Harler, Jr., 47 Hardy Road, Levittown, PA 19056.

International Christian Fellowship, 1028 East College Avenue, Wheaton, IL 60187.

International Christian Leprosy Mission, 6917 S.W. Oak Drive, Portland, OR 97223.

International Christian Ministries, c/o Dr. Clifford Wilson, Director, 1838 Ross Avenue, St. Louis, MO 63141.

International Christian Organization, (See Intercristo).

International Christian Relief, 801 Haddon Avenue, Collingswood, NJ 08108.

International Christian Youth, 756 Haddon Avenue, Collingswood, NJ 08108.

International Christian Youth Exchange, 74 Trinity Place — Room 610, New York, NY 10006.

The International Church of Ageless Wisdom (*Psychic*), c/o Rev. Muriel E. Matalucci, P.O. Box 101, Wyalusing, PA 18853.

International Church of Spiritual Vision (*New Age*), P.O. Box 2627, Reno, NV 89505.

International Church of the Foursquare Gospel (*Pentecostal*), Angelus Temple, 1100 Glendale Blvd., Los Angeles, CA 90026.

International Committee on English in the Liturgy (*Catholic*), 1234 Massachusetts Avenue, N.W., Washington, DC 20005.

International Community of Christ (*Psychic*), 643 Ralston Street, Reno, NV 89503.

International Conference of Gay and Lesbian Jews, P.O. Box 7566, Philadelphia, PA 19101.

International Conference of Police Chaplains, 1200 Nakomis Drive, N.E., Albuquerque, NM 87112.

International Conference of the Old Catholic Church, (Represented in the U.S. by the Polish National Catholic Church).

International Congregational Council, (See World Alliance of Reformed Churches — Presbyterian and Congregational).

International Congregational Fellowship, c/o Dr. Leslie Deinstadt, 2915 West Ranch Road, Mequon, WI 53092.

International Congress for the Peace of Jerusalem, P.O. Box 500, San Juan Capistrano, CA 92693.

International Convention of Faith Churches & Ministries (*Pentecostal*), P.O. Box 7302, Tulsa, OK 74105.

International Convention of Original Free Will Baptists, (See General Conference of Original Free Will Baptists).

International Convention of the Christian Churches (*Disciples of Christ*), (See Christian Church — Disciples of Christ).

International Cooperation Council (*New Age*), (See Unity-in-Diversity Council).

International Council of Christian Churches, 756 Haddon Avenue, Collingswood, NJ 08108.

International Council of Community Churches, (See National Council of Community Churches).

International Council of Hindu Churches, c/o Markandeya Peruman, General Secretary, P.O. Box 4603, Kailua, HI 96740.

The International Council of Religious Education, (See the National Council of Churches of Christ in the U.S.A.).

International Council on Biblical Inerrancy, P.O. Box 13261, Oakland, CA 94661.

International Cultural Foundation (*Unification Church*), P.O. Box 3939, Grand Central Station, New York, NY 10017.

International Deliverance Churches (*Pentecostal*), P.O. Box 353, Dallas, TX 75221.

International Documentation on the Contemporary Church, (See IDOC/North America).

International Evangelism Crusades, Inc. (*Pentecostal*), 7970 Woodman — Suite 114, Van Nuys, CA 91402.

International Federation of Catholic Alumnae, 416 Administration Bldg., Catholic University of America, Washington, DC 20064.

International Fellowship of Evangelical Students, P.O. Box 270, Madison, WI 53701.

International Fellowship of Fundamentalists, c/o Dr. Leon F. Maurer, P.O. Box 2142, Terre Haute, IN 47802.

International Fortean Organization, 7317 Baltimore Avenue, College Park, MD 20740.

International Foundation for Biblical Studies, Inc., 423 First National Bank Bldg., Peoria, IL 61602.

International Foundation for EWHA Woman's University (*United Methodist*), 475 Riverside Drive — Room 627, New York, NY 10115.

International Foundation for Integral Psychology (*New Age*), 10921 Wilshire Blvd. — Suite 901, Los Angeles, CA 90024.

International General Assembly of Spiritualists, 1809 East Bayview Blvd., Norfolk, VA 23503.

International Ghost Registry, 369-J Western Drive, Santa Cruz, CA 95060.

International Gospel League, Inc., 854 East Washington Blvd., Pasadena, CA 91104.

International Grail Movement (*Catholic*), Loveland Road, Loveland, OH 45140.

International Hebrew Christian Alliance, c/o Dr. David Bronstein, Secretary, P.O. Box 758, Palm Harbor, FL 33563.

International Holiness Church, (See The Wesleyan Church).

International Holiness Mission of England, (See Church of the Nazarene).

International Holistic Center, Inc. (*New Age*), P.O. Box 15103, 616 East Oregon, Phoenix, AZ 85102.

International Hospital Christian Fellowship — USA Branch, P.O. Box 4004, San Clemente, CA 92672.

International I Ching Studies Institute, (See Taoist Sanctuary).

International Institute of the Heart of Jesus (*Catholic*), 7700 Blue Mound Road, Milwaukee, WI 53213.

International League for the Repatriation of Russian Jews, 315 Church Street, New York, NY 10013.

International Liaison for Volunteer Service (*Catholic*), (See International Liaison, U.S. Catholic Coordinating Center for Lay Volunteer Ministries).

International Liaison, U.S. Catholic Coordinating Center for Lay Volunteer Ministries, 1234 Massachusetts Avenue, N.W., Washington, DC 20005.

International Liberal Catholic Church, c/o Most Rev. Edmund W. Sheehan, 840 Fairview Road, Ojai, CA 93023.

International Lutheran Center for Church Renewal, 2701 Rice Street, St. Paul, MN 55113.

International Lutheran Deaf Association, 1333 South Kirkwood Road, St. Louis, MO 63122.

International Lutheran Fellowship, c/o E. Edward Tornow, 2918 Edgewood Drive, Fargo, ND 58102.

International Lutheran Laymen's League (*Lutheran Church-Missouri Synod*), 2185 Hampton Avenue, St. Louis, MO 63139.

International Lutheran Women's Missionary League (*Lutheran Church-Missouri Synod*), 3558 South Jefferson Avenue, St. Louis, MO 63118.

International Mahavir Mission (*Jainism*), 722 Tompkins Avenue, Staten Island, NY 10305.

International Meditation Society (*Hindu*), 17310 Sunset Blvd., Pacific Palisades, CA 90272.

International Metaphysical Association, Inc., 20 East 68th Street — 10-D, New York, NY 10021.

International Methodist Historical Society, (See World Methodist Historical Society).

International Methodist Historical Union, (See World Methodist Historical Society).

International Ministerial Association, Inc. (*Pentecostal*), 9455 Lackland Road, St. Louis, MO 63114.

International Ministerial Federation, Inc., 724 Clark Street, Fresno, CA 93701.

International Mission Radio Association (*Catholic*), c/o Rev. Michael Mullen, St. John's University, Jamaica, NY 11439.

International Missions (*Interdenominational Foreign Mission Association of North America*), P.O. Box 323, Wayne, NJ 07470.

International New Thought Alliance, 7314 East Stetson Drive, Scottsdale, AZ 85251.

International Order of St. Luke, the Physician, 61 Broad Street, Elizabeth, NJ 07201.

International Order of the Alhambra (*Catholic*), 4200 Leeds Avenue, Baltimore, MD 21229.

International Order of the King's Daughters and Sons, 34 Vincent Avenue, Chautauqua, NY 14722.

International Organization for Masoretic Studies, c/o Harry M. Orlinski, Hebrew Union College, Jewish Institute of Religion, Brookdale Center, One West 4th Street, New York, NY 10012.

International Organization for Septuagint and Cognate Studies, c/o Albert Pietersma, University of Toronto, Toronto, Ontario M5S 1A1, Canada.

International Organization of Awareness (*Psychic*), 1648 Alencastre Street, Honolulu, HI 96816.

International Pentecostal Assemblies, (See The International Pentecostal Church of Christ).

The International Pentecostal Church of Christ, P.O. Box 263, London, OH 43140.

International Pentecostal Press Association, c/o Dr. O. W. Polen, Secretary-Treasurer, 1080 Montgomery Avenue, Cleveland, TN 37311.

International Prayer Fellowship, P.O. Box 578, Lake Junaluska, NC 28745.

International Prison Ministry, Inc., c/o Chaplain Ray, P.O. Box 63, Dallas, TX 75221.

International Reform Federation, 120 Maryland Avenue, N.E., Washington, DC 20002.

International Religious Liberty Association, c/o W. Melvin Adams, Secretary, General Conference of Seventh-day Adventists, 6840 Eastern Avenue, Washington, DC 20012.

International School of Yoga and Vedanta, (See Yoga Research Foundation).

International Seamen's Center, P.O. Box 4033, Brownsville, TX 78520.

International Sivananda Yoga Society (*Hindu*), 8157 Sunset Blvd., Los Angeles, CA 90046.

International Society for Krishna Consciousness (ISKCON) (*Hindu*), c/o Srisri Radha Krsna Temple, 3764 Watseka Avenue, Los Angeles, CA 90034.

International Society of Bible Collectors, P.O. Box 2485, El Cajon, CA 92021.

International Society of Christian Endeavor, 1221 East Broad Street, P.O. Box 1110, Columbus, OH 43216.

International Students, Inc., Star Ranch — Box C, Colorado Springs, CO 80901.

International Union of Gospel Missions, P.O. Box 10780, Kansas City, MO 64118.

International Wholistic Center, Inc. (*New Age*), 2125 Stirling Road, Ft. Lauderdale, FL 33312.

International Yoga Society (*Hindu*), 6111 S.W. 74th Avenue, Miami, FL 33143.

Interreligious Foundation for Community Organizations, 348 Convent Avenue, New York, NY 10031.

Interseminary Movement, (See the National Council of Churches of Christ in the U.S.A.).

Interseminary Theological Education for Ministry, 175 9th Avenue, New York, NY 10011.

Inter-University Committee on Israel, (See America-Israel Cultural Foundation).

Inter-Varsity Christian Fellowship, 233 Langdon Street, Madison, WI 53703.

Inter-Varsity Missions, (See Inter-Varsity Christian Fellowship).

Intuitus Center (*New Age*), 326 Argonne Circle, Santa Barbara, CA 93105.

The Invisible Ministry, (See Church of the Trinity).

Iowa Inter-Church Forum, 317 East 5th Street, Des Moines, IA 50309.

"Irvingites", (See Catholic Apostolic Church).

ISKCON, (See International Society for Krishna Consciousness).

The Islamic Center, 2551 Massachusetts Avenue, N.W., Washington, DC 20008.

Islamic Center of New York, One Riverside Drive, New York, NY 10023.

Islamic Center of San Francisco, 400 Crescent Avenue, San Francisco, CA 94110.

Islamic Centers of America, 601 California — Suite 300, San Francisco, CA 94108.

Islamic Mission of America, 143 State Street, Brooklyn NY 11201.

Islamic Science Organization, P.O. Box 1810, Fort Walton, FL 32548.

Islamic Seminary and Publications, Inc., 55 West 42nd Street, New York, NY 10036.

Islamic Service Organization, 99 Woodview Drive, Old Bridge, NJ 08857.

Israel Aliya Center (*Jewish*), 515 Park Avenue, New York, NY 10022.

Israel Histadrut Foundation (*Jewish*), 33 East 67th Street, New York, NY 10021.

Israelite House of David as Reorganized by Mary Purnell, P.O. Box 187, Benton Harbor, MI 49022.

Israel's Evangelistic Missions, Inc., P.O. Box 3734, Oak Park, MI 48237.

Italian Baptist Association of America, (See Association of Evangelicals for Italian Mission).

Italian Baptist Missionary Association, (See Association of Evangelicals for Italian Mission).

Italian Catholic Federation of California, Central Council, 1801 Van Ness Avenue — Suite 330, San Francisco, CA 94109.

Italian Christian Churches, (See Christian Church of North America).

The J. Willard Marriott Family Foundation (*Mormon*), c/o Mrs. Kay Bodeen, 5161 River Road, Washington, DC 20016.

Jack Van Impe Ministries, P.O. Box J, Royal Oak, MI 48068.

Jacobite Apostolic Church, (See The American Catholic Church, Archdiocese of New York; see also The American Catholic Church — Syro Antiochian).

Jacques Marchais Center for Tibetan Art (*Buddhist*), 338 Lighthouse Avenue, Staten Island, NY 10306.

J.A.D.E. Center, (Joint American-Asian Devotion and Education), Drawer A, Atascadero, CA 93422.

Jain Center of America, 85 Memphis Avenue, Staten Island, NY 10312.

Jain Center of Greater Boston, 83 Fuller Brook Road, Wellesley, MA 02181.

Jain Center of Greater Cleveland, c/o Dr. K. C. Bhaiji, 13579 Ridge Road, North Royalton, OH 44133.

Jain Meditation International Center, 120 East 86th Street, New York, NY 10028.

Jain Society of Chicago, 653 West Aldine Avenue, Chicago, IL 60657.
Jain Society of Rochester, 80 Treebrook Drive, Rochester, NY 14625.
James Robison Evangelistic Association, P.O. Box 18489, Fort Worth, TX 76118.
Japan Evangelical Mission, 9047 Burke Avenue North, Seattle, WA 98103.
Japan International Christian University Foundation, Inc., 475 Riverside Drive — Room 720, New York, NY 10115.
Japan North American Commission on Cooperative Mission, 475 Riverside Drive — Room 618, New York, NY 10115.
Japanese Evangelical Missionary Society, c/o Rev. Sam Tonomura, Executive Director, 112 North San Pedro Street, Los Angeles, CA 90012.
Jehovah's Witnesses, 107 Columbia Heights, Brooklyn, NY 11201.
Jemez Bodhi Mandala (*Buddhist*), P.O. Box 44, Jemez Springs, NM 87025.
Jen Sen Association for the Examination of the Buddhist & Taoist Teachings, 146 Waverly Place, San Francisco, CA 94108.
Jerry Barnard Ministries, 590 Fir Street, San Diego, CA 92101.
Jerry Savelle Evangelistic Association, P.O. Box 2228, Forth Worth, TX 76113.
Jersey Shore Pagan Way (*Neo-Paganism*), P.O. Box 2015, Neptune City, NJ 07753.
Jesuit Center for Social Studies (*Catholic*), Georgetown University, Washington, DC 20057.
Jesuit Council for Theological Reflection (*Catholic*), c/o Edward Finn, S.J., 1100 West Wells Street, Milwaukee, WI 53233.
Jesuit Educational Association (*Catholic*), (See Jesuit Secondary Education Association; see also Association of Jesuit Colleges and Universities).
Jesuit Missions (*Catholic*), 1717 Massachusetts Avenue, N.W. — Room 402, Washington, DC 20036.
Jesuit Philosophical Association of the United States and Canada (*Catholic*), St. Joseph's College, 2448 North 54th Street, Philadelphia, PA 19131.
Jesuit Research Council of America (*Catholic*), (See Association of Jesuit Colleges and Universities).
Jesuit Secondary Education Association (*Catholic*), 1717 Massachusetts Avenue, N.W. — Suite 402, Washington, DC 20036.
Jesuit Seismological Association (*Catholic*), St. Louis University, P.O. Box 8099, Pierre Laclede Station, St. Louis, MO 63156.
Jesuit Volunteer Corps (*Catholic*), Laurence L. Gooley, S.J., Director, P.O. Box 3928, Portland, OR 97208.
Jesus Caritas Fraternity of Fr. Charles de Foucauld (*Catholic*), c/o Patricia M. Collins, 3843 North Spaulding, Chicago, IL 60618.
Jesus Church (*Pentecostal*), c/o Samuel E. Officer, P.O. Box 652, Cleveland, TN 37311.
Jesus Festivals, P.O. Box 7447, Orlando, FL 32854.
Jesus Northwest (*Pentecostal*), P.O. Box 7718, Salem, OR 97303.
Jesus Only Apostolic Church of God (*Pentecostal*), (See Assemblies of the Lord Jesus Christ).
Jesus People Information Center, Inc., 4338 3rd Avenue, Sacramento, CA 95817.
Jesus People, U.S.A., 4707 North Malden, Chicago, IL 60640.
Jesus to the Communist World, Inc., P.O. Box 11, Glendale, CA 91209.
Jewish Academy of Arts and Sciences, Gregory Corner Northfield Avenue, West Orange, NJ 07052.

Jewish Agency for Israel, (See United Israel Appeal).

Jewish Alternatives to Zionism, (See American Jewish Alternatives to Zionism).

Jewish Association for Services for the Aged, 222 Park Avenue South, New York, NY 10003.

Jewish Board of Guardians, 120 West 57th Street, New York, NY 10019.

Jewish Book Council, 15 East 26th Street, New York, NY 10010.

Jewish Braille Institute of America, 110 East 30th Street, New York, NY 10016.

Jewish Chautauqua Society, 838 5th Avenue, New York, NY 10021.

Jewish Committee to Help Animals, 225 West 106th Street, New York, NY 10025.

Jewish Community Relations Council of New York, Inc., 111 West 40th Street — Suite 2600, New York, NY 10018.

Jewish Conciliation Board of America, 120 West 57th Street, New York, NY 10019.

Jewish Cultural Clubs and Societies, 1133 Broadway, New York, NY 10010.

Jewish Defense League, 76 Madison Avenue, New York, NY 10016.

Jewish Draft and Military Counseling Center, 1740 Judson Street, Evanston, IL 60201.

Jewish Educators' Assembly of America, 155 5th Avenue, New York, NY 10010.

Jewish Family Service, 33 West 60th Street, New York, NY 10023.

Jewish Family Welfare Society of Brooklyn, (See Jewish Family Service).

Jewish Folk Schools of New York, 575 Sixth Avenue, New York, NY 10009.

Jewish Foundation for Education of Girls, (See Jewish Foundation for Education of Women).

Jewish Foundation for Education of Women, 120 West 57th Street, New York, NY 10019.

Jewish Free Loan Association, 6505 Wilshire Blvd., Los Angeles, CA 90048.

Jewish Funeral Directors of America, 1170 Rockville Pike, Rockville, MD 20852.

Jewish Guild for the Blind, 15 West 65th Street, New York, NY 10023.

Jewish Information Bureau, 250 West 57th Street, New York, NY 10019.

Jewish Labor Bund, 25 East 78th Street, New York, NY 10021.

Jewish Labor Committee, 25 East 78th Street, New York, NY 10021.

Jewish Lawyers Guild, 299 Broadway, New York, NY 10007.

Jewish Librarians Association, (See Association of Jewish Libraries).

Jewish Library Association, (See Association of Jewish Libraries).

Jewish Media Service, National Jewish Welfare Board, 15 East 26th Street, New York, NY 10010.

Jewish Ministers Cantors Association of America and Canada, Three West 16th Street, New York, NY 10011.

Jewish Minorities Research, 16 East 85th Street, New York, NY 10028.

Jewish Museum, 1109 Fifth Avenue, New York, NY 10028.

The Jewish Music Council, 15 East 26th Street, New York, NY 10010.

Jewish National Fund, 42 East 69th Street, New York, NY 10021.

Jewish Occupational Council, (See National Association of Jewish Vocational Services).

Jewish Peace Fellowship, 420 Riverside Drive, New York, NY 10025.

Jewish Pharmaceutical Society of America, 525 Ocean Parkway, Brooklyn, NY 11218.

Jewish Publication Society of America, 117 South 17th Street, Philadelphia, PA 19103.

Jewish Reconstructionist Foundation, Inc., 432 Park Avenue South — Suite 1206-08, New York, NY 10016.

Jewish Restitution Successor Organization, 15 East 26th Street, New York, NY 10010.

Jewish Science Society, 111 West 57th Street, New York, NY 10019.

Jewish Social Service Association, (See Jewish Family Service).

Jewish Society of America, 28-13 Steinway Street, Long Island City, NY 11103.

Jewish Society of Americanists, (See Jewish Society of America).

Jewish Statistical Bureau, 1182 Broadway, New York, NY 10001.

Jewish Student Press Service, 15 East 26th Street — Suite 1350, New York, NY 10010.

Jewish Teachers Association, 45 East 33rd Street, New York, NY 10016.

Jewish Theatrical Guild of America, 1501 Broadway, New York, NY 10036.

Jewish Vacation Association, (See Association of Jewish Sponsored Camps).

Jewish Vegetarian Society, c/o Judah Grosberg, 68-38 Yellowstone Blvd., Forest Hills, NY 11375.

Jewish Voice Broadcasts, Inc., P.O. Box 6, Phoenix, AZ 85001.

Jewish War Veterans of the U.S.A., 1712 New Hampshire Avenue, N.W., Washington, DC 20009.

Jewish War Veterans of the U.S.A. — National Ladies Auxiliary, 1712 New Hampshire Avenue, N.W., Washington, DC 20009.

Jews for Jesus, 60 Haight Street, San Francisco, CA 94102.

Jimmy Swaggart Evangelistic Association, Baton Rouge, LA 70821.

Jodo Mission (*Buddhist*), 1429 Makiki Street, Honolulu, HI 96822.

The John Carroll Society (*Catholic*), 1666 K Street, N.W., Washington, DC 20006.

John LaFarge Institute (*Catholic*), 106 West 56th Street, New York, NY 10019.

John Milton Society, (See John Milton Society for the Blind).

John Milton Society for the Blind, 475 Riverside Drive — Room 824, New York, NY 10115.

John Osteen Ministries, P.O. Box 23117, Houston, TX 77028.

John R. Rice Associates, c/o Sword of the Lord, P.O. Box 1099, Murfreesboro, TN 37130.

John XXIII Ecumenical Center, Fordham University, 2502 Belmont Avenue, Bronx, NY 10458.

John Wesley Fellowship and the Frances Asbury Society of Ministers, P.O. Box 11585, Atlanta, GA 30355.

The Johnnie Colemon Institute, (See Christ Universal Temple).

Joint Commission on Church Music (*Episcopal*), (See Standing Commission on Church Music).

Joint Commission on Missionary Education (*National Council of Churches*), (See Commission on Education for Mission).

Joint Council on Research in Pastoral Care and Counseling, P.O. Box 5184, 507 North Lombardy, Richmond, VA 23220.

Joint Distribution Committee (*Jewish*), (See American Jewish Joint Distribution Committee).

Joint Distribution Committee for Relief of Jewish War Sufferers, (See American Jewish Joint Distribution Committee).

Joint Educational Development, (Protestant Ecumenical Partnership), 341 Ponce de Leon Avenue, N.E. — Room 322, Atlanta, GA 30308.

Joint Passover Association of the City of New York (*Jewish*), 33 West 60th Street, New York, NY 10023.

Joint Strategy and Action Committee, Inc., 475 Riverside Drive — Room 903, New York, NY 10115.

Joint Washington Office for Social Concern, (See Unitarian Universalist Association — Washington Office for Social Concern).

"Joni and Friends", (Joni Eareckson), P.O. Box 3225, Woodland Hills, CA 91365.

Jubilee, Inc., c/o Judy Alexander, President, P.O. Box 12236, Philadelphia, PA 19144.

Jubilee Partners, P.O. Box 274, Comer, GA 30629.

Judaic Heritage Society, P.O. Box 2022, New York, NY 10163.

Jude 3, (See Christian Apologetics: Research and Information Service).

The Judean Society, Inc. (*Catholic*), 1075 Spacepark Way — No. 336, Mountain View, CA 94043.

Jungle Aviation and Radio Service, Inc., c/o James Baptista, Director, P.O. Box 248, Waxhaw, NC 28173.

Junior Catholic Daughters of America, 10 West 71st Street — Suite 401, New York, NY 10023.

Junior Hadassah (*Jewish*), (See Hashachar).

Junior Slovak Catholic Sokol, 205 Madison Street, Passaic, NJ 07055.

Justice and Peace Center (*Catholic*), c/o Dr. Joseph A. Grau, Executive Director, 3900 North Third Street, Milwaukee, WI 53212.

JWB, (National Jewish Welfare Board), 15 East 26th Street, New York, NY 10010.

Ka Hale Hoano Hou O Ke Akua, (The Hallowed House of God, the King of Kings and Lord of Lords), 1760 Nalani, Honolulu, HI 96819.

Ka Makua Mau Loa, (The Church of the Living God), 1629 Bernice Street, Honolulu, HI 96817.

Kagyu Droden Kunchab (*Buddhist*), 3746 21st Street, San Francisco, CA 94110.

Kailas Shugendo (*Buddhist*), 2362 Pine Street, San Francisco, CA 94115.

Kaliashram, P.O. Box 461, Bowling Green Station, New York, NY 10004.

Kansas Yearly Meeting of Friends, c/o David Smitherman, 2018 Maple, Wichita, KS 67213.

Kanuga Episcopal Center, P.O. Drawer 250, Hendersonville, NC 28739.

Kappa Gamma Pi (*Catholic*), c/o Dr. Sally Ann Vonderbrink, President, 5747 Colerain Avenue, Cincinnati, OH 45239.

Kappeler Institute (*New Thought*), c/o Mrs. Elizabeth Robinson, 2235 Seventh Street, East Meadow, NY 11554.

Karl Barth Society of North America, c/o H. M. Rumscheidt, Atlantic School of Theology, 640 Francklyn Street, Halifax, Nova Scotia B3H 3B5, Canada.

Karma Dzong Meditation Center (*Buddhist*), 1111 Pearl Street, Boulder, CO 80302.

Karma Tingay Ling (*Buddhist*), 501 Edgewood Road, San Mateo, CA 94402.

Karma Triyana Dharmachakra (*Buddhist*), Meads Mountain Road, Woodstock, NY 12498.

Karme-Choling, (Tail of the Tiger Buddhist Community), Star Route, Barnet, VT 05821.

Katharsis (*Communal*), 468 Morse, Sunnyvale, CA 94086.
Kathryn Kuhlman Foundation (*Pentecostal*), Park Bldg., 351 5th Avenue, Pittsburgh, PA 15222.
Katolicky Delnik, (See Catholic Workman).
Ke Anaima O Ka Hoomana Hawaii Ponoi, P.O. Box 1075, Kealakekua, HI 96750.
Kealaokalamalama Church, 1207 Prospect Street, Honolulu, HI 96822.
Keepers of the Ancient Mysteries (*Witchcraft*), P.O. Box 34464, Bethesda, MD 20034.
Kenn Mann Ministries, P.O. Box 6656, San Jose, CA 95150.
Kenneth Copeland Evangelistic Association, Inc., P.O. Box 8720, Fort Worth, TX 76112.
Kenneth Gaub Evangelistic Association, P.O. Box 1, Yakima, WA 98907.
Kenneth Hagin Ministries, P.O. Box 50126, Tulsa, OK 74150.
Kentucky Council of Churches, 1500 West Main Street, Lexington, KY 40505.
Kentucky Mountain Holiness Association, c/o Lela G. McConnell, Jackson, KY 41339.
Keren Kayemeth Leisrael, (See Jewish National Fund).
Kerista Consciousness Church (*New Age*), 543 Frederick Street, San Francisco, CA 94117.
Keshavashram International Center, Vedic Sanatana Dharma (*Hindu*), P.O. Box 260, Warrenton, VA 22186.
Kethra E'da Foundation, Inc. (*Psychic*), P.O. Box 11672, Palo Alto, CA 94306.
King Jesus Ministries, c/o Neal R. Williams, 345 Wabasha — Suite 810, St. Paul, MN 55102.
Kingdom of Yahweh (*Psychic*), c/o Dr. Joseph Jeffers, P.O. Box 50338, Jacksonville Beach, FL 32250.
Kingdom Truth Assembly, 1125 Stuyvesant Avenue, Irvington, NJ 07111.
Kirpal Ruhani Satsang (*Sikhism*), c/o Bernadine Chard, 442 Beloit, Kensington, CA 94707.
The Knight Federation Church, c/o Lydia Stalnaker, 535 Fifth Avenue, New York, NY 10017.
Knights Hospitaller, (See Hospitaller Order of St. John of Jerusalem).
Knights of Columbus (*Catholic*), One Columbus Plaza, New Haven, CT 06510.
Knights of Lithuania (*Catholic*), 2455 West 47th Street, Chicago, IL 60632.
Knights of Malta, (See Sovereign Order of Saint John of Jerusalem).
Knights of Peter Claver (*Catholic*), 1821 Orleans Avenue, New Orleans, LA 70116.
Knights of St. John (*Catholic*), 6517 Charles Avenue, Parma, OH 44129.
Knights of St. John Supreme Commandery (*Catholic*), 1603 South Bedford Avenue, Evansville, IN 47713.
Knights of the Immaculata (*Catholic*), (Franciscan Friars of Marytown), 1600 West Park Avenue, Libertyville, IL 60048.
Kodesh Church of Immanuel (*Holiness*), c/o Rev. Fred Almond, 1336 North Hobart Street, Philadelphia, PA 19131.
Koinonia Community, P.O. Box 5744, Baltimore, MD 21208.
Koinonia Foundation, 1400 Greenspring Valley Road, Stevenson, MD 21153.
Koinonia Partners (*Communal*), Route 2, Americus, GA 31709.
Kolel Shomre Hachomos (*Jewish*), Five Beekman Street, New York, NY 10038.
Konko-Kyo Church (*Shinto*), c/o Rev. Alfred Y. Tsuyuki, 2924 East First Street, Los Angeles, CA 90033.

Korea International Mission, Inc., c/o David J. Cho, President, 3423 East Chapman, Orange, CA 92669.

Korean Christian Missions of Hawaii, 1832 Liliha Street, Honolulu, HI 96817.

Korean Relief, Inc., 3827 34th Street, Mount Rainier, MD 20822.

Korean Society for Religious Studies in North America, P.O. Box 8257, University Station, Grand Forks, ND 58202.

Koreshan Unity (*Communal*), c/o Claude J. Rahn, 2012 28th Avenue, Vero Beach, FL 32960.

Kotohira Jinsha Temple (*Shinto*), 1045 Kama Lane, Honolulu, HI 96817.

Krimmer Mennonite Brethren Conference, (See Mennonite Brethren Church of North America).

Kripalu Center for Holistic Health (*New Age*), P.O. Box 120, Summit Station, PA 17979.

Kripalu Yoga Ashram, Seven Walters Road, Sumneytown, PA 18084.

Krishnamurti Foundation of America (*Hindu*), P.O. Box 216, Ojai, CA 93023.

Krotona Institute of Theosophy, P.O. Box 433, Ojai, CA 93023.

Kundalini Clinic for Counseling and Research (*Hindu*), 1628 Union Street, San Francisco, CA 94123.

The Kundalini Research Foundation, Ltd. (*Hindu*), 475 Fifth Avenue, New York, NY 10017.

Kundalini Science Center, 722 Tompkins Avenue, Staten Island, NY 10305.

Kurth Religious Trust (*Lutheran*), 2100 South 43rd Street, Milwaukee, WI 53219.

Kwan Yin Temple (*Buddhist*), 170 North Vineyard Street, Honolulu, HI 96817.

Kwan Yin Zen Temple (*Buddhist*), RFD 2, Temple Road, Woodhull, NY 14898.

La Bergerie-Inner Space Foundation (*New Age*), P.O. Box 5417, Santa Barbara, CA 93108.

Labor Zionist Alliance (*Jewish*), 575 Sixth Avenue, New York, NY 10009.

L'Abri Fellowship Foundation, 49 Lynnbrook, Southborough, MA 01772.

Labsum Shedrub Ling — Lamaist Buddhist Monastery of America, P.O. Box 306-A, R.D. No. 1, Washington, NJ 07882.

Ladies Catholic Benevolent Association, (See Loyal Christian Benefit Association).

Lady Sara's Coven (*Neo-Paganism*), P.O. Box 204, Wolf Creek, OR 97497.

Ladygrove (*Witchcraft*), P.O. Box 171, Pocono Manor, PA 18349.

"Laestadians", (See Apostolic Lutheran Church of America).

Laffey-McHugh Foundation (*Catholic*), Farmers Bank Bldg., 919 North Market Street, Wilmingtom, DE 19801.

Lake Erie Association Yearly Meeting (*Friends*), c/o Ann Arbor Monthly Meeting, 1420 Hill Street, Ann Arbor, MI 48104.

The Lama Foundation (*Communal*), P.O. Box 444, San Cristobal, NM 87564.

Lamaist Buddhist Monastery of America, (See Labsum Shedrub Ling).

Lamb of God Church (*Pentecostal*), 612 Isenberg Street, Honolulu, HI 96826.

Lamp Light Cassette Fellowship, P.O. Box Y, Elyria, OH 44036.

Land House (*Gurdjieff*), P.O. Box 801, Monte Rio, CA 95462.

Landmark Baptists, c/o Dr. I. K. Cross, P.O. Box 848, Bellflower, CA 90706.

Language Institute for Evangelism, c/o Dr: Kenneth P. Wendling, President, P.O. Box 200, Alhambra, CA 91802.

Laodicean Home Missionary Movement, Seven Overbrook Lane, Levittown, PA 19055.

LAOS Inc. (*National Council of Churches*), 4920 Piney Branch Road, N.W., Washington, DC 20011.

Las Hermanas (*Catholic*), 187 Clayton Avenue, San Jose, CA 95110.

Last Day Messenger Assemblies, P.O. Box 17056, Portland, OR 97217.

Last Day Messengers (*Psychic*), P.O. Box 766, Ft. Lauderdale, FL 33302.

Last Day Ministries, P.O. Box 9, Lindale, TX 75771.

Latin America Mission, P.O. Box 341368, Coral Gables, FL 33134.

Latin American Council of Christian Churches (*Pentecostal*), 328 East Jefferson Street, Brownsville, TX 78520.

Latin-American Council of the Pentecostal Church of God of New York, Inc., 115 East 125th Street, New York, NY 10035.

Latin Liturgy Association (*Catholic*), c/o Dr. James Hitchcock, 6158 Kingsbury Blvd., St. Louis, MO 63112.

The Latvian Evangelical Lutheran Church in America, c/o Rev. Arturs Voitkus, President, 3438 Rosedale Avenue, Montreal, Quebec H4B 2G6, Canada.

Lausanne Committee for World Evangelization, P.O. Box 1100, Wheaton, IL 60187.

Lay Mission-Helpers Association (*Catholic*), c/o Rev. Msgr. Lawrence O'Leary, Director, 1531 West Ninth Street, Los Angeles, CA 90015.

Layman Tithing Foundation, 202 South State Street — Room 624, Chicago, IL 60604.

Layman's Missionary Movement (*Southern Baptist Convention*), (See Southern Baptist Convention, Brotherhood Commission).

Laymen's Commission of the American Council of Christian Churches, Valley Forge, PA 19482.

Laymen's Holiness Association of Minnesota, the Dakotas, and Montana, (See Church of the Nazarene).

Laymen's Home Missionary Movement, 2101-13 South 11th Street, Philadelphia, PA 19148.

Laymen's Movement for a Christian World, (See Wainwright House Center for Development of Human Resources).

Laymen's National Bible Committee, 815 Second Avenue — Suite 512, New York, NY 10017.

Laymen's National Committee, (See Laymen's National Bible Committee).

Laymen's Overseas Service (*National Council of Churches*), (See LAOS Inc.).

Leadership Conference of Women Religious of the U.S.A. (*Catholic*), 1302 18th Street, N.W. — Suite 701, Washington, DC 20036.

League for National Labor in Israel (*Jewish*), 55 West 42nd Street — Room 924, New York, NY 10036.

League for Religious Freedom in Israel (*Jewish*), (See American Friends of Religious Freedom in Israel).

League for Yiddish (*Jewish*), 200 West 72nd Street, New York, NY 10023.

League of Night Adoration in the Home (*Catholic*) (See Night Adoration in the Home).

League of Prayer for Unity (*Catholic*), Graymoor, Garrison, NY 10524.

League of St. Dymphna (*Catholic*), 3000 Erie Street South, P.O. Box 4, Massillon, OH 44646.

League of Tarcisians (*Catholic*), Three Adams Street, Fairhaven, MA 02719.

League of Tarcisians of the Sacred Heart (*Catholic*), (See League of Tarcisians).

League of Winant Volunteers, (See The Winant and Clayton Volunteers, Inc.).

League to Uphold Congregational Principles, Inc., P.O. Box 26499, Milwaukee. WI 53213.

Lectorium Rosicrucianum (*Occult*), P.O. Box 517, Pleasant Valley, NY 12569.

Legion of Mary (*Catholic*), P.O. Box 1313, St. Louis, MO 63188.

Lemurian Fellowship (*Occult*), P.O. Box 397, Ramona, CA 92065.

Lend A Hand Society (*Unitarian Universalist*), 34¹/₂ Beacon Street, Boston, MA 02108.

Leo Baeck Institute (*Jewish*), 129 East 73rd Street, New York, NY 10021.

Leonardt Foundation (*Catholic*), 1801 Avenue of the Stars — Suite 500, Los Angeles, CA 90067.

Leroy Jenkins Evangelistic Association, P.O. Box F, Delaware, OH 43015.

Lester Sumrall Evangelistic Association, Inc., P.O. Box 12, South Bend, IN 46624.

Letters of Interest Associates (*Plymouth Brethren*), P.O. Box 294, Wheaton, IL 60187.

Lewis Foundation (*Catholic*), (See Frank J. Lewis Foundation).

The Liberal Catholic Church (Miranda, California), Bear Butte Road and U.S. Freeway 101, Miranda, CA 95553.

The Liberal Catholic Church — Province of the United States of America, c/o Rev. Lawrence Williams, P.O. Box 1051, Ojai, CA 93023.

Liberal Religious Education Directors Association (*Unitarian Universalist Association*), 25 Beacon Street, Boston, MA 02108.

Liberal Religious Peace Fellowship (*Unitarian Universalist*), c/o Ruth Neuendorffer, 15 Dixon Street, Tarrytown, NY 10591.

Liberal Religious Youth (*Unitarian Universalist*), 25 Beacon Street, Boston, MA 02108.

Libertarian Council of Churches, 1220 Larnel Place, Los Altos, CA 94022.

Liberty Corner Mission, (See Fellowship Deaconry, Inc.).

Library and Archives of the Church Historical Society (*Episcopal*), 606 Rathervue Place, Austin, TX 78705.

Liebenzell Mission of U.S.A., Inc., c/o Board of Trustees, Schooleys Mountain, NJ 07870.

Life and Advent Union, (See Advent Christian Church).

Life in the Spirit Ministries (*Pentecostal*), 154 North Greece Road, Hilton, NY 14468.

Life Institute (*New Age*), 60 East 13th Street, New York, NY 10003.

Life Messengers, P.O. Box 1967, Seattle, WA 98111.

Life Science Church, P.O. Box 1708, Twin City Airport, MN 55111.

Life Science Institute, 1500 Boston Avenue, Fort Pierce, FL 33450.

Life Study Fellowship (*New Thought*), Noroton, CT 06820.

Life Understanding Foundation, c/o William T. Cox, President, 741 Rosarita Lane, Santa Barbara, CA 93105.

Lifegate, Inc., P.O. Box 1771, Martinsville, IN 46151.

Lifeliners (*Pentecostal Holiness Church, International*), c/o Rev. Jim Eby, General Director, P.O. Box 12526, Oklahoma City, OK 73157.

Light-for-the-Lost (*Assemblies of God*), 1445 Boonville, Springfield, MO 65802.

Light Haven (*New Age*), 3512 McCoy, S.E., Grand Rapids, MI 49506.

Light of Divine Truth Foundation, 8624 Granby Street, Norfolk, VA 23503.

Light of the Universe (*New Age*), 161 North Sandusky Street, Tiffin, OH 44883.

Light of Truth Church, c/o Nelson White, P.O. Box 3125, Pasadena, CA 91103.

The Light of Yoga Society (*Hindu*), 12429 Cedar Road, Cleveland Heights, OH 44106.

The Lighted Way (*New Age*), 1515 Palisades Drive, Pacific Palisades, CA 90272.

Lighthouse Gospel Tract Foundation, c/o Bill Maupin, 3140 East Greenlee Road, Tucson, AZ 85716.

Lindenself Foundation (*New Age*), P.O. Box 2321, Chapel Hill, NC 27514.

The Lindisfarne Association (*New Age*), c/o The Lindisfarne Press, R.D. 2, East Alford Road, West Stockbridge, MA 01266.

The Lindisfarne Center (*New Age*), c/o Cathedral of St. John the Divine, 1047 Amsterdam Avenue, New York, NY 10025.

The Lindisfarne Fellows' House (*New Age*), c/o Zen Center, Green Gulch Farm, Sausalito, CA 94965.

The Lindisfarne Institute (*New Age*), c/o Baca Grande Ranch, Crestone, CO 81131.

Literacy and Evangelism International, c/o Rev. Robert F. Rice, Director, 1800 South Jackson Avenue, Tulsa, OK 74107.

Lithuanian American Catholic Services, 351 Highland Blvd., Brooklyn, NY 11207.

Lithuanian American Roman Catholic Federation, 351 Highland Blvd., Brooklyn, NY 11207.

Lithuanian Catholic Alliance, 73 South Washington Street, Wilkes-Barre, PA 18701.

Lithuanian Catholic Graduate Association "Ateitis", c/o J. B. Laucka, President, 4921 78th Avenue, Hyattsville, MD 20784.

Lithuanian Catholic Press Society, 4545 West 63rd Street, Chicago, IL 60629.

Lithuanian Catholic Religious Aid, Inc., 351 Highland Blvd., Brooklyn, NY 11207.

Lithuanian Roman Catholic Alliance of America, (See Lithuanian Catholic Alliance).

Lithuanian Roman Catholic Federation of America, 8761 West Outer Drive, Detroit, MI 48219.

Lithuanian Roman Catholic Priests' League of America, 351 Highland Blvd., Brooklyn, NY 11207.

Little Brothers of the Gospel, 58 East 4th Street, New York, NY 10003.

Little Brothers of the Poor, 1658 West Belmont Avenue, Chicago, IL 60657.

Little Flower Mission League (*Catholic*), P.O. Box 25, Plaucheville, LA 71362.

Little Flower Society (*Catholic*), 11343 South Michigan Avenue, Chicago, IL 60628.

Little Sisters of the Gospel, 223 East 10th Street, New York, NY 10003.

Little Synagogue (*Jewish*), 27 East 20th Street, New York, NY 10003.

The Liturgical Conference, 810 Rhode Island Avenue, N.E., Washington, DC 20018.

Liturgy Committee, National Conference of Catholic Bishops, 1312 Massachusetts Avenue, N.W., Washington, DC 20005.

Living Bibles International, 342 Gundersen Drive, Wheaton, IL 60187.

Living Church Foundation (*Episcopal*), 407 East Michigan Street, Milwaukee, WI 53202.

Living Faith Community (*Episcopal*), 1206 Broad Avenue East, Spokane, WA 99207.

Living, Loving, Learning Center (*New Age*), c/o Rev. Golda Sirota, Director, 19722 Grandview Drive, Topanga, CA 90290.

Living Word Ministries, P.O. Box 958, North Hollywood, CA 91603.

The (Local) Church, (Witness Lee), c/o Stream Publishers, P.O. Box 20755, Los Angeles, CA 90006.

Logos International Fellowship, Inc., 201 Church Street, Plainfield, NJ 07060.

Logos Ministry for Orthodox Renewal, 2707 South Calhoun Street, Fort Wayne, IN 46807.

Long Island Gardnerians (*Witchcraft*), P.O. Box 56, Commack, NY 11725.

Longchen Nyingthig Buddhist Society, P.O. Box 302, Harris, NY 12742.

Longyear Historical Society (*Christian Science*), Mary Baker Eddy Museum, 120 Seaver Street, Brookline, MA 02146.

Lorain Association (*New Age*), c/o David Spangler, P.O. Box 941, Belmont, CA 94002.

Lord's Acre Plan, P.O. Box 27, Hayesville, NC 28904.

Lord's Covenant Church, Inc., c/o Rev. Sheldon Emry, P.O. Box 5334, Phoenix, AZ 85010.

Lord's Day Alliance of the U.S., 2930 Flowers Road South — Suite 107, Atlanta, GA 30341.

Lord's New Church Which Is Nova Hierosolyma (*Swedenborgian*), Creek Road, Bryn Athyn, PA 19009.

The Lord's Own Tape Ministry, Inc., 5529 Granada Road, Fort Myers, FL 33907.

Lord's Way Inn Ministries, Inc., 846 5th Avenue, San Diego, CA 92101.

The Los Angeles Council of Churches, 760 South Westmoreland Avenue, Los Angeles, CA 90005.

Lotus Ashram (*Psychic*), P.O. Box 39, Fabens TX 79838.

The Louis Foundation (*New Age*), Eastsound, WA 98245.

Louisiana Interchurch Conference, 440 North Foster Drive — Suite 106, Baton Rouge, LA 70806.

Love in Action, P.O. Box 2655, San Rafael, CA 94902.

The Love Project (*New Age*), P.O. Box 7601, San Diego, CA 92107.

Lowell Lundstrom Ministries, Inc., Sisseton, SD 57262.

Loyal Christian Benefit Association, 305 West 6th Street, Erie, PA 16507.

The Loyola Foundation, Inc. (*Catholic*), 308 C Street, N.E., Washington, DC 20002.

Lubavitch Youth Organization (*Jewish*), 770 Eastern Parkway, Brooklyn, NY 11213.

Lucien B. and Katherine E. Price Foundation, Inc. (*Catholic*), 896 Main Street, Manchester, CT 06040.

Lucis Trust, 866 United Nations Plaza — Suite 566-7, New York, NY 10164.

Ludendorff Study Group (*Teutonic-Nordic*), P.O. Box 3235, Wichita, KS 67201.

Ludhiana Christian Medical College Board, U.S.A., Inc., 475 Riverside Drive — Room 250, New York, NY 10115.

Luis Palau Evangelistic Team, Inc., P.O. Box 1173, Portland, OR 97207.

Luther Union, (See Lutheran Brotherhood).

Lutheran Academy for Scholarship, 908 Wood Street, Valparaiso, IN 46383.

Lutheran Benevolent Association, P.O. Box 228, Alma, MO 64001.

Lutheran Bible Ministries, c/o Rev. Victor Albers, Executive Director, 705 Pomander Walk, Teaneck, NJ 07666.

Lutheran Bible Translators, Inc., P.O. Box 5566, Orange, CA 92667.

Lutheran Braille Evangelism Association, 660 East Montana Avenue, St. Paul, MN 55106.

Lutheran Braille Workers, Inc., c/o Mrs. Bernard Loewe Koehler, Executive Director, 11735 Peach Tree Circle, Yucaipa, CA 92399.

Lutheran Brotherhood, 701 Second Avenue South, Minneapolis, MN 55402.

Lutheran Camp Association, 5020 West Wolfram, Chicago, IL 60641.

Lutheran Campus Ministry Association, c/o Rev. Richard Stewart, Central State University, Box 386, Wilberforce, OH 45384.

Lutheran Charisciples, (See Charis Life Ministries).

Lutheran Charismatic Renewal Services, P.O. Box 14344, University Station, Minneapolis, MN 55414.

Lutheran Church and Indian People, 600 West 12th Street, Sioux Falls, SD 57104.

Lutheran Church in America, 231 Madison Avenue, New York, NY 10016.

Lutheran Church Library Association, 122 West Franklin Avenue, Minneapolis, MN 55404.

The Lutheran Church-Missouri Synod, 1333 South Kirkwood Road, St. Louis, MO 63122.

Lutheran Church of Latvia in Exile, (See The Latvian Evangelical Lutheran Church in America).

Lutheran Church Women (*Lutheran Church in America*), 2900 Queen Lane, Philadelphia, PA 19129.

Lutheran Churches of the Reformation, c/o Rev. Paul G. Koch, 117 Vermont Street, La Crosse, IN 46348.

Lutheran Collegians (*Wisconsin Evangelical Lutheran Synod*), 3512 West North Avenue, Milwaukee, WI 53208.

Lutheran Council in the U.S.A., 360 Park Avenue South, New York, NY 10010.

Lutheran Deaconess Association, c/o Deaconess Hall, Valparaiso, IN 46383.

Lutheran Deaconess Community (*Lutheran Church in America*), 801 Merion Square Road, Gladwyne, PA 19035.

Lutheran Education Association, 7400 Augusta Street, River Forest, IL 60305.

Lutheran Educational Conference of North America, 475 L'Enfant Plaza, S.W., West Bldg. — Suite 2720, Washington, DC 20024.

Lutheran Evangelism Association, P.O. Box 10021, Phoenix, AZ 85064.

Lutheran Evangelistic Movement, 13 South 9th Street, Minneapolis, MN 55402.

Lutheran Foundation for Religious Drama, St. Peter's Center, 16 East 56th Street, New York, NY 10022.

Lutheran Fraternities of America, 728 Penobscot Bldg., Detroit, MI 48226.

Lutheran Free Church, (See The American Lutheran Church).

Lutheran Free Church (Not Merged), (See Association of Free Lutheran Congregations).

Lutheran Girl Pioneers (*Wisconsin Evangelical Lutheran Synod*), c/o Mrs. Jean Masewicz, 1611 Caledonia Street, La Crosse, WI 54601.

Lutheran Guild of Suomi Synod, (See Lutheran Church Women).

Lutheran Historical Conference, c/o Concordia Historical Institute, 801 DeMun Avenue, St. Louis, MO 63105.

Lutheran Hospital Association of America, 840 North Lake Shore Drive — Room 607 W, Chicago, IL 60611.

Lutheran Hospitals and Homes Society of America, P.O. Box 2087, Fargo, ND 58107.

Lutheran Human Relations Association, c/o Charles and Susan Ruehle, Sherman Park Lutheran Church, 2703 North Sherman Blvd., Milwaukee, WI 53210.

Lutheran Immigration and Refugee Services, 360 Park Avenue South, New York, NY 10010.

Lutheran Immigration Service, (See Lutheran Immigration and Refugee Services).

Lutheran Laymen's League, (See International Lutheran Laymen's League).

Lutheran Laymen's Movement, 231 Madison Avenue, New York, NY 10016.

Lutheran Library for the Blind, 3558 South Jefferson Avenue, St. Louis, MO 63118.

Lutheran Medical Mission Association, Lutheran Professional Bldg. — Suite 115, 3535 South Jefferson Avenue, St. Louis, MO 63118.

Lutheran Ministries in Higher Education, 178 Bennett Avenue, New York, NY 10040.

Lutheran Mission Societies, c/o Corey Hjalseth, President, P.O. Box 549, Cordova, AK 99574.

Lutheran Mutual Life, Heritage Way, Waverly, IA 50677.

Lutheran Peace Fellowship, 168 West 100th Street, New York, NY 10025.

Lutheran Pioneers, Inc. (*Wisconsin Evangelical Lutheran Synod*), P.O. Box 66, Burlington, WI 53105.

Lutheran Resources Commission — Washington, 1346 Connecticut Avenue, N.W. — Suite 823, Washington, DC 20036.

Lutheran Science Institute, c/o Prof. Gerald Mallmann, 4821 19th Avenue, Kenosha, WI 53140.

Lutheran Seamen's Center, (See Seamen and International House).

Lutheran Society for Worship, Music, and the Arts, c/o Daniel C. Brockopp, Executive Secretary, Valparaiso University, Valparaiso, IN 46383.

Lutheran Student Association of America, (See Lutheran Student Movement — USA).

Lutheran Student Movement — USA, 35 East Wacker Drive — Suite 1847, Chicago, IL 60601.

Lutheran Women's Missionary League, (See International Lutheran Women's Missionary League).

Lutheran Women's Missionary Society (*Wisconsin Evangelical Lutheran Synod*), c/o Mrs. Ralph T. Schmidt, Sr., 250 Circle Drive, Oconomowoc, WI 53066.

Lutheran World Action, (See Lutheran Council in the U.S.A.).

Lutheran World Federation — USA National Committee, 360 Park Avenue South, New York, NY 10010.

Lutheran World Ministries, (See Lutheran World Federation — USA National Committee).

Lutheran World Relief, 360 Park Avenue South, New York, NY 10010.

Lutheran Youth Encounter, 2500 39th Avenue, N.E., Minneapolis, MN 55421.

Lutherans Alert, P.O. Box 7186, Tacoma, WA 98407.

Lutherans Concerned for Gay People, P.O. Box 19114A, Los Angeles, CA 90019.

Lutherans for Life, P.O. Box 988, 275 North Syndicate, St. Paul, MN 55104.

Lutherans for Life (*Wisconsin Evangelical Lutheran Synod*), c/o Christ the King Evangelical Lutheran Church, 100 West Michigan Avenue, Palatine, IL 60067.

Lydia in America, P.O. Box 20236, San Jose, CA 95160.

Maalin Bakodesh Society (*Jewish*), 26 Canal Street, New York, NY 10002.

MacDonald Foundation (*Catholic*), (See Marquis George MacDonald Foundation, Inc.).

Macedonia Baptist Association, (See Christian Unity Baptist Association).

Macedonia Ministries, Inc., 9500 Comstock, Little Rock, AR 72209.

Macedonian Orthodox Church, c/o Macedonian Orthodox Church of SS. Peter and Paul, 51st and Virginia Streets, Gary, IN 46409.

Madrakara Festivals (*Neo-Paganism*), P.O. Box 82, Occidental, CA 95465.

The Magi Center, Inc. (*Psychic*), 565 Pearson Road, P.O. Box 1166, Paradise, CA 95969.

The Magick Circle (*Neo-Paganism*), R.D. No. 2, Camelot, North Adams, MA 01247.

Maharishi International University, (International Meditation Society), Fairfield, IA 52556.

Mahikari of America, 6470 Foothill Blvd., Tujunga, CA 91042.

Maine Council of Churches, P.O. Box 512, Auburn, ME 04210.

The Maitreya World Foundation, Inc. (*Buddhist*), 63 Coolidge Road, Boston, MA 02123.

Maitri Center of Buddhist Psychology, Old Forge Road, Wingdale, NY 12594.

Malankara (Indian) Orthodox Church, American Diocese, c/o Rev. Dr. M. E. Idiculla, Secretary, 68 Second Street, Geneseo, NY 14454.

Malbis Memorial Foundation (*Greek Orthodox*), P.O. Box 218, Daphne, AL 36526.

The Mandala Society (*New Age*), P.O. Box 1233, Del Mar, CA 92014.

Mann Ranch Seminars (*New Age*), P.O. Box 570, Ukiah, CA 95482.

Manosophy, Inc. (*New Thought*), 1964 Anaheim Avenue, Costa Mesa, CA 92627.

MAP International, P.O. Box 50, Wheaton, IL 60187.

Maranatha Ministries, P.O. Box 1799, Gainesville, FL 32602.

The Margaret Coffin Prayer Book Society (*Episcopal*), Beatrice M. Osgood, Clerk, One Joy Street, Boston, MA 02108.

Marian Movement of Priests (*Catholic*), c/o Rev. Albert G. Roux, P.O. Box 8, St. Francis, ME 04774.

Mariavite Old Catholic Church — Province of North America, 2803 Tenth Street, Wyandotte, MI 48192.

Marietta Center for New Age Wicca (*Witchcraft*), c/o Dr. John Beasley, 306 Hill Street, Marietta, GA 30060.

Mariological Society of America (*Catholic*), c/o The Marian Library, University of Dayton, Dayton, OH 45469.

Mariska Aldrich Memorial Foundation (*New Age*), 2512 Komo Mai Drive, Pearl City, HI 96782.

Mark-Age (*Psychic*), 565 East Channel Road, Santa Monica, CA 90402.

Markham Prayer Card Apostolate (*Catholic*), 60 Compton Road, Cincinnati, OH 45215.

Marquette League for Catholic Indian Missions, 1011 First Avenue, New York, NY 10022.

Marquis George MacDonald Foundation, Inc. (*Catholic*), 120 Broadway — Room 3121, New York, NY 10005.

Marriott Family Foundation (*Mormon*), (See The J. Willard Marriott Family Foundation).

Martin Tananbaum Foundation, Inc. (*Jewish*), c/o David T. Goldstick, 551 Fifth Avenue, New York, NY 10017.
Martinist Institute of Spiritual Science, c/o Grand Lodge, 15 Outlook Road, Mattapan, MA 02126.
Martinist Order, (See Neo-Pythagorean Gnostic Church).
The Maryheart Crusaders (*Catholic*), 22 Button Street, Meriden, CT 06450.
Maryland Churches United, 3107 North Charles Street, Baltimore, MD 21218.
Mass Media Ministries, 2116 North Charles Street, Baltimore, MD 21218.
Massachusetts Catholic Order of Foresters, (See Catholic Association of Foresters)
Massachusetts Convention of Congregational Ministers, c/o Rev. Paul E. Sinn, Moderator, Eight Town Square, Plymouth, MA 02360.
Massachusetts Council of Churches, 14 Beacon Street, Boston, MA 02108.
Matagiri Sri Aurobindo Center (*Hindu*), Mt. Tremper, NY 12457.
Matri Satsang (*Hindu*), P.O. Box 117, Carmichael, CA 95608.
Max Stern Foundation, Inc. (*Jewish*), 700 South 4th Street, Harrison, NJ 07029.
Max Weinreich Center for Advanced Jewish Studies, 1048 Fifth Avenue, New York, NY 10028.
The Mayan Order (*Occult*), P.O. Box 2710, San Antonio, TX 78299.
Mazdaznan Association (*Zoroastrian*), 1159 South Norton Avenue, Los Angeles, CA 90019.
Meadowlark Holistic Health Center (*New Age*), (See Friendly Hills Fellowship).
Measure of Faith Ministries (*Pentecostal*), P.O. Box 1294, Jonesboro, AR 72401.
The Media Outreach Agency (*Church of God — Seventh Day*), P.O. Box 33677, Denver, CO 80233.
Medical Assistance Program, (See MAP International).
Medical Mission Sisters (*Catholic*), 8400 Pine Road, Philadelphia, PA 19111.
Meditation Center of Awareness (*New Age*), c/o Rev. Ruth Lambek, Director, 1756 North Hill Avenue, Pasadena, CA 91104.
Meditation Group for the New Age, P.O. Box 566, Ojai, CA 93023.
Meditation International Center (*Jainism*), 120 East 86th Street, New York, NY 10028.
The Meditology Foundation (*New Age*), P.O. Box 514, Woodland Hills, CA 91364.
Megiddo Mission Church, 481 Thurston Road, Rochester, NY 14619.
Meher Baba League, Inc. (*Sufism*), 2131 University Avenue — Room 336, Berkeley, CA 94704.
Meher Spiritual Center (*Sufism*), P.O. Drawer 1519, North Myrtle Beach, SC 29582.
Melodyland Christian Center, 1730 South Clementine, Anaheim, CA 92802.
Members of "The Church Which Is Christ's Body", P.O. Box 1122, Charlottesville, VA 22902.
Memorial Foundation for Jewish Culture, 15 East 26th Street, New York, NY 10010.
Men for Missions International, P.O. Box A, Greenwood, IN 46142.
Men for the Ministry Foundation (*Episcopal*), c/o Rev. Canon C. Leslie Glenn, President, 16 Kalorama Circle, N.W., Washington, DC 20008.
Men of Goodwill, (See World Goodwill).
Men of the Sacred Heart (*Catholic*), c/o The Shrine of the Sacred Heart, Harleigh, PA 18225.

Mennonite Board of Education, P.O. Box 1142, Elkhart, IN 46515.

Mennonite Brethren Church of North America, c/o Mennonite Brethren Publishing House, Hillsboro, KS 67063.

Mennonite Brethren in Christ, (See The Missionary Church).

The Mennonite Central Committee, 21 South 12th Street, Akron, PA 17501.

Mennonite Church, 528 East Madison Street, Lombard, IL 60148.

Mennonite Church Historical Committee, 1700 South Main Street, Goshen, IN 46526.

Mennonite Disaster Service, 21 South 12th Street, Akron, PA 17501.

Mennonite Economic Development Associates, c/o Lloyd J. Fisher, Executive Director, 21 South 12th Street, Akron, PA 17501.

Mennonite Health Assembly, P.O. Box 370, Elkhart, IN 46514.

Mennonite Historical Library, Bluffton College, Bluffton, OH 45817.

Mennonite Medical Association, c/o Erland Walter, 3003 Benham Avenue, Elkhart, IN 46514.

Mennonite Renewal Services, P.O. Box 722, Goshen, IN 46526.

Mennonite World Conference, c/o Paul N. Kraybill, Executive Secretary, 528 East Madison Street, Lombard, IL 60148.

Merlin Carothers Foundation of Praise, P.O. Box 2518, Escondido, CA 92025.

Message for America, (See Lowell Lundstrom Ministries, Inc.).

Messiah's World Crusade, (See The Universal Industrial Church of the New World Comforter).

Messianic Jewish Alliance of America, 3601 West Devon Avenue — Room G-9, Chicago, IL 60659.

The Messianic Jewish Movement International, P.O. Box 30313, Washington, DC 20014.

Meta Tantay Indian Foundation (*Native American*), c/o Rolling Thunder, P.O. Box 707, Carlin, NV 89822.

The Metaphysical Arts Center, 2315 University Blvd., Houston, TX 77005.

Metaphysical Science Association, P.O. Box 6454, Metropolitan Station, Los Angeles, CA 90055.

Metaphysics & Parapsychology Institute, Inc., c/o Renee Linn, Director, 225 East 74th Street, New York, NY 10021.

The Methodist Church, (See The United Methodist Church).

Methodist Committee for Overseas Relief, (See United Methodist Committee on Relief).

Methodist Council on Youth Ministry, (See National Youth Ministry Organization).

Methodist Episcopal Church, (See The United Methodist Church).

Methodist Episcopal Church, South, (See The United Methodist Church).

The Methodist Federation for Social Action, Inc. (*United Methodist Church*), Shalom House, 76 Clinton Avenue, Staten Island, NY 10301.

Methodist Historical Union, (See World Methodist Historical Society).

Methodist Peace Fellowship, 5123 Truman Road, Kansas City, MO 64127.

The Methodist Protestant Church (*Holiness*), 325 East McDowell Road, P.O. Box 1468, Jackson, MS 39205.

Methodist Protestant Church, (See The United Methodist Church).

Metropolitan Christian Council of Philadelphia, 1501 Cherry Street, Philadelphia, PA 19102.

Metropolitan Church Association (*Holiness*), 323 Broad Street, Lake Geneva, WI 53147.

Metropolitan Community Church, 1046 South Hill Street, Hollywood, CA 90015.

Metropolitan Spiritual Churches of Christ, 4315 South Wabash, Chicago, IL 60653.

The Mevlana Foundation (*Sufism*), P.O. Box 305, Boulder, CO 80306.

Mexican Mission Ministries, Inc., P.O. Box 636, Pharr, TX 78577.

Miami Friends of Teilhard de Chardin, 1030 N.E. 128th Street, Miami, FL 33161.

Michigan Council of Churches, 205 West Saginaw, P.O. Box 10206, Lansing, MI 48901.

The Michigan Metaphysical Society, 3036 West Twelve Mile Road, Berkley, MI 48072.

Mid Hudson Pagan Grove (*Witchcraft*), P.O. Box 504, Glenham, NY 12527.

The Midnight Call, P.O. Box 704, Hamilton, OH 45012.

Midwest Challenge, 8200 Grand Avenue South, Minneapolis, MN 55420.

Midwest Holiness Association (*Holiness*), (See Evangelical Wesleyan Church).

Midwest Pagan Council, P.O. Box 664, Chicago Heights, IL 60411.

Migrant/Field Ministry (*National Council of Churches*), 475 Riverside Drive — Room 572, New York, NY 10115.

Miletus Church, 140 North Barry Avenue, Wayzata, MN 55391.

Militarism and Education Program of United Ministries in Education, 1451 Dundee Avenue, Elgin, IL 60120.

Military Chaplains Association of the U.S.A., 7758 Wisconsin Avenue — Suite 401, Washington, DC 20014.

Millennium Guild, 40 Central Park South, New York, NY 10019.

Million Testaments Campaigns, 1211 Arch Street, Philadelphia, PA 19107.

Mind Development Association (*Psychic*), P.O. Box 24571, St. Louis, MO 63141.

Ministerial and Missionary Alliance of the Original Trinity Apostolic Faith, Inc. (*Pentecostal*), (See Full Gospel Evangelistic Association).

Ministerial Interfaith Association, 110 East 125th Street, New York, NY 10035.

Ministers in Medical Education, Society for Health and Human Values, c/o Dr. Russell McIntyre, College of Medicine and Dentistry of New Jersey, 88 Sky-line Drive, Morristown, NJ 07960.

Ministries in Public Education, (See United Ministries in Education).

Ministries of Vision, P.O. Box 4130, Medford, OR 97501.

Ministries to Blacks in Higher Education, c/o Elwyn D. Rawlings, Howard University, Box 822, Washington, DC 20059.

Ministry and Life Programs, c/o Rev. Joel Garner, Director, St. Norbert Abbey, 1016 North Broadway, De Pere, WI 54115.

Ministry of Christ, P.O. Box 306, Colby, WI 54421.

Ministry of Christ Church, 4241 Usona Road, Mariposa, CA 95338.

Ministry of Divine Love, P.O. Box 2815, La Mesa, CA 92041.

Minnesota Baptist Convention, 5000 Golden Valley Road, Minneapolis, MN 55422.

Minnesota Bible Fellowship, Inc., P.O. Box 8295, Minneapolis, MN 55408.

Minnesota Christian Writer's Guild, c/o Dorothy Larson, Secretary, 7340 Brunswick Avenue North, Minneapolis, MN 55443.

Minnesota Church of the Wicca (*Witchcraft*), P.O. Box 8854, Minneapolis, MN 55408.

Minnesota Council of Churches, 122 West Franklin Avenue, Minneapolis, MN 55404.

Minnesota Zen Meditation Center, 3343 East Calhoun Parkway, Minneapolis, MN 55408.

The Miracle Connection (*New Age*), c/o Mrs. J'Nevelyn Terrell, Director, 510 South Burnside Avenue, Los Angeles, CA 90036.

Miracle Life Revival, Inc. (*Pentecostal*), P.O. Box 20707, Phoenix, AZ 85036.

Miracle Revival Fellowship (*Pentecostal*), Miracle Valley, AZ 85645, (See also Don Stewart Evangelistic Association).

Mirrer Yeshiva Central Institute (*Jewish*), 1791-5 Ocean Parkway, Brooklyn, NY 11223.

Mission Aviaton Fellowship, P.O. Box 202, Redlands, CA 92373.

Mission Doctors Association (*Catholic*), 1531 West Ninth Street, Los Angeles, CA 90015.

Mission of the Month Club (*Catholic*), c/o Trinity Missions, P.O. Box 30, Silver Spring, MD 20910.

Mission to Catholics, P.O. Box 19280, San Diego, CA 92119.

Mission to Mormons, P.O. Box 322, Roy, UT 84067.

Missionary and Soul Winning Fellowship, 350 East Market Street, North Long Beach, CA 90805.

Missionary Association of Catholic Women, Inc., 1425 North Prospect Avenue, Milwaukee, WI 53202.

Missionary Bands of the World (*Holiness*), (See The Wesleyan Church).

Missionary Cenacle Apostolate (*Catholic*), 3501 Solly Avenue, Philadelphia, PA 19136.

The Missionary Church, 3901 South Wayne Avenue, Fort Wayne, IN 46807.

Missionary Church Association, (See The Missionary Church).

Missionary Dispensary Bible Research, P.O. Box 5296, Buena Park, CA 90622.

Missionary Education Movement, (See Commission on Education for Mission).

The Missionary Education Movement of the United States and Canada, (See the National Council of Churches of Christ in the U.S.A.).

Missionary Engineering, (See Mission Aviation Fellowship).

Missionary Fellowship of Baptist Churches, (See Independent Bible Baptist Missions).

Missionary Information Exchange, c/o Robert B. Hicks, P.O. Box 664, Warren, MI 48090.

Missionary Internship, Inc., P.O. Box 457, Farmington, MI 48024.

Missionary Literature Distributors (*Grace Gospel Fellowship*), c/o Rollie Phipps, Director, 7514 Humbert Road, Godfrey, IL 62035.

Missionary Methodist Church of America (*Holiness*), c/o Rev. Dan S. Hardin, Forest City Missionary Methodist Church, Forest City, NC 28043.

The Missionary Research Library, 3041 Broadway, New York, NY 10027.

Missionary Revival Crusade, 102 East Lyon, Laredo, TX 78040.

Missionary Services, Inc., P.O. Box 853, Wheaton, IL 60187.

Missionary Union of the Clergy in the U.S.A. (*Catholic*), (See Pontifical Missionary Union in the U.S.A.).

Missionary Vehicle Association, Inc. (*Catholic*), 514 Allegheny River Blvd., P.O. Box 63, Oakmont, PA 15139.

Missions Advanced Research and Communication Center, c/o World Vision International, 919 West Huntington Drive, Monrovia, CA 91016.

Missions, Inc., c/o Richard L. Shope, President, Zion Road, R.D. 5, Bellefonte, PA 16823.

Missions to Japan, Inc. (*Pentecostal*), P.O. Box 1203, Campbell, CA 95008.

Missions to Military (*Baptist*), P.O. Box 6, Norfolk, VA 23501.

Missouri Council of Churches, P.O. Box 839, Jefferson City, MO 65101.

Missouri Synod (*Lutheran*), (See The Lutheran Church-Missouri Synod).

Missouri Valley Conference Yearly Meeting of Friends (*Unaffiliated*), c/o Kenton Allen, 1423 Woodland Street, Wichita, KS 67203.

Mita Movement (*Pentecostal*), Calle Duarte 235, Hato Rey, PR 00919.

Mizrachi National Education Committee (*Jewish*), (See National Council for Torah Education).

Mizrachi Palestine Fund (*Jewish*), 25 West 26th Street, New York, NY 10010.

Mizrachi Women's Organization of America (*Jewish*), (See American Mizrachi Women).

Mohawk Christian Fellowship, c/o Stephen J. Myers, Jr., Executive Director, P.O. Box 99, Johnstown, NY 12095.

The Monka Retreat, c/o Samuel George Partridge, Golden Sierra Printing Co., 116 Mercury Drive, Grass Valley, CA 95945.

Montana Association of Churches, 1511 Poly Drive, Billings, MT 59102.

Moody Church, 1630 North Clark Street, Chicago, IL 60614.

Moody Institute of Science, 12000 East Washington Blvd., Whittier, CA 90606.

Moonfire Coven (*Witchcraft*), P.O. Box 395, Littleton, CO 80120.

"Moonies" (See The Unification Church).

Moonrise and Church of the Celtic Cross (*Neo-Paganism*), P.O. Box 5558, Atlanta, GA 30307.

Moorish Divine and National Movement in North America, 4233 South Calumet Avenue, Chicago, IL 60653.

Moorish Science Temple of America, c/o Reynold N. El, 3810 South Wabash Avenue, Chicago, IL 60653.

Moral Alternatives, c/o Rabbi Francis Barry Silberg, Congregation Emanu-El B'ne Jeshurun, 2419 East Kenwood Blvd., Milwaukee, WI 53211.

Moral Majority, Inc., P.O. Box 190, Forest, VA 24551.

Moral Re-Armament, 124 East 40th Street — Suite 701, New York, NY 10016.

Morality in Media, Inc. (*Catholic*), 475 Riverside Drive, New York, NY 10115.

Moravian Archives, Southern Province of the Moravian Church, Drawer M, Salem Station, Winston-Salem, NC 27108.

Moravian Church in America (Unitas Fratrum), Northern Province: 69 West Church Street, P.O. Box 1245, Bethlehem, PA 18018, Southern Province: 459 South Church Street, Winston-Salem, NC 27101.

Moravian Historical Society, 214 East Center, Nazareth, PA 18064.

Moravian Music Foundation, P.O. Box Z, Salem Station, Winston-Salem, NC 27108.

More Men for the Ministry Foundation (*Episcopal*), c/o Rev. Canon C. Leslie Glenn, President, 16 Kalorama Circle, Washington, DC 20008.

Mormon History Association, P.O. Box 7010, University Station, Provo, UT 84602.

Morningland (*New Age*), 2600 East 7th, Long Beach, CA 90804.

Morris Cerullo World Evangelism, (See World Evangelism).

Morris Pratt Institute Association (*Spiritualist*), 11811 Watertown Plank Road, Wauwatosa, WI 53226.

Moslem Mosque, 104 Powers Street, Brooklyn, NY 11211.
Mother Cabrini League (*Catholic*), 2520 Lakeview Avenue, Chicago, IL 60614.
Mother Earth Church, 469 Pacific, Monterey, CA 93940.
Mother Thunder Mission (*Episcopal*), P.O. Box 579, New York, NY 10011.
Motivation Development Centre (*New Age*), P.O. Box 25643, Albuquerque, NM 87125.
Mt. Calvary Holy Church of America (*Holiness*), 9-15 Otisfield Street, Boston, MA 02121.
Mt. Helion Sanctuary, (See Embassy of the Gheez-Americans).
Mount Hermon Christian Conference Center, P.O. Box 597, Mount Hermon, CA 95041.
Mt. Sinai Holy Church of America (*Pentecostal*), c/o Bishop Mary E. Jackson, 1601 North Broad Street, Philadelphia, PA 19122.
Mt. Zion Sanctuary, 21 Dayton Street, Elizabeth, NJ 07202.
Mountain Brook Studies (*New Thought*), c/o William Samuel, P.O. Box 9206, Mountain Brook, AL 35213.
Movement for a Better World (*Catholic*), P.O. Box H, Far Rockaway, NY 11691.
Movement for Religious Renewal, (See The Christian Community).
Movement of Spiritual Inner Awareness (*New Age*), P.O. Box 3935, Los Angeles, CA 90051.
Movimiento Familiar Cristiano (*Catholic*), 6932 Thrush Drive, Houston, TX 77087.
Mu Farm (*Communal*), Route 1 — Box 143, Yoncalla, OR 97499.
Munedowk Foundation, Inc. (*New Age*), Route 1 — Box 268, Kiel, WI 53042.
Muni Sushil Yogville (*Jainism*), Route 51, Burlington Flats, NY 13315.
Murphy Center for Liturgical Research (*Catholic*), P.O. Box 81, University of Notre Dame, Notre Dame, IN 46556.
Muslim Students Association, Al-Amin Mosque, 3702 West 11th Avenue, Gary, IN 46404.
The Muslim Students' Association of the United States and Canada, P.O. Box 38, Plainfield, IN 46168.
Muslim Women's Childbirth Education Association, 94 11th Street, Newark, NJ 07107.
The Mustard Seed, Inc., c/o Mrs. Lillian R. Dickson, President, 1377 East Colorado Street, Glendale, CA 91205.
Nalanda Foundation (*Buddhist*), 1345 Spruce Street, Boulder, CO 80302.
NARCONON (*Church of Scientology*), 90 Windon Avenue, Allston, MA 02134.
Naropa Institute (*Buddhist*), 1111 Pearl Street, Boulder, CO 80302.
Narragansett Indian Church, c/o Rev. Harold Mars, 61 Highland Avenue, Wakefield, RI 02879.
Narramore Christian Foundation, P.O. Box 5000, 1409 North Walnut Grove Avenue, Rosemead, CA 91770.
Narrow Way Ministries, P.O. Box 367, Holbrook, NY 11741.
Nation of Islam, (See The World Community of Islam in the West).
National Academy for Adult Jewish Studies (*United Synagogue of America*), 155 Fifth Avenue, New York, NY 10010.
National Academy of Religion and Mental Health, (See Institutes of Religion and Health).
National Alliance of Czech Catholics, 2657-59 South Lawndale Avenue, Chicago, IL 60623.

National and International Pentecostal Missionary Union, (See The International Pentecostal Church of Christ).

National Apostolate with Mentally Retarded Persons (*Catholic*), P.O. Box 4588, Washington, DC 20017.

National Assembly of Religious Brothers (*Catholic*), 9001 New Hampshire Avenue, Silver Spring, MD 20903.

National Assembly of Women Religious (*Catholic*), 1307 South Wabash Avenue, Chicago, IL 60605.

National Association for the Advancement of Orthodox Judaism, Inc., 132 Nassau Street, New York, NY 10038.

National Association for the Promotion of Holiness, (See Christian Holiness Association).

National Association for the Self-Supporting Active Ministry, 14 Beacon Street — No. 715, Boston, MA 02108.

National Association of Biblical Instructors, (See American Academy of Religion).

National Association of Catholic Alumni Clubs, (See Catholic Alumni Clubs, International).

National Association of Catholic Chaplains, 1312 Massachusetts Avenue, N.W., Washington, DC 20005.

National Association of Christian Colleges and Universities, 4516 Nancy Drive, Salt Lake City, UT 84120.

National Association of Christian Marriage Counselors, Inc., 11611 Webb Chapel Road, Dallas, TX 75229.

National Association of Christian Schools, P.O. Box 550, Wheaton, IL 60187.

National Association of Church Business Administrators, Northeast National Bank Tower — Suite 324, 7001 Grapevine Hwy., Forth Worth, TX 76118.

National Association of Church Personnel Administrators (*Catholic*), 426 East 5th Street, Cincinnati, OH 45202.

National Association of College and University Chaplains and Directors of Religious Life, c/o Rev. Robert Young, Duke University, Durham, NC 27706.

National Association of College and University Ministers, (See National Campus Ministry Association).

National Association of Congregational Christian Churches, P.O. Box 1620, Oak Creek, WI 53154.

National Association of Diocesan Ecumenical Officers (*Catholic*), c/o Rev. Alex J. Brunett, 17500 Farmington Road, Livonia, MI 48152.

National Association of Directors of Christian Education, 7101 Nicollet Avenue South, Minneapolis, MN 55423.

National Association of Ecumenical Staff, 475 Riverside Drive — Room 870, New York, NY 10115.

National Association of Episcopal Schools, 815 Second Avenue, New York, NY 10017.

National Association of Evangelicals, P.O. Box 28, Wheaton, IL 60187.

National Association of Free Will Baptists, 1134 Murfreesboro Road, Nashville, TN 37217.

National Association of Health and Welfare Ministries of the United Methodist Church, 1200 Davis Street, Evanston, IL 60201.

National Association of Hebrew Day School Administrators (*Jewish*), 22 East 28th Street, New York, NY 10016.

National Association of Hebrew Day School PTA's, 229 Park Avenue South,
New York, NY 10003.
National Association of Hillel Directors (*Jewish*), (See International Association
of Hillel Directors).
National Association of Holiness Churches, c/o Rev. Dale L. Hallaway, Gen.
Secretary, P.O. Box 1065, Hobe Sound, FL 33455.
National Association of Jewish Center Workers, (See Association of Jewish
Center Workers).
National Association of Jewish Family, Children's and Health Services, 1175
College Avenue, Columbus, OH 43209.
National Association of Jewish Homes for the Aged, 2525 Centerville Road,
Dallas, TX 75228.
National Association of Jewish Vocational Services, 600 Pennsylvania Avenue,
S.E., Washington, DC 20003.
National Association of Kingdom Evangelicals, c/o Gospel Temple, 16205
Highway 7, Minnetonka, MN 55343.
National Association of Laity (*Catholic*), c/o Dr. Joseph Skehan, 638 East 3rd
Street, Bloomsburg, PA 17815.
National Association of Ministers' Wives, c/o Muriel Lemon Johnson, Presi-
dent, 128 Pennsylvania Avenue, Roosevelt, NY 11575.
The National Association of Native Religious (*Catholic*), c/o Brother Lorenzo
Martin, Coordinator, P.O. Box B, Fort Defiance, AZ 86504.
National Association of Pastoral Musicians (*Catholic*), 225 Sheridan Street,
Washington, DC 20011.
National Association of Priest Pilots (*Catholic*), c/o Rev. John Hemann, 1701
Mulberry Street, Waterloo, IA 50703.
National Association of Professors of Hebrew, c/o Zev Garber, Los Angeles
Valley College, 5800 Fulton Avenue, Van Nuys, CA 91401.
National Association of Schools and Colleges of the United Methodist Church,
P.O. Box 871, Nashville, TN 37202.
National Association of Seventh-day Adventist Dentists, P.O. Box 101, Loma
Linda, CA 92354.
National Association of Synagogue Administrators (*Jewish*), 8100 Stevenson
Road, Baltimore, MD 21208.
National Association of Temple Administrators (*Jewish-Reform*), 838 5th
Avenue, New York, NY 10021.
National Association of Temple Educators (*Jewish-Reform*), 838 5th Avenue,
New York, NY 10021.
National Association of Temple Secretaries (*Jewish-Reform*), (See National
Association of Temple Administrators).
The National Association of the Holy Name Society (*Catholic*), 516 North Front
Street, Minersville, PA 17954.
National Baptist Brotherhood (*National Baptist Convention of America*), c/o Dr. Ira
L. Clark, President, 3615 Rosedale Street, Houston, TX 77004.
National Baptist Convention, (See National Baptist Convention, U.S.A.).
National Baptist Convention of America, c/o Albert E. Chew, Secretary, 2823
North Houston, Fort Worth, TX 76106.
National Baptist Convention of America, Foreign Mission Board, c/o Rev.
Robert H. Wilson, Executive Secretary, P.O. Box 223665, Dallas, TX 75222.

National Baptist Convention of America, Senior Woman's Auxiliary, c/o Mrs. Fannie C. Thompson, President, 516 East Waverly Street, Tucson, AZ 85705.

National Baptist Convention, U.S.A., c/o Rev. J. H. Jackson, 405 East 31st Street, Chicago, IL 60616.

National Baptist Convention, U.S.A., Foreign Mission Board, c/o Rev. William J. Harvey, III, Secretary, 701 South 19th Street, Philadelphia, PA 19146.

National Baptist Convention, U.S.A., Laymen's Movement, c/o Walter Cade, President, 537 North 82nd Street, Kansas City, KS 66112.

National Baptist Convention, U.S.A., Woman's Auxiliary Convention, c/o Mrs. Mary O. Ross, President, 584 Arden Park, Detroit, MI 48202.

National Baptist Deacons Convention of America, c/o Phillip A. Smith, President, 1107 Trewellyn Avenue, Penllyn, PA 19422.

National Baptist Evangelical Life and Soul-Saving Assembly of the U.S.A., 441 Monroe Avenue, Detroit, MI 48226.

National Bar Mitzvah Club (*Jewish*), (See American Zionist Youth Foundation).

National Bible Museum, c/o Rev. Lewie H. Miller, Jr., P.O. Box 287, Gatlinburg, TN 37738.

National Black Catholic Clergy Caucus, House of Peace, 1702 West Walnut Street, Milwaukee, WI 53205.

National Black Catholic Seminarians Association, c/o Brother Arthur Anderson, Catholic Theological Union, 5401 South Cornell, Chicago, IL 60615.

National Black Evangelical Association, P.O. Box 42565, Atlanta, GA 30311.

National Black Lay Catholic Caucus, 1945 Webb, Detroit, MI 48206.

National Black Sisters Conference (*Catholic*), P.O. Box 28216, Philadelphia, PA 19131.

National Buddhist Women's Associations, c/o Buddhist Churches of America, 1710 Octavia Street, San Francisco, CA 94109.

National Bureau of Federated Jewish Women's Organizations, c/o Federation of Jewish Women's Organizations, 55 West 42nd Street, New York, NY 10036.

National Campus Ministry Association, c/o Allyn D. Axelton, President, 18302 Plummer Street, Northridge, CA 91325.

National Cathedral Association, Washington Cathedral, Washington, DC 20016.

National Catholic Apostleship of the Sea Conference, (See Apostleship of the Sea in the United States).

National Catholic Bandmasters' Association, Box 523, Notre Dame University, Notre Dame, IN 46556.

National Catholic Business Education Association, c/o Sr. Marian James Deegan, Elizabeth Seton College, 1061 North Broadway, Yonkers, NY 10706.

National Catholic Cemetery Conference, 710 North River Road, Des Plaines, IL 60016.

National Catholic Coalition for Responsible Investment, c/o Helen Sanders, 3900 North Third Street, Milwaukee, WI 53212.

National Catholic Committee on Scouting, c/o Boy Scouts of America, 1325 Walnut Hill Lane, Irving, TX 75062.

National Catholic Community Service, 1146 19th Street, N.W., Washington, DC 20036.

National Catholic Conference for Interracial Justice, 1200 Varnum Street, N.E., Washington, DC 20017.

National Catholic Conference for Seafarers, c/o All Saints Church, 215 East 10th Street, Houston, TX 77008.

National Catholic Development Conference, 119 North Park Avenue, Rockville Centre, NY 11570.

National Catholic Disaster Relief Committee, 1346 Connecticut Avenue, N.W. — Suite 307, Washington, DC 20036.

National Catholic Educational Association, One Dupont Circle — Suite 350, Washington, DC 20036.

National Catholic Forensic League, 44 Cherry Street, Plymouth, PA 18651.

National Catholic Guidance Conference, (See Association for Religious and Value Issues in Counseling).

National Catholic Lay Celebration of Evangelization, c/o Paulist Office for Evangelization, 3031 4th Street, N.E., Washington, DC 20017.

National Catholic Music Educators Association, (See National Association of Pastoral Musicians).

National Catholic News Service, c/o United States Catholic Conference, 1312 Massachusetts Avenue, N.W., Washington, DC 20005.

National Catholic Office for the Deaf, c/o Rev. David Walsh, Director, Trinity College, Washington, DC 20017.

National Catholic Pharmacists Guild of the United States, 1012 Surrey Hills Drive, St. Louis, MO 63117.

National Catholic Rural Life Conference, 4625 N.W. Beaver Drive, Des Moines, IA 50323.

National Catholic Society of Foresters, 35 East Wacker Drive, Chicago, IL 60601.

National Catholic Stewardship Council, One Columbia Place, Albany, NY 12207.

National Catholic Vocation Council, 1307 South Wabash Avenue, Chicago, IL 60605.

National Catholic Women's Union, 3835 Westminster Place, St. Louis, MO 63108.

National Catholic Youth Organization Federation, c/o Rev. Rudy Beranek, Director, 1312 Massachusetts Avenue, N.W., Washington, DC 20005.

National Center Confraternity of Christian Doctrine (*Catholic*), (See United States Catholic Conference).

National Center for Church Vocations (*Catholic*), (See National Catholic Vocation Council).

The National Center for Urban Ethnic Affairs (*Catholic*), 1521 16th Street, N.W., Washington, DC 20036.

National Center of Religious Education (*Catholic*), (See United States Catholic Conference).

National Center of the Confraternity of Christian Doctrine (*Catholic*), (See Religious Education/CCD).

National Chaplain's Association, Gatlinburg, TN 37738.

National Christ Child Society (*Catholic*), 1610 N.E. Siskiyou Street, Portland, OR 97212.

National Christian Action Coalition, P.O. Box 1745, Washington, DC 20013.

National Christian Association, 850 West Madison Street, Chicago, IL 60607.

National Christian Leadership Conference for Israel, 1629 K Street, N.W. — Suite 700, Washington, DC 20006.

National Christian School Education Association, 464 Malin Road, Newtown Square, PA 19073.

National Christian Secretaries Association, 8000 East Girard — Suite 709, Denver, CO 80231.

National Church and School of Wicca (*Witchcraft*), P.O. Box 1502, New Bern, NC 28560.

National Church Goods Association (*Catholic*), 1114 Greenfield Lane, Mt. Prospect, IL 60056.

National Church Growth Research Center, P.O. Box 3760, Washington, DC 20007.

National Church Music Fellowship, c/o William W. Tromble, President, Houghton College, Houghton, NY 14744.

National Clergy Conference on Alcoholism (*Catholic*), (See National Clergy Council on Alcoholism and Related Drug Problems).

National Clergy Council on Alcoholism and Related Drug Problems (*Catholic*), 3112 Seventh Street, N.E., Washington, DC 20017.

National Coalition of American Nuns (*Catholic*), 1305 South Wabash Avenue — Suite 202, Chicago, IL 60605.

National Colored Spiritualist Association of the U.S.A., 14228 Wisconsin, Detroit, MI 48238.

National Committee for A Human Life Amendment, Inc. (*Catholic*), 1707 L Street, N.W. — Suite 400, Washington, DC 20036.

National Committee for Amish Religious Freedom, 30650 Six Mile Road, Livonia, MI 48152.

National Committee for Labor Israel (*Jewish*), 33 East 67th Street, New York, NY 10021.

National Committee for the Furtherance of Jewish Education, 824 Eastern Parkway, Brooklyn, NY 11213.

National Community Relations Advisory Council (*Jewish*), (See National Jewish Community Relations Advisory Council).

National Conference of Black Churchmen, 900 James Robertson Parkway, Nashville, TN 37203.

National Conference of Catholic Bishops, 1312 Massachusetts Avenue, N.W., Washington, DC 20005.

National Conference of Catholic Charities, 1346 Connecticut Avenue, N.W. — Suite 307, Washington, DC 20036.

National Conference of Catholic Guidance Councils, (See Association for Religious and Value Issues in Counseling).

National Conference of Christians and Jews, 43 West 57th Street, New York, NY 10019.

National Conference of Diocesan Directors of Religious Education — CCD (*Catholic*), 1312 Massachusetts Avenue, N.W., Washington, DC 20005.

National Conference of Independent Catholic and Orthodox Jurisdictions, c/o Chancery Office, 805 Tijeras, N.W., Albuquerque, NM 87102.

National Conference of Jewish Communal Service, (See Conference of Jewish Communal Service).

National Conference of Religious Vocations Directors of Men (*Catholic*), 1307 South Wabash Avenue — Suite 350, Chicago, IL 60605.

National Conference of Synagogue Youth (*Jewish-Orthodox*), 116 East 27th Street, New York, NY 10016.

National Conference of Vicars for Religious (*Catholic*) c/o Rev. Joseph A. Galante, 222 North 17th Street, Philadelphia, PA 19103.

National Conference of Yeshiva Principals (*Jewish*), 229 Park Avenue South, New York, NY 10003.

National Conference on Ministry to the Armed Forces, 5100 Wisconsin Avenue, N.W. — Suite 310, Washington, DC 20016.

National Conference on Soviet Jewry (*Jewish*), 10 East 40th Street — Suite 907, New York, NY 10016.

National Congress of Jewish Deaf, 9102 Edmonston Court — No. 302, Green-belt, MD 20770.

National Council for Art in Jewish Life, 15 East 84th Street, New York, NY 10028.

National Council for Jewish Education, 114 Fifth Avenue, New York, NY 10011.

National Council for Telephone Ministries, (See Contact Teleministries USA).

National Council for Torah Education (*Jewish*), c/o Religious Zionists of America, 25 West 26th Street, New York, NY 10010.

National Council of American Baptist Men (*American Baptist Churches in the U.S.A.*), (See American Baptist Men).

National Council of American Baptist Women (*American Baptist Churches in the U.S.A.*), (See American Baptist Women).

National Council of Beth Jacob Schools (*Jewish*), (See Federated Council of Beth Jacob Schools).

National Council of Catholic Laity, P.O. Box 14525, Cincinnati, OH 45214.

National Council of Catholic Men, c/o William H. Sandweg, 4712 Randolph Drive, Annandale, VA 22003.

National Council of Catholic Women, c/o United States Catholic Conference, 1312 Massachusetts Avenue, N.W., Washington, DC 20005.

National Council of Churches, (See National Council of Churches of Christ in the U.S.A.).

National Council of Churches Energy Project, 475 Riverside Drive — Room 572, New York, NY 10115.

National Council of Churches of Christ in the U.S.A., 475 Riverside Drive, New York, NY 10115.

National Council of Community Churches, 89 East Wilson Bridge Road, Worthington, OH 43085.

National Council of Jewish Correctional Chaplains, (See American Jewish Correctional Chaplains Association).

National Council of Jewish Federations and Welfare Funds, (See Council of Jewish Federations, Inc.).

National Council of Jewish Prison Chaplains, (See American Jewish Correctional Chaplains Association).

National Council of Jewish Women, 15 East 26th Street, New York, NY 10010.

National Council of the Young Men's Christian Associations of the United States of America, 101 North Wacker Drive, Chicago, IL 60606.

National Council of United Presbyterian Men, 475 Riverside Drive — Room 1149, New York, NY 10115.

National Council of Young Israel (*Jewish*), Three West 16th Street, New York, NY 10011.

National Council on Alcoholism, Department of Alcoholism and Religion, c/o Rev. Jack C. White, 733 Third Avenue, New York, NY 10017.

National Council on Jewish Audio-Visual Materials, c/o American Jewish Congress, 15 East 84th Street, New York, NY 10028.

The National Council on Religion and Public Education, Inc., c/o Dr. Daryl B. Adrian, Executive Director, Ball State University, Muncie, IN 47306.

National Council on Religion in Higher Education, (See Society for Values in Higher Education).

National Council on Woman's Work (*American Baptist Churches in the U.S.A.*), (See American Baptist Women).

National Cursillo Movement (*Catholic*), P.O. Box 210226, Dallas, TX 75211.

National CYO Federation (*Catholic*), c/o United States Catholic Conference, 1312 Massachusetts Avenue, N.W., Washington, DC 20005.

National Diocesan Press (*Episcopal*), (See Episcopal Communicators).

National Ecumenical Coalition, P.O. Box 3554, Georgetown Station, Washington, DC 20007.

National Education Council of the Christian Brothers (*Catholic*), (See Regional Education Council of the Christian Brothers).

National Educators Fellowship, 1410 West Colorado, Pasadena, CA 91105.

National Emergency Committee of Clergy Concerned About Vietnam, (See Clergy and Laity Concerned).

National Evangelical Lutheran Church, (See The Lutheran Church-Missouri Synod).

National Farm Worker Ministry, 1430 West Olympic Blvd., Los Angeles, CA 90015.

National Federation for Decency, P.O. Box 1398, Tupelo, MS 38801.

National Federation of Catholic Physicians' Guilds, 850 Elm Grove — Suite 11, Elm Grove, WI 53122.

National Federation of Christian Life Communities, 3700 West Pine Blvd., St. Louis, MO 63108.

National Federation of Diocesan Catholic Youth Councils, (See National CYO Federation).

National Federation of Jewish Men's Clubs, 475 Riverside Drive — Suite 244, New York, NY 10115.

National Federation of Laymen (*Catholic*), P.O. Box 56058, Chicago, IL 60656.

National Federation of Priests' Councils (*Catholic*), 1307 South Wabash Avenue, Chicago, IL 60605.

National Federation of Spiritual Directors (*Catholic*), c/o Rev. Robert B. Sidner, St. Meinrad Seminary, St. Meinrad, IN 47577.

National Federation of Temple Brotherhoods (*Jewish-Reform*), 838 Fifth Avenue, New York, NY 10021.

National Federation of Temple Sisterhoods (*Jewish-Reform*), 838 5th Avenue, New York, NY 10021.

National Federation of Temple Youth (*Jewish-Reform*), 835 5th Avenue, New York, NY 10021.

National Federation of the Fundamentalist Fellowship (*Baptist*), (See Conservative Baptist Association of America).

National Fellowship of Brethren Churches, 1108 Chestnut Avenue, Winona Lake, IN 46590.

National Fellowship of Brethren Ministers, (See National Fellowship of Grace Brethren Ministers).

National Fellowship of Disciple Directors (*Disciples of Christ*), (See Association of Christian Church Educators).

National Fellowship of Grace Brethren Ministers, c/o Ralph Colburn, Secretary, 3490 La Jara, Long Beach, CA 90805.

National Fellowship of Methodist Musicians, (See Fellowship of United Methodist Musicians).

National Foundation for Jewish Culture, 122 East 42nd Street, New York, NY 10017.

National Fraternal Council of Churches, 1225 N Street, N.W., Washington, DC 20005.

National Fraternity of the Secular Franciscan Order — USA (*Catholic*), c/o Mary R. Teoli, Executive Secretary, 1901 Prior Road, Wilmington, DE 19809.

National Guild of Catholic Psychiatrists, c/o Peter A. Santucci, M.D., 118 North Brook Lane, Bethesda, MD 20014.

National Guild of Churchmen, Inc. (*Episcopal*), 44-660 San Pablo Avenida, Palm Desert, CA 92260.

National Guilds of St. Paul (*Catholic*), c/o Rev. Leonard B. Nienaber, Monastery of the Visitation, Cardome, Georgetown, KY 40324.

National Hebrew Culture Council (*Jewish*), 1776 Broadway, New York, NY 10019.

National Holiness Association, (See Christian Holiness Association).

National Huguenot Federation, (See National Huguenot Society).

National Huguenot Society, c/o Mrs. Luther D. Swanstrom, 9027 South Damen Avenue, Chicago, IL 60620.

National Institute for Campus Ministries, 885 Centre Street, Newton Centre, MA 02159.

National Institute for Lay Training (*Episcopal*), 175 9th Avenue, New York, NY 10011.

National Institute for the Word of God (*Catholic*), 487 Michigan Avenue, N.E., Washington, DC 20017.

National Institute of Biblical Studies, Inc., 4001 North Dixie Highway — No. 204, Pompano Beach, FL 33064.

National Institute on the Holocaust, P.O. Box 2147, Philadelphia, PA 19103.

National Interfaith Coalition on Aging, Inc., 298 South Hull Street, P.O. Box 1924, Athens, GA 30603.

National Interreligious Conference on Peace, (See World Conference on Religion and Peace).

National Interreligious Service Board for Conscientious Objectors, Washington Bldg. — Room 550, 15th and New York Avenue, N.W., Washington, DC 20005.

National Interreligious Task Force on Criminal Justice, c/o Joint Strategy and Action Committee, 475 Riverside Drive — Room 1700A, New York, NY 10115.

National Interreligious Task Force on Soviet Jewry, 1307 South Wabash Avenue — Room 221, Chicago, IL 60605.

National Jewish Committee on Scouting, c/o Boy Scouts of America, P.O. Box 350, Dayton, NJ 08810.

National Jewish Community Relations Advisory Council, 55 West 42nd Street — Room 1530, New York, NY 10036.

National Jewish Hospitality Committee and Information Centers, 437 Chestnut Street — Room 426, Philadelphia, PA 19106.

National Jewish Information Service, 5174 West 8th Street, Los Angeles, CA 90036.

National Jewish Music Council, 15 East 26th Street, New York, NY 10010.
National Jewish Welfare Board, (See JWB).
National Laymen for Christ, P.O. Box 316, Childersburg, AL 35044.
National League for Separation of Church and State, P.O. Box 2832, San Diego, CA 92112.
National Liberal League, (See National League for Separation of Church and State).
National Lutheran Campus Ministry, 35 East Wacker Drive — Suite 1847, Chicago, IL 60601.
National Lutheran Council, (See Lutheran Council in the U.S.A.).
National Lutheran Editors and Managers Association, c/o Augsburg Publishing House, 426 South 5th Street, Minneapolis, MN 55415.
National Lutheran Parent — Teacher League (*Lutheran Church-Missouri Synod*), 3558 South Jefferson Avenue, St. Louis, MO 63118.
National Metaphysics Institute, Inc., 326 South LaBrea Avenue, Los Angeles, CA 90036.
National Negro Evangelical Association, (See National Black Evangelical Association).
National Network of Episcopal Clergy Associations, c/o Rev. Richard J. Kirk, 110 North Warson Road, St. Louis, MO 63124.
National Newman Chaplains Association, (See Catholic Campus Ministry Association).
National Office for Black Catholics, 1234 Massachusetts Avenue, N.W., Washington, DC 20005.
National Organization for Continuing Education of Roman Catholic Clergy, Inc., c/o Rev. Robert M. Schwartz, 212 North Moore, St. Paul, MN 55104.
National ORT League (*Jewish*), 817 Broadway, New York, NY 10003.
National Presbyterian Church, (See Presbyterian Church in America).
National Presbyterian Health and Welfare Association, (See United Presbyterian Health, Education and Welfare Association).
National Presbyterian Missions, Inc., c/o Donald J. MacNair, 12330 Conway Road, St. Louis, MO 63141.
National Primitive Baptist Convention of the U.S.A., P.O. Box 2355, Tallahassee, FL 32301.
The National Protestant Council on Higher Education, (See the National Council of Churches of Christ in the U.S.A.).
National Psychic Science Association, c/o Rev. William Daut, President, 39 George Street, Paterson, NJ 07503.
National Ramah Commission (*Jewish*), 3080 Broadway, New York, NY 10027.
National Reform Association, 45 South Bryant Avenue, Pittsburgh, PA 15202.
National Religious Broadcasters, P.O. Box 2254R, Morristown, NJ 07960.
National Religious Formation Conference (*Catholic*), 1234 Massachusetts Avenue, N.W., Washington, DC 20005.
National Religious Liberty Association, (See International Religious Liberty Association).
National Service Board for Religious Objectors, (See National Interreligious Service Board for Conscientious Objectors).
National Sisters Communication Service (*Catholic*), c/o Sister Elizabeth Thoman, 1962 South Shenandoah Street, Los Angeles, CA 90034.
National Sisters Vocation Conference (*Catholic*), 1307 South Wabash Avenue — Suite 201, Chicago, IL 60605.

National Society for Hebrew Day Schools, 229 Park Avenue South, New York, NY 10003.

The National Society of Universalists, Inc., (See The Christian Congregation, Inc.).

National Spiritual Alliance of the United States of America (*Spiritualist*), c/o Mrs. Wilma M. Doucette, Secretary, 14 Edgewood Street, Stafford Springs, CT 06076.

National Spiritual Assembly of the Baha'is of the United States, 112 Linden Avenue, Wilmette, IL 60091.

National Spiritual Science Center, 5605 16th Street, N.W., Washington, DC 20011.

National Spiritualist Association of Churches, c/o Rev. Alice M. Hull, Secretary, P.O. Box 128, Cassadaga, FL 32706.

National Street Ministry, (See Worldshakers For Christ).

National Sunday School Association, P.O. Box 28, Wheaton, IL 60187.

National Teaching Institute of The Orthodox Baha'i Faith in the United States, P.O. Box 1424, Las Vegas, NM 87701.

National Third Order Federation (*Catholic*), (See National Fraternity of the Secular Franciscan Order — USA).

National Union of Christian Schools, (See Christian Schools International).

National United Church Ushers Association, c/o Robert Allen, 5009 South Prairie, Chicago, IL 60615.

National Woman's Christian Temperance Union, 1730 Chicago Avenue, Evanston, IL 60201.

National Women's Conference of the American Ethical Union, Two West 64th Street, New York, NY 10023.

National Women's League of the United Synagogue of America, (See Women's League for Conservative Judaism).

National Workshop on Christian-Jewish Relations, 3501 South Lake Drive, Milwaukee, WI 53207.

National Yokefellow Prison Ministry, Inc., 112 Old Trail North, Shamokin Dam, PA 17876.

National Young Buddhist Association, c/o Buddhist Churches of America, 1710 Octavia Street, San Francisco, CA 94109.

National Young Judaea (*Jewish*), 50 West 58th Street, New York, NY 10019.

National Youth Ministry Organization (*United Methodist Church*), P.O. Box 840, Nashville, TN 37202.

The Native American Theological Association, Minnesota Church Center — Room 310, 122 West Franklin Avenue, Minneapolis, MN 55404.

Native Preacher Company, 888 Seventh Avenue — Suite 400, New York, NY 10019.

Navajo Missions, Inc., P.O. Box 1230, Farmington, NM 87401.

The Navigators, P.O. Box 6000, Colorado Springs, CO 80934.

Near East Archaeological Society, 978 Orchard Lakes, St. Louis, MO 63141.

Nebraska Christian Evangelizing Association, c/o First Christian Church, Lexington, NE 68850.

Nelson Glueck School of Biblical Archaeology, c/o Hebrew Union College — Jewish Institute of Religion, One West 4th Street, New York, NY 10012.

Neo-American Church (*Psychic*), Mandalit, Elk Ridge, Redway, CA 95560.

Neo-Animist Church (*Neo-Paganism*), P.O. Box 429, Miami Springs, FL 33166.

Neo-Dharma (*Buddhist*), c/o Dr. Douglas Burns, 2648 Graceland Avenue, San Carlos, CA 94070.

Neo-Dianic Faith (*Neo-Paganism*), c/o W. Holman Keith, Contez Hotel, 375 Columbia Avenue, Los Angeles, CA 90017.

Neo-Pythagorean Gnostic Church (*Occult*), c/o Michael P. Bertiaux, P.O. Box 1554, Chicago, IL 60690.

Neosho Valley Holiness Association, (See Fire Baptized Holiness Church — Wesleyan).

"Nestorian" Church, (See Holy Apostolic and Catholic Church of the East — Assyrian).

Netherlands Reformed Congregations, c/o Rev. A. M. Den Boer, P.O. Box 42, East Norwich, Ontario NOJ 1PO, Canada.

Neturei Karta of U.S.A. (*Jewish*), G.P.O. Box 2143, Brooklyn, NY 11202.

Network (*Catholic*), 224 D Street, S.E., Washington, DC 20003.

Nevada Association of Humane Studies, 1756 Industrial Road, Las Vegas, NV 89102.

New Age Action Group, P.O. Box 3481, Alexandria, VA 22302.

New Age Assembly Church, c/o Rev. Roger C. Hight, 6433 Long Meadow, Corpus Christi, TX 78413.

New Age Bible and Philosophy Center, 1139 Lincoln Blvd., Santa Monica, CA 90403.

The New Age Caucus, c/o Daniel Maziarz, Director, 4800 South Sepulveda Blvd., Culver City, CA 90230.

New Age Center, 265 South Broadway, Hicksville, NY 11801.

New Age Center for Holistic Health, 2100 Mediterranean Avenue, Virginia Beach, VA 23451.

New Age Church of Truth, Christ Light Community, Star Route 2, Deming, NM 88030.

New Age Communications, P.O. Box 1047, Pacific Grove, CA 93950.

New Age Communications, Inc., 32 Station Street, Brookline Village, MA 02146.

New Age Community Church World Wide, c/o Dr. Ben Winter, P.O. Box 4069, Palm Springs, CA 92262.

New Age Ecumenical Monastic Community, P.O. Box 32849, Nimitz Station, San Antonio, TX 78216.

New Age Foundation, P.O. Box 601, Eatonville, WA 98328.

New Age Information Service, P.O. Box 1043, Corvallis, OR 97330.

New Age Meditation Camps, P.O. Box 396, New Lebanon, NY 12125.

The New Age Network, Inc., 1619 Broadway — Suite 409, New York, NY 10019.

New Age Psychic Center, 1701 West Lake Avenue, Glenview, IL 60025.

New Age Teachings, P.O. Box 477, Brookfield, MA 01506.

The New Age Wellness Center, 9000 S.W. 87th Street — Suite 201, Miami, FL 33173.

New Angelus (Great White Brotherhood) (*New Age*), 130 Southern, P.O. Box 3274, Corpus Christi, TX 78404.

New Apostolic Church of North America, 3753 North Troy Street, Chicago, IL 60618.

New Apostolic Community, (See New Apostolic Church of North America).

New Aquarian Masters' Educational Association, Fund for New Age Youth, Inc., c/o Lynn F. Perkins, P.O. Box 146, Lake Luzerne, NY 12846.

New Beginnings: Ex-Christian Scientists for Jesus, 1550 South Anaheim Blvd. — Suite C, Anaheim, CA 92805.

New Bethel Church of God in Christ — Pentecostal, c/o Bishop A. D. Bradley, First and Market Streets, Richmond, CA 94801.

New Christian Crusade Church, P.O. Box 3247, Hollywood, CA 90028.

New Congregational Methodist Church, c/o Bishop Joe E. Kelley, 354 East Ninth Street, Jacksonville, FL 32206.

The New Covenant Apostolic Order (*Evangelical Orthodox Church*), c/o Bishop Gordon T. Walker, 6867 Pasado Road, Isla Vista, CA 93017.

New Creation Bible Students, 307 White Street, Hartford, CT 06106.

The New Creations, Inc. (*Pentecostal*), P.O. Box 1584, 6400 National Road East, Richmond, IN 47374.

New Dimensions Foundation (*New Age*), c/o Michael Toms, President, 267 States Street, San Francisco, CA 94114.

The New Directions Evangelistic Association, P.O. Box 2347, Burlington, NC 27215.

New England Evangelical Baptist Fellowship, c/o Dr. John Viall, 40 Bridge Street, Newton, MA 02158.

New England Hindu Temple, Inc., 100 Albion Road, Wellesley, MA 02181.

New England Methodist Historical Society Library, Boston University, School of Theology, 745 Commonwealth Avenue, Boston, MA 02215.

New Hampshire Council of Churches, 24 Warren Street, P.O. Box 1107, Concord, NH 03301.

New Hope Crusades (*Pentecostal*), Fairfax, OK 74637.

New Horizons Youth Ministries, 2720 44th Street, S.E., Grand Rapids, MI 49508.

New Humanist Associates, (See American Humanist Association).

New Jersey Center of Truth (*New Thought*), c/o Rev. Patricia Limerick-Andries, P.O. Box 3054, East Orange, NJ 07019.

New Jersey Council of Churches, 116 North Oraton Parkway, East Orange, NJ 07017.

The New Jerusalem Army, (See The True Church of Jesus Christ Restored, Inc.).

New Jewish Media Project, (See Jewish Media Service).

New Life Christian Center (and related congregations), 804 Windsor Road, Arnold, MD 21012.

New Life Films & Cassettes (*Catholic*), P.O. Box 2008, Kansas City, KS 66110.

New Life Foundation, P.O. Box 684, Boulder City, NV 89005.

New Life, Inc., P.O. Box 11303, Knoxville, TN 37919.

New Life International, P.O. Box 11511, Fresno, CA 93773.

New Life League, 7654 West Berwyn Avenue, Chicago, IL 60656.

New Life Ministries, c/o Rev. Neil C. Macaulay, President, 345 West Palmetto Park Road, Boca Raton, FL 33432.

New Life Ministries, Inc., c/o Gregory P. Gulley, Director, P.O. Box 10851, Raleigh, NC 27605.

New Life U.S.A., P.O. Box 1050, Gresham, OR 97030.

New Mennonites, (See The Missionary Church).

New Mexico Inter-Church Agency, 525 San Pedro, N.E., Albuquerque, NM 87108.

New Mexico Psychic Research Association, Inc., P.O. Box 9264, Albuquerque, NM 87119.

The New Order of Christ, P.O. Box 13023, Salem, OR 97309.

New Psychiana, c/o Psychiana Study Center, 4069 Stephens Street, San Diego, CA 92103.

New Reformed Church of All Worlds — Milwaukee Synod (*Neo-Paganism*), P.O. Box 1423, Milwaukee, WI 53201.

New Reformed Order of the Golden Dawn (*Witchcraft*), P.O. Box 23243, Oakland, CA 94623.

New Testament Association of Independent Baptist Churches, 1079 Westview Drive, Rochelle, IL 61068.

New Testament Church Fellowship, 422 Walnut Avenue, Burbank, CA 91501.

New Testament Church of God (*Holiness*), c/o Rev. G. W. Pendleton, 307 Cockrell Hill Road, Dallas, TX 75211.

New Testament Colloquium, Department of Religious Thought, University of Pennsylvania, Philadelphia, PA 19104.

New Testament Holiness Church, Inc., P.O. Box 24409, Dallas, TX 75224.

New Thought Episcopal Church, c/o Dr. William E. Kemery, 384^1/$_2$ Third Street — Suites C & D, Chula Vista, CA 92010.

New Thought Ministries, Inc., 2561 Pinetree Drive, Miami Beach, FL 33140.

New Transport for Christ, (See Transport for Christ International).

New Tribes Mission, Sanford, FL 32771.

New Wiccan Church (*Witchcraft*), P.O. Box 162046, Sacramento, CA 95816.

New World Avatar Cosmic Link, Inc., P.O. Box 15545, Colorado Springs, CO 80935.

New World Club (*Jewish*), 2121 Broadway, New York, NY 10023.

New York Association for New Americans (*Jewish*), 225 Park Avenue South, New York, NY 10003.

New York Bible Society, (See New York International Bible Society).

New York Board of Rabbis (*Jewish*), 10 East 73rd Street, New York, NY 10021.

New York Committee for the Investigation of Paranormal Occurrences, c/o Hans Holzer, 140 Riverside Drive, New York, NY 10024.

New York Conference of the Pilgrim Holiness Church, (See Pilgrim Holiness Church of New York State, Inc.).

The New York C.S. Lewis Society, c/o Mrs. John Kirkpatrick, Secretary, 466 Orange Street, New Haven, CT 06511.

New York Guild for the Jewish Blind, (See Jewish Guild for the Blind).

New York International Bible Society, 45 East 46th Street, New York, NY 10017.

New York State Council of Churches, Inc., 3049 East Genesee Street, Syracuse, NY 13224.

New York Training School for Deaconesses (*Episcopal*), c/o Rev. Paul Moore, Jr., President, 117 Chestnut Drive, Barnegat, NJ 08005.

New York Zen Center (*Buddhist*), 440 West End Avenue, New York, NY 10024.

N.E.W.S. Church, c/o Rev. Nathan Klopfenstein, Route 2, Kendallville, IN 46755.

Nexus (*Neo-Paganism*), P.O. Box 45061, Dallas, TX 75245.

Nichiren Mission (*Buddhist*), 3058 Pali Highway, Honolulu, HI 96817.

Nichiren Shoshu of America (*Buddhist*), 1351 Ocean Front, Santa Monica, CA 90401.

Night Adoration in the Home (*Catholic*), Three Adams Street, Fairhaven, MA 02719.

Nipponzan Myohoji (*Buddhist*), 2674 South Vermont Avenue, Los Angeles, CA 90007.

Nocturnal Adoration Society of the United States (*Catholic*), 194 East 76th Street, New York, NY 10021.

Non-stipendiary Training and Operations Program, (See National Association for the Self-Supporting Active Ministry).

The Norcliffe Fund (*Catholic*), 1001 Fourth Avenue, Seattle, WA 98104.

North Africa Mission, 239 Fairfield Avenue, Upper Darby, PA 19082.

North America Indian Mission, Inc., 115 Tulalip Road, N.E., Marysville, WA 98270.

North American Academy of Ecumenists, c/o Rev. John E. Brandon, Consultation on Church Union, 228 Alexander Street, Princeton, NJ 08540.

North American Academy of Liturgy, c/o John Barry Ryan, Secretary-Treasurer, Manhattan College, Bronx, NY 10471.

North American Association of the International Constantinian Order, 21435 Amulet Drive, Cupertino, CA 95014.

North American Baptist Association, (See Baptist Missionary Association of America).

North American Baptist Conference, One South 210 Summit Avenue, Oakbrook Terrace, IL 60181.

North American Baptist Fellowship, 1628 16th Street, N.W., Washington, DC 20009.

North American Baptist General Conference, (See North American Baptist Conference).

North American Christian Convention, (See Christian Churches and Churches of Christ).

North American Federation of Secular Franciscans (*Catholic*), (See National Fraternity of the Secular Franciscan Order — USA).

North American Federation of the Third Order of St. Francis (*Catholic*), (See National Fraternity of the Secular Franciscan Order — USA).

North American Free Church Federation, P.O. Box 3208, Columbus, OH 43210.

North American Grand Priories of the Hospitaller Order of St. John of Jerusalem, (See Hospitaller Order of St. John of Jerusalem).

North American Islamic Trust, 7216 South Madison Avenue — Suite S, Indianapolis, IN 46227.

North American Jewish Students' Network, 15 East 26th Street — Suite 1350, New York, NY 10010.

North American Jewish Youth Council, 515 Park Avenue, New York, NY 10022.

North American Liturgy Resources, c/o Raymond P. Bruno, President, 2110 West Peoria Avenue, Phoenix, AZ 85029.

North American Old Roman Catholic Church, c/o Bishop Lane, 2820 North Lincoln, Chicago, IL 60657.

North American Old Roman Catholic Church, c/o Most Rev. John E. Schweikert, 4200 North Kedvale Avenue, Chicago, IL 60641.

The North American Old Roman Catholic Church (Archdiocese of New York), c/o Most Rev. James H. Rogers, 236 Wyona Street, G.P.O. Box 1647, Brooklyn, NY 11202.

North American Old Roman Catholic Church Utrecht Succession, c/o Most Rev. E. R. Verostek, 3519 Roosevelt Avenue, Richmond, CA 94805.

North American Patristic Society, c/o Department of Religious Studies, John Carroll University, University Heights, Cleveland, OH 44118.

North American Paul Tillich Society, Inc., c/o Prof. Allen O. Miller, Department of Systematic Theology and Philosophy, Eden Seminary, Webster Groves, MO 63119.

North Carolina Council of Churches, Bryan Bldg. — Suite 201A, Raleigh, NC 27605.

North Carolina Mount Union Association of Regular Baptists, (See Christian Unity Baptist Association).

North Dakota Conference of Churches, 107^1/$_2$ North 4th Street, Bismarck, ND 58501.

North Pacific Yearly Meeting of Friends (*Unaffiliated*), c/o Ann Stever, Clerk, Steering Committee, 715 37th Avenue, Seattle, WA 98122.

North Shore Christian Fellowship, 66-134 Kam Highway, Haleiwa, HI 96712.

North Star Ministries, P.O. Box 926, Grass Valley, CA 95945.

Northeast Regional Pastoral Center for Hispanics (*Catholic*), 487 Park Avenue, New York, NY 10022.

Northern Baptist Convention, (See American Baptist Churches in the USA).

Northern California Ecumenical Council, 942 Market Street — No. 702, San Francisco, CA 94102.

Northwest Yearly Meeting of Friends, c/o Richard H. Beebe, P.O. Box 190, Newberg, OR 97132.

Northwestern Holiness Association, (See Evangelical Church of North America).

Norwegian-Danish Evangelical Free Church Association, (See Evangelical Free Church of America).

The Norwegian Lutheran Church of America, (See The American Lutheran Church).

Norwegian Synod, (See The American Lutheran Church).

Norwegian Synod of the American Evangelical Lutheran Church, (See Evangelical Lutheran Synod).

The Nostradamus Society (*Psychic*), P.O. Box 401, Matawan, NJ 07747.

NOVUS (*New Age*), (Network of Vitally United Souls), 33 Ark Row, Tiburon, CA 94920.

Nu Age Ashram, 1115 Chapala, Santa Barbara, CA 93101.

Nubian Islamic Hebrew Mission, 833 St. John's Place, Brooklyn, NY 11216.

Nurses Christian Fellowship, 233 Langdon, Madison, WI 53703.

Nusbaum Family Foundation (*Jewish*), (See Sol Nusbaum Family Foundation, Inc.).

Nyingma Institute (*Buddhist*), 1815 Highland Place, Berkeley, CA 94709.

Oahspe Foundation (*Psychic*), 2425 Siskiyou Blvd., Ashland, OR 97520.

Oaken Moon Pagan Association, 242 Brentborough on Broadmeade, Sheridan, OR 97378.

Oasis Fellowship, Inc. (*Psychic*), c/o George White, P.O. Box O, Florence, AZ 85232.

O.C. Ministries, (Overseas Crusades), 3033 Scott Blvd., P.O. Box 66, Santa Clara, CA 95052.

Occult Studies Foundation of Providence, P.O. Box 32, Kingston, RI 02881.

Odiyan Center of Nyingma Culture (*Buddhist*), 2425 Hillside Avenue, Berkeley, CA 94704.

Office for Church in Society (*United Church of Christ*), 105 Madison Avenue, New York, NY 10016.

Office for Film & Broadcasting of the U.S. Catholic Conference, 1011 First Avenue, New York, NY 10022.

Office of Gay Concerns, Unitarian Universalist Association, 25 Beacon Street, Boston, MA 02108.

Office of New Directions, 2341 University Avenue, Bronx, NY 10468.

Office of the Presiding Bishop's Suffragan for Chaplaincies to Military, Prisons and Hospitals (*Episcopal*), 815 Second Avenue, New York, NY 10017.

Ohio Bible Fellowship, c/o Rev. John Ashbrook, 5733 Hopkins Road, Mentor, OH 44060.

Ohio Council of Churches, Inc., 89 East Wilson Bridge Road, Columbus, OH 43085.

Oklahoma Conference of Churches, c/o Rt. Rev. Gerald N. McAllister, President, P.O. Box 1098, Oklahoma City, OK 73101.

Oklahoma Indian Ministries, Inc., 701 N.W. 82nd Street, Oklahoma City, OK 73114.

Olazabal Latin-American Council of Churches, Inc. (*Pentecostal*), Tabernaculo Bethesda, 1925 East First Street, Los Angeles, CA 90033.

Olcott Library and Research Center (*The Theosophical Society in America*), P.O. Box 270, Wheaton, IL 60187.

Old Believers (*Russian Orthodox*), Marion County, Woodburn, OR 97071.

Old Catholic Archdiocese for the Americas and Europe, (See Christ Catholic Exarchate of Americas and Eastern Hemisphere).

Old Catholic Church in America, c/o Archdiocesan Chancery, P.O. Box 433, Woodstock, NY 12498.

Old Catholic Church in North America, c/o Most Rev. Charles V. Hearn, 2210 Wilshire Blvd. — Suite 382, Santa Monica, CA 90403.

Old Catholic Church of the West, (See The Antiochian Orthodox Christian Archdiocese of North America — Western Rite).

Old Catholic Church — Philadelphia, Pennsylvania, (See The Antiochian Orthodox Christian Archdiocese of North America — Western Rite).

Old Christian Initiate, (See The Church of Revelation).

Old Christian Reformed Church of Grand Rapids, Michigan, (See Free Reformed Churches of North America).

Old Episcopal Church, c/o Rt. Rev. Jack C. Adam, P.O. Box 2424, Mesa, AZ 85204.

Old German Baptist Brethren, c/o Elder Clement Skiles, Route 1 — Box 140, Bringhurst, IN 46913.

Old Order Amish Mennonite Church, c/o Raber's Book Store, Baltic, OH 43804.

Old Order (Reidenbach) Mennonite Church, c/o Bishop Amos M. Martin, New Holland, PA 17557.

Old Order River Brethren (Yorkers), c/o Bishop Daniel M. Sipling, 356 East High Street, Elizabethtown, PA 17022.

Old Order (Wisler) Mennonite Church, c/o Henry W. Riehl, Route 1, Columbiana, OH 44408.

Old Roman Catholic Church, c/o Most Rev. Richard A. Marchena, 348 West 14th Street, New York, NY 10014.

Old Roman Catholic Church (English Rite), c/o Most Rev. Francis P. Facione, 3827 Old Creek Road, Troy, MI 48084.

The Old Roman Catholic Church (Orthodox Orders), c/o Rev. Earl Anglin James, 460 Danforth Avenue, Toronto, Ontario, Canada.

Olympic Jewish Study Group, 1042 Corona, Port Townsend, WA 98368.

Omega Fellowship, 2756 North Main Street, Santa Ana, CA 92701.

Omega Institute for Holistic Studies (*New Age*), P.O. Box 571, Lebanon Springs, NY 12114.

Omni Foundation (*New Age*), 3007 Santa Monica Blvd., Santa Monica, CA 90404.

Omnitheistic Church (*Neo-Paganism*), P.O. Box 4322, Berkeley, CA 94704.

OMS International, (Oriental Missionary Society), 1200 Fry Road, P.O. Box A, Greenwood, IN 46142.

One Nation Under God (*Pentecostal*), P.O. Box 62524, Virginia Beach, VA 23462.

One World Crusade, (See The Unification Church).

One World Family, (See Universal Industrial Church of the New World Comforter).

O'Neil Foundation (*Catholic*), (See Cyril F. and Marie E. O'Neil Foundation; See also the W. O'Neil Foundation).

Ongoing Ambassadors for Christ (*Lutheran*), 3009 Thomas, Wichita Falls, TX 76308.

Ontario Old Roman Catholic Church, c/o Most Rev. Nelson D. Hillyer, Five Manor Road West, Toronto, Ontario, Canada.

Ontological Society (*New Age*), P.O. Box 328, Loveland, CO 80537.

The Ontology Library (*New Age*), P.O. Box 4116, Santa Barbara, CA 93103.

Open Air Campaigners, 128 College Avenue, Wheaton, IL 60187.

Open Bible Evangelistic Association (*Pentecostal*), (See Open Bible Standard Churches, Inc.).

Open Bible Standard Churches, Inc. (*Pentecostal*), 2020 Bell Avenue, Des Moines, IA 50315.

"The Open Door of Love", (See Church of Tzaddi).

Open Doors With Brother Andrew, Inc., P.O. Box 2020, Orange, CA 92669.

The Open Goddess (*Witchcraft*), 142 Buckness Avenue, Woodbridge, NJ 07095.

The Open Minds, 2148 Conwell Avenue, Philadelphia, PA 19115.

Open Way (*New Age*), Route 2 — Box 217, Celina, TN 38551.

Opus Dei (*Catholic*), 330 Riverside Drive, New York, NY 10025.

Oral Roberts Association, Tulsa, OK 74171.

Orbit Family, c/o E. Blanche Pritchett, Route 4, Arlington, WA 98223.

Order of Divine Love (*New Age*), c/o Bishop Michael Francis Itkin, 7985 Santa Monica Blvd. — Suite 219, West Hollywood, CA 90046.

Order of Huna International (*Psychic*), c/o Dr. Sage King, 2617 Lincoln Blvd., Santa Monica, CA 90405.

Order of Omega (*New Age*), 6418 South 39th Avenue, Phoenix, AZ 85041.

Order of Osirus (*Witchcraft*), P.O. Box 654, Kearney, NE 68847.

Order of St. Anne (*Episcopal*), Lincoln, MA 01773.

Order of St. Luke, 2243 Front Street, San Diego, CA 92101.

Order of St. Luke the Physician of America, P.O. Box 1252, York, PA 17405.

The Order of St. Vincent (*Episcopal*), 60 Rockledge Drive, Pelham, NY 10803.

Order of Sons of Zion (*Jewish*), (See Bnai Zion).

The Order of Teachers of the Children of God (*Episcopal*), 5870 East 14th Street, Tucson, AZ 85711.

Order of the Alhambra (*Catholic*), (See International Order of the Alhambra).

Order of the Black Ram (*Satanism*), 15731 Garrison, Southgate, MI 48195.

Order of the Circle Cross, P.O. Box 707, Delta, CO 81416.

The Order of the Daughters of the King (*Episcopal*), Episcopal Church Center, 815 Second Avenue, New York, NY 10017.

Order of the Healing Christ, 814 Broad Street, Chattanooga, TN 37402.

The Order of the Holy Cross (*Episcopal*), c/o Holy Cross Monastery, West Park, NY 12493.

The Order of the Holy Family (*Episcopal*), c/o Saint Andrew's Abbey, 2015 Glenarm Place, P.O. Box 2169, Denver, CO 80201.

Order of Thelema (*Occult*), 4445 36th Street, San Diego, CA 92116.

Ordo Templi Dianos and Coven of Diana (*Witchcraft*), P.O. Box 291, Westerville, OH 43081.

Ordo Templi Orientis (*Occult*), c/o Hymenaeus Alpha, Caliph, P.O. Box 2043, Dublin, CA 94566.

Ordo Templi Orientis (*Occult*), P.O. Box 2303, Berkeley, CA 94702.

Ordo Templi Orientis (*Occult*), c/o D. Smith, 1566 Ixora, North Fort Myers, FL 33903.

Ordo Templi Orientis, Broken Mountain Lodge (*Occult*), 178 Cosey Beach Avenue, East Haven, CT 06512.

Ordo Templi Satanas (*Satanism*), c/o Temple of Moloch, P.O. Box 8423, Louisville, KY 40208.

Orient Crusades, (See O.C. Ministries).

Oriental Boat Mission, (See International Missions).

Oriental Missionary Crusade, Inc., c/o Ernest A. Reb, President and Founder, P.O. Box 507, Pasadena, CA 91102.

Oriental Missionary Society, (See OMS International).

Oriental Missionary Society Holiness Conference of North America, c/o Rev. Akira Kuroda, Los Angeles Holiness Church, 3660 South Gramercy Place, Los Angeles, CA 90018.

Original Allegheny Conference of the Wesleyan Methodist Church (*Holiness*), (See Allegheny Wesleyan Methodist Connection).

Original Church of God (*Holiness*), c/o Bishop Th. R. Jeffries, 653 Roscoe, Akron, OH 44306.

The (Original) Church of God, Inc. (*Pentecostal*), P.O. Box 3086, Chattanooga, TN 37404.

The (Original) Church of the Living God, Pillar and Ground of Truth, 2132 Nicholas Street, Philadelphia, PA 19121.

Original Kleptonian Neo-American Church, (See Neo-American Church).

Original Pentecostal Church of God, 2206 Andrew Jackson Way, Huntsville, AL 35811.

Orinoco River Mission, c/o David L. Coots, General Director, 234 East Colorado Blvd., Pasadena, CA 91101.

Orthodox-Catholic Church of America, c/o His Grace Bishop George A. Hyde, P.O. Box 1273, Anderson, SC 29621.

Orthodox Catholic Missionary Cenobite of the Hispanic Rite, c/o Fr. Patrick Cubillos, 158-18 Riverside Drive West, New York, NY 10032.

The Orthodox Catholic Patriarchate of America, c/o Most Rev. Peter A. Zurawetzky, 946 Leesville Avenue, Rahway, NJ 07065.

The Orthodox Church in America, Route 25A — Box 675, Syosset, NY 11791.

Orthodox Church in America, Department of History and Archives, c/o Archbishop Sylvester, Chairman, Route 25A — Box 675, Syosset, NY 11791.

Orthodox Episcopal Church of God, c/o Raymond L. Broshears, St. Timothy's Church, 26 Seventh Avenue, San Francisco, CA 94118.

Orthodox Lutheran Conference, (See Concordia Lutheran Conference).

The Orthodox Presbyterian Church, 7401 Old York Road, Philadelphia, PA 19126.

Orthodox Reformed Church, 3628 South Chestnut, Grandville, MI 49418.

Orthodox Roman Catholic Movement, c/o Fr. Robert McKenna, 15 Pepper Street, P.O. Box 237, Monroe, CT 06468.

The Orthodox Syrian Church of India, (The Syrian Orthodox Church of Malabar), c/o Very Rev. K. M. Simon, 12 Edwin Street, Ridgefield Park, NJ 07660.

Orthodox Theological Society in America (*Eastern Orthodox*), 19 Meriam Street, Lexington, MA 02173.

Orthodox Youth of America, (See Society of Orthodox Youth Organizations).

Osborn Foundation, P.O. Box 10, Tulsa, OK 74102.

O'Shaughnessy Foundation (*Catholic*), (See I.A. O'Shaughnessy Foundation, Inc.).

Other Americans, Inc., (See American Atheists).

The Other Side, Inc., c/o John Alexander, President, P.O. Box 12236, Philadelphia, PA 19144.

Our Church in the Garden (*New Age*), c/o Pat Thompson, P.O. Box 16230, Houston, TX 77022.

Our Lady of Enchantment (*Witchcraft*), P.O. Box 69, New Bern, NC 28560.

Our Lady of Endor Coven, the Ophite Cultus Satanas (*Satanism*), 808 West Central Avenue, Toledo, OH 43610.

Outreach, Inc., P.O. Box 6, Salem, OR 97308.

Overseas Ambassadors, (See Sports Ambassadors).

Overseas Christian Servicemen's Center, P.O. Box 10308, Denver, CO 80210.

Overseas Crusades, (See O.C. Ministries).

Overseas Episcopal Dioceses, 815 Second Avenue, New York, NY 10017.

Overseas Foundation, Inc. (*Jewish*), 511 Fifth Avenue, New York, NY 10017.

Overseas Migration Services of the American Jewish Joint Distribution Committee, (See HIAS).

Overseas Ministries Study Center, c/o Rev. Gerald H. Anderson, Director, P.O. Box 2057, 6315 Ocean Avenue, Ventnor, NJ 08406.

Overseas Missionary Fellowship, 404 South Church Street, Robesonia, PA 19551.

Oxford Group Movement, (See Moral Re-Armament).

Ozar Hatorah (*Jewish*), 411 5th Avenue, New York, NY 10016.

PACE, (Practical Apologetics & Christian Evangelism), 1944 North Tustin Avenue — Suite 118, Orange, CA 92665.

Pacific and Asian American Center for Theology and Strategies, 1798 Scenic Avenue, Berkeley, CA 94709.

Pacific Broadcasting Association, P.O. Box 941, Wheaton, IL 60187.

Pacific Coast Khalsa Diwan Society, (See Sikh Foundation).

Pacific Garden Mission, 646 South State Street, Chicago, IL 60605.

Pacific Yearly Meeting of Friends (*Unaffiliated*), c/o Eleanor Foster, 118 Miles Street, Santa Cruz, CA 95060.

PADRES, (Padres Asociados para Derechos Religiosos Educativos y Sociales) (*Catholic*), 3112 West Ashby Place, San Antonio, TX 78228.

Pagan Information Council (*Neo-Paganism*), c/o Ron Parshley, 11 Washington Way, Lawrence, MA 01843.

Pagan Way (*Neo-Paganism*), P.O. Box 215, Lindenwold, NJ 08021.

Palma Christi Center (*New Age*), c/o Marilyn Danner, Director, 105 North Plaza Trail — Suite 114, P.O. Box 2400, Virginia Beach, VA 23452.

Palolo Kannondo Temple (*Buddhist*), 3326 Paalea Street, Honolulu, HI 96816.

Pan American Council for the Preservation of the Hellenic Orthodox Church and the Hellenic Language, P.O. Box 65, Oak Park, IL 60303.

Pan American Union of Baptist Men, P.O. Box 388, Yazoo City, MS 39194.

The Pansophic Institute (*Buddhist*), P.O. Box 42324, Portland, OR 97242.

Pantheism, c/o Eugene Austin, P.O. Box 104, Foley, MO 63347.

The Pantheon, P.O. Box 620, Tujunga, CA 91042.

Paracelsus Research Society, P.O. Box 6006, Sugar House Station, Salt Lake City, UT 84106.

Parapsychological Association, c/o Executive Secretariat, P.O. Box 7503, Alexandria, VA 22307.

Parapsychology Association of Riverside, Inc., c/o Jean Griffin, President, 3756 Elizabeth Street, Riverside, CA 92506.

Parapsychology Foundation, 29 West 57th Street, New York, NY 10019.

Paris Foreign Mission Society (*Catholic*), c/o Rev. Leon Roncin, Superior General, 930 Ashbury Street, San Francisco, CA 94117.

Parish Evaluation Project (*Catholic*), 1307 South Wabash Avenue, Chicago, IL 60605.

Parthenon West (*Hellenic Paganism*), P.O. Box 613, Richton Park, IL 60471.

Partners in Mission (*Episcopal*), 815 Second Avenue, New York, NY 10017.

Partners in Mission (*Lutheran*), P.O. Box 31456, St. Louis, MO 63131.

Partnership in Mission, c/o Robert DeMoss, 1564 Edge Hill Road, Abington, PA 19001.

Partnership in Mission, (See Bibles for the World).

The Pasadena Awareness Center (*New Age*), 1083 Atchison Street, Pasadena, CA 91104.

Past Savio Movement (*Catholic*), c/o Savio Club National Office, Filors Lane, West Haverstraw, NY 10993.

Pastoral Bible Institute, P.O. Box 3252, Chouteau Station, St. Louis, MO 63110.

Pastoral Leadership Development, Inc. (*Catholic*), c/o Sr. Ellen L. Burns, Rockhurst College, 5225 Troost, Kansas City, MO 64110.

Pastors Institute of Applied Theology, P.O. Box 441, Franklin, KY 42134.

Pat Dupree Evangelistic Association, Inc., P.O. Box 2250, Daytona Beach, FL 32015.

Pathway Enrichment Center, 2129 Perrysville Avenue, Pittsburgh, PA 15214.

Patriarchal Parishes of the Russian Orthodox Church in the U.S.A., c/o St. Nicholas Patriarchal Cathedral, 15 East 97th Street, New York, NY 10029.

Paulist League (*Catholic*), 415 West 59th Street, New York, NY 10019.

Pax Christi-USA (*Catholic*), 3000 North Mango Avenue, Chicago, IL 60634.

Pax Romana — American Graduate and Professional Commission (*Catholic*), c/o Prof. Thomas E. Bird, Queens College, CUNY, Flushing, NY 11367.

Peace Fellowship of Presbyterians, (See United Presbyterian Peace Fellowship).

Peace Mission Movement, Woodmont, Gladwyne, PA 19035.

Pegasus (*Neo-Paganism*), P.O. Box 1225, Green Valley, AZ 85614.

Peniel Missions, Incorporated (*Holiness*), 4500 63rd Street, Sacramento, CA 95820.

Pennsylvania Conference of the Mennonite Brethren in Christ Church, (See Bible Fellowship Church).

The Pennsylvania Council of Churches, 900 South Arlington Avenue, Harrisburg, PA 17109.

Pensacola Theological Institute, 1220 East Blount Street, Pensacola, FL 32503.

Pentecost Bands of the World (*Holiness*), (See The Wesleyan Church).

Pentecost Faith Mission of Bedford (*Holiness*), (See Faith Mission Church).

Pentecostal Assemblies of Jesus Christ, (See United Pentecostal Church, International).

Pentecostal Assemblies of the United States of America, (See Pentecostal Church of God).

Pentecostal Assemblies of the World, Inc., 3040 North Illinois Street, Indianapolis, IN 46208.

Pentecostal Church, Inc., (See United Pentecostal Church, International).

Pentecostal Church of Christ, (See The International Pentecostal Church of Christ).

Pentecostal Church of God, Messenger Plaza, 221 Main Street, Joplin, MO 64801.

Pentecostal Church of Scotland (*Holiness*), (See Church of the Nazarene).

Pentecostal Church of the Nazarene (*Holiness*), (See Church of the Nazarene).

Pentecostal Church of Zion, Inc., c/o Zion College of Theology, P.O. Box 110, French Lick, IN 47432.

Pentecostal Conquerors (*United Pentecostal Church International*), c/o Donald E. Deck, President, 8855 Dunn Road, Hazelwood, MO 63042.

Pentecostal Evangelical Church, c/o Rev. Ernest Beroth, P.O. Box 4218, Spokane, WA 99202.

Pentecostal Faith Challengers, Bridgeville, CA 95526.

Pentecostal Fellowship of North America, c/o Dr. Roy M. Chappell, Secretary, P.O. Box 850, Joplin, MO 64801.

Pentecostal Fire-Baptized Holiness Church, Toccoa, GA 30577.

Pentecostal Free-Will Baptist Church, (See Pentecostal Fire-Baptized Holiness Church).

The Pentecostal Free Will Baptist Church, Inc., P.O. Box 1568, Dunn, NC 28334.

Pentecostal Holiness Church, International, P.O. Box 12609, Oklahoma City, OK 73157.

The Pentecostal Renewal Service Committee, c/o Rev. Carlton Spencer, Elim Fellowship, 7245 College, Lima, NY 14485.

Pentecostal Rescue Mission of Binghamton, New York (*Holiness*), (See Pilgrim Holiness Church of New York State, Inc.).

The Pentecostal Union (*Holiness*), (See Pillar of Fire).

Pentecostal World Conference, c/o Dr. Thomas F. Zimmerman, 1445 Boonville Avenue, Springfield, MO 65802.

The People of Holy Earth, 51 Rossmore Road — 3rd Floor, Jamaica Plain, MA 02130.

People of the Living God (*Communal*), 2101 Prytania Street, New Orleans, LA 70130.

"People Plus", c/o Joni Eareckson, P.O. Box 3225, Woodland Hills, CA 91365.

People's Christian Church (*Adventist*), 165 West 105th Street, New York, NY 10025.

People's Christian Coalition, 1309 L Street, N.W., Washington, DC 20005.

The People's Church Collective, c/o Bishop Mikhail F. Itkin, 716 North Irving Blvd. — Studio 303, Hollywood, CA 90038.

People's Institute of Applied Religion, Helena, AL 35080.

People's Methodist Church, (See Evangelical Methodist Church).

Perfect Liberty Order, 700 South Adams Street, Glendale, CA 91205.

Persecuted Church Commission, P.O. Box 1000, Kingston, NY 12401.

Persian Church, (See Holy Apostolic and Catholic Church of the East — Assyrian).

Personal Christianity, 14952 East Pacific Avenue, Baldwin Park, CA 91706.

Personal Creative Freedoms Foundation, (See Eductivism).

Personal Freedom Foundation, 7915 Milbury Road, Baltimore, MD 21207.

Personal Freedom Outreach, P.O. Box 26062, St. Louis, MO 63136.

P'eylim — American Yeshiva Student Union (*Jewish*), Three West 16th Street, New York, NY 10011.

The Phenix Society, Inc. (*New Age*), c/o Jerome Ellison, P.O. Box 25, Guilford, CT 06437.

Phenomenon of Man Project (*New Age*), P.O. Box 836, South Pasadena, CA 91030.

Phil deVries Ministries, Inc., 948 Elmwood Avenue, West Chester, PA 19380.

Philadelphia Conference on Reformed Theology, 17th and Spruce Streets, Philadelphia, PA 19103.

Philadelphia Coordinating Council on the Holocaust, 1520 Locust Street — 5th Floor, Philadelphia, PA 19102.

Philadelphia Yearly Meeting of the Religious Society of Friends, 1515 Cherry Street, Philadelphia, PA 19102.

Philadelphian Institute, Inc. (*New Age*), 401 Patterson Street, P.O. Box 98, Sulphur Springs, AR 72768.

Philangeli (*Catholic*), (Friends of the Angels), c/o Viatorian Fathers, 1115 East Euclid Avenue, Arlington Heights, IL 60004.

Philanthropic Assembly — The Church of the Kingdom of God, 709 74th Street, North Bergen, NJ 07047.

The Philippian Fellowship, P.O. Box 164, North Syracuse, NY 13212.

The Phillips Foundation (*Jewish*), c/o Samuel H. Maslon, 1800 Midwest Plaza, Minneapolis, MN 55402.

Philo Institute, Inc., 555 South Woodlawn Avenue, Chicago, IL 60637.

Philosophical Heritage Institute (*New Age*), P.O. Box 80849, Fairbanks, AK 99708.

Philosophical Research Society (*Occult*), 3910 Los Feliz Blvd., Los Angeles, CA 90027.

Phoenix Akashic Corporation (*New Age*), 24522 Bunbury Drive, El Toro, CA 92630.

The Phoenix Institute (*New Thought*), P.O. Box 2431, San Diego, CA 92112.

The Pilgrim, (See Pilgrim Fellowship).

Pilgrim Fellowship, 1211 Arch Street, Philadelphia, PA 19107.

Pilgrim Holiness Church, (See The Wesleyan Church).

Pilgrim Holiness Church of New York State, Inc., c/o Rev. Andrew J. Whitney, 32 Cadillac Avenue, Albany, NY 12205.

Pilgrim's Mission, Inc., P.O. Box 424, Los Angeles, CA 90053.

Pillar of Fire (*Holiness*), Zarephath, NJ 08890.

The Pillsbury Foundation (*Baptist*), P.O. Box 187, 1831 Chestnut Street, St. Louis, MO 63166.

Pioneer Clubs, (See Pioneer Ministries).

Pioneer Girls, (See Pioneer Ministries).

Pioneer Ministries, P.O. Box 788, 27 West 130th Street, Wheaton, IL 60187.

The Pioneer Tract Society, P.O. Box 619, Henderson, NC 27536.

Pioneer Women, The Women's Labor Zionist Organization of America (*Jewish*), 200 Madison Avenue, New York, NY 10016.

Pious Union of Prayer (*Catholic*), c/o St. Joseph's Home, P.O. Box 288, Jersey City, NJ 07303.

Pious Union of St. Joseph for Dying Sinners (*Catholic*), (See Pious Union of St. Joseph for the Dying).

Pious Union of St. Joseph for the Dying (*Catholic*), 110 West Madison Street, Chicago, IL 60602.

Pious Union of the Holy Spirit (*Catholic*), 30 Gedney Park Drive, White Plains, NY 10605,

Pirchei Agudath Israel (*Jewish*), Five Beekman Street — Room 910, New York, NY 10038.

Pittsburgh Association of Individual Freedom, P.O. Box 131, Allison Park, PA 15101.

Plymouth Brethren (Exclusive): Tunbridge Wells Brethren, c/o Bible Truth Publishers, 239 Harrison Street, Oak Park, IL 60304.

Plymouth Brethren (Open), 218 West Willow, P.O. Box 294, Wheaton, IL 60187.

Poale Agudath Israel of America (*Jewish*), 156 5th Avenue — Suite 811, New York, NY 10010.

Pocket Testament League, 117 Main Street, Lincoln Park, NJ 07035.

Poets for Christ, c/o Gene Rickett, Route 4, Tennessee Drive, Seymour, TN 37865.

Polish Beneficial Association, 2595 Orthodox, Philadelphia, PA 19137.

Polish Evangelical Missionary Association, Inc., 2624 North Fairfield Avenue, Chicago, IL 60647.

Polish National Catholic Church of America, 529 East Locust Street, Scranton, PA 18505.

Polish Roman Catholic Union of America, 984 Milwaukee Avenue, Chicago, IL 60622.

Pontifical Association of the Holy Childhood (*Catholic*), (See Holy Childhood Association).

Pontifical Institute for Foreign Missions (*Catholic*), c/o Rev. Charles A. Minck, 9800 Oakland Avenue, Detroit, MI 48211.

Pontifical Mission for Palestine, c/o Catholic Near East Welfare Association, 1011 First Avenue, New York, NY 10022.

Pontifical Missionary Union in the U.S.A. (*Catholic*), 366 Fifth Avenue, New York, NY 10001.

Postal Satsang (*New Age*), P.O. Box 468, Cambridge, MA 02138.

Praise the Lord Fellowship, c/o Christian Outreach Center, Route 2 — Box 110, Hillsboro, MO 63050.

Prana Yoga Ashram (*Hindu*), c/o Swami Sivalingam, 488 Spruce Street, Berkeley, CA 94708.

Prayer-A-Gram Foundation, Inc., P.O. Box 8127, Station D, Ft. Wayne, IN 46808.

The Prayer Book Society (*Episcopal*), 120 Village Square — Suite 2, Louisville, KY 40243.

Prayer Family International, P.O. Box 10021, Phoenix, AZ 85064.

Prayer Therapy Institute, c/o Community Church by the Bay, 1807 Westcliff Drive, Newport Beach, CA 92660.

Prema Fellowship and World Community, Route 4 — Box 265, Bedford, VA 24523.

Pre-Millennial Baptist Missionary Fellowship, (See World Baptist Fellowship; see also Baptist Bible Fellowship, International).

Presbyterian Charismatic Communion, 2245 N.W. 39th Street, Oklahoma City, OK 73112.

Presbyterian Church in America, c/o Rev. Morton H. Smith, Stated Clerk, P.O. Box 312, Brevard, NC 28712.

Presbyterian Church in the United States, 341 Ponce de Leon Avenue, N.E., Atlanta, GA 30308.

The Presbyterian Church in the U.S.A., (See The United Presbyterian Church in the United States of America).

Presbyterian Church of America, (See The Orthodox Presbyterian Church).

Presbyterian Churchmen United, (See Presbyterian Church in the United States).

Presbyterian Evangelistic Fellowship, (See Presbyterian Church in the United States).

Presbyterian Foundation (*Presbyterian Church in the United States*), P.O. Box 847A, Montreat, NC 28757.

Presbyterian Gay Caucus, P.O. Box 2073, Chicago, IL 60690.

Presbyterian Historical Society (*United Presbyterian Church in the U.S.A*), 425 Lombard Street, Philadelphia, PA 19147.

Presbyterian Lay Committee (*United Presbyterian Church in the U.S.A.*), 1727 Delancey Place, Philadelphia, PA 19103.

Presbyterian Ministers' Fund, 1809 Walnut Street, Philadelphia, PA 19103.

Presbyterian Missionary Committee, (See Interchurch Medical Assistance).

Presbyterians United for Biblical Concerns (*United Presbyterian Church in the U.S.A.*), c/o Mathew J. Welde, Executive Secretary, Buckwalter Road, Spring City, PA 19475.

Presbyterians United for Biblical Confessions, (See Presbyterians United for Biblical Concerns).

Price Foundation (*Catholic*), (See Lucien B. and Katherine E. Price Foundation, Inc.).

Priests' Eucharistic League (*Catholic*), 194 East 76th Street, New York, NY 10021.

Priest's Fellowship of the North American Old Roman Catholic Church, St. Augustine's Cathedral, 236 Wyona Street, Brooklyn, NY 11207.

Priests of the Sacred Heart (*Catholic*), Sacred Heart Monastery, Hales Corners, WI 53130.

Primitive Advent Christian Church, c/o Hugh W. Good, Secretary, 395 Frame Road, Elkview, WV 25071.

Primitive Baptist Association of the Regular Predestinarian Faith and Order, (No address available; group in fellowship with the Union Primitive Baptist Association of Old School or Predestinarian Faith and Order).

Primitive Baptist Conference of New Brunswick, Maine, and Nova Scotia, c/o Saint John Valley Bible Camp, Hartland, New Brunswick, Canada.

Primitive Baptist Library, 107 Elm Lane, Streamwood, IL 60103.

Primitive Baptists, c/o Elder W. H. Cayce, South Second Street, Thornton, AR 71766.

Primitive Baptists — Absolute Predestination, c/o Elder David V. Spangler, Route 1 — Box 539, Beechwood Lane, Danville, VA 24541.

Primitive Baptists — Black, c/o Elder W. J. Berry, Primitive Baptist Library, Route 2, Elon College, NC 27244.

Primitive Baptists Progressive, c/o The Banner Herald, P.O. Box 4168, Martinez, GA 30907.

Primitive Church of Jesus Christ (*Mormon*), (See Church of Jesus Christ of Erie).

The Primitive Church of Jesus Christ (*Pentecostal*), c/o Elder Johnny Wilson, Bethel Church of Jesus Christ, Highway 19 North, Inglis, FL 32649.

Primitive Methodist Church, U.S.A., c/o Rev. G. Kenneth Tyson, President, 408 East Market Street, Scranton, PA 18509.

Prince of Peace Movement, (See Superet Light Center).

Princeton Religion Research Center, P.O. Box 5, Hopewell, NJ 08525.

Prison Ashram Project, 2459 Fawn Creek Lane, Escondido, CA 92026.

Prison Fellowship, P.O. Box 40562, Washington, DC 20016.

Prison Mission Association (*Grace Gospel Fellowship*), P.O. Box 3397, Riverside, CA 92519.

The Prison Monastery Project (*Buddhist*), Vajrapani Institute, 1140 7th Street, Santa Monica, CA 90403.

Pristine Egyptian Orthodox Church (*Neo-Paganism*), 5017 North Clark Street, Chicago, IL 60640.

Pritzker Foundation (*Jewish*), Two First National Plaza — 30th Floor, Chicago, IL 60603.

Pro Ecclesia Foundation (*Catholic*), 663 Fifth Avenue, New York, NY 10022.

Pro Maria Committee (*Catholic*), 22 Second Avenue, Lowell, MA 01854.

Probe Ministries, International, 12011 Coit Road — Suite 107, Dallas, TX 75251.

The Process (*Psychic*), c/o Ken Humphreys, Three Eleanor Street, Stratford, CT 06497.

Program for the Study of New Religious Movements in America, Graduate Theological Union, 2465 LeConte Avenue, Berkeley, CA 94709.

Progressive Dunkers, (See National Fellowship of Brethren Churches).

Progressive National Baptist Convention, Inc., 601 50th Street, N.E., Washington, DC 20019.

Progressive National Baptist Convention, Inc., Women's Auxiliary, c/o Ms. Peggy A. Garnett, President, 313 Oak Street, Cincinnati, OH 45216.

Project Equality, Inc., 4049 Pennsylvania Avenue — Suite 207, Kansas City, MO 64111.

"Project Joshua", (See ACTS 17).

Project L.O.R.D., c/o Youth With A Mission, 7085 Battlecreek Road, S.E., Salem, OR 97302.

"Project Pearl", (See Open Doors with Brother Andrew, Inc.).

"Project Servant Program", c/o Rev. Paul Anderson, Trinity Lutheran Church, 1450 West 7th Street, San Pedro, CA 90732.

Project Sonlight, P.O. Box 1783, Santa Ana, CA 92702.

Promethean Coven (*Witchcraft*), P.O. Box 383, Mastic Beach, NY 11951.

Prophetic Herald Ministry, P.O. Box 7, Spokane, WA 92210.

The Prosperos (*Sufism*), 1441 4th Street, P.O. Box 1400, Santa Monica, CA 90406.

Protect America's Children, c/o Anita Bryant, 300 Broad Street, Selma, AL 36701.

Protestant Center, Inc., (See Interchurch Center).

Protestant Church-Owned Publishers Association, 127 9th Avenue North, Nashville, TN 37234.

Protestant Conference (*Lutheran*), c/o Rev. Gerald Hinz, Secretary, Shiocton, WI 54170.

Protestant Episcopal Church, 815 Second Avenue, New York, NY 10017.

Protestant Film Commission, (See the National Council of Churches of Christ in the U.S.A.).

Protestant Guild for the Blind, 456 Belmont Street, Watertown, MA 02172.

The Protestant Health and Welfare Assembly, 1701 East Woodfield Road — Suite 311, Schaumburg, IL 60195.

Protestant Lawyers Association of Brooklyn, (See Protestant Lawyers Association of New York).

Protestant Lawyers Association of New York, c/o Ilse G. Coe, Secretary, 187 Hicks Street — Apt. 4C, Brooklyn, NY 11201.

Protestant Radio and Television Center, c/o Peter Kontos, President, 1727 Clifton Road, N.E., Atlanta, GA 30329.

Protestant Radio Commission, (See the National Council of Churches of Christ in the U.S.A.).

Protestant Reformed Churches in America, 16515 South Part Avenue, South Holland, IL 60473.

Protesting Christian Reformed Churches, (See Protestant Reformed Churches in America).

"Protes'tnts" (*Lutheran*), (See Protestant Conference).

The Providence Association of the Ukrainian Catholics in America (Ukrainian Catholic Fraternal Benefit Society), 817 North Franklin Street, Philadelphia, PA 19123.

Providence Mission Homes, Inc., c/o William J. Gribble, President, 1421 Glengary Road, Pasadena, CA 91105.

Providence Zen Center (*Buddhist*), 528 Pound Road, RFD 5, Cumberland, RI 02864.

PSI (New Age), (Center for Psycho-Spiritual Integration), 140 Mayhew Way — Suite 400, Pleasant Hill, CA 94523.

Psi Groups Associated (*New Age*), P.O. Box 31751, Omaha, NE 68131.

Psychedelic Venus Church (*Neo-Paganism*), P.O. Box 4163, Sather Gate Station, Berkeley, CA 94704.

Psychiana Study Center, 4069 Stephens Street, San Diego, CA 92103.

Psychic Consultations Ltd., P.O. Box 8323, La Crescenta, CA 91214.

Psychic Diastrophism Center, P.O. Box 50262, Tucson, AZ 85703.

Psychic Phenomena Research Foundation, (See Congregational Church of Practical Theology).

The Psychic Register International, P.O. Box 11288, Phoenix, AZ 85061.

Psychic Research and Training Center, 807 Haddon Avenue, Collingswood, NJ 08108.

Psychic Science Institute, 3117 Arundel Avenue, Alexandria, VA 22306.

Psychical Aid Foundation, P.O. Drawer 49047, Tucson, AZ 85717.

Psychical Research Foundation, P.O. Box 3356, Chapel Hill, NC 27514.

Psychics United for Peace, c/o Dr. Kolai Babb, Universal Awareness Research Center, 252 Tunxis Road, West Hartford, CT 06107.

PsychoDynamics Foundation, P.O. Box 837, Coronado, CA 92118.

Psychologists Interested in Religious Issues, c/o American Psychological Association, 1200 17th Street, N.W., Washington, DC 20036.

Psychosynthesis Associates (*New Age*), 228 Santa Monica Blvd. — No. 7, Santa Monica, CA 90401.

Psychosynthesis Training Center (*New Age*), c/o High Point Foundation, 647 North Madison Avenue, Pasadena, CA 91101.

Psynetics Research and Education Foundation (*New Age*), 1212 East Lincoln Avenue, Anaheim, CA 92805.

PTL Club, c/o Jim Bakker, Charlotte, NC 28279.

Public Education Religion Studies Center, c/o Department of Religion, Wright State University, Dayton, OH 45431.

Pyramid Church of Truth and Light (*New Age*), c/o Rev. Steele M. Goodman, 2426 G Street, Sacramento, CA 95816.

Pyramid Zen Society (*Buddhist*), P.O. Box 16021, Pittsburgh, PA 15242.

Quaker Project on Community Conflict, 15 Rutherford Place, New York, NY `10003.

Quaker Theological Discussion Group, c/o Viola Purvis, Clerk, 316 Marks Street, Orlando, FL 32803.

Quimby Center (*Psychic*), c/o Dr. Neva Dell Hunter, P.O. Box 453, Alamogordo, NM 88310.

Qumran Desert Center (*New Age*), P.O. Box 41985, Tucson, AZ 85717.

Quong Ming Buddhism and Taoism Society, 1104 Powell, San Francisco, CA 94108.

R. Gordon White Ministries International, P.O. Box 433, Pine Lake, GA 30072.

Rabbinical Alliance of America (*Jewish-Orthodox*), 156 5th Avenue — Suite 807, New York, NY 10010.

Rabbinical Assembly (*Jewish-Conservative*), 3080 Broadway, New York, NY 10027.

Rabbinical Council of America (*Jewish-Orthodox*), 1250 Broadway, New York, NY 10001.

Rabbinical Council of the Syrian and Near Eastern Sephardic Jews, 2030 Ocean Parkway, Brooklyn, NY 11223.

Radha Soami (*Sikhism*), P.O. Box 7667, Riverside, CA 92513.

Radiant Love Foundation (*New Age*), 741 Rosarita Lane, Santa Barbara, CA 93105.

Radiant School of the Seekers and Servers (*Psychic*), 624 South Mt. Shasta Blvd., Mt. Shasta, CA 96067.

Radio Missions (*Baptist*), P.O. Box 6250, New Orleans, LA 70174.

Railroad Evangelistic Association, c/o Herman Rose, Route 4, Phillips Road, Spencer, IN 47460.

The Rainbow Center (*New Age*), c/o Diane Halliday, Director, 4901 Densmore Avenue, Encino, CA 91436.

Rainbow Family of Living Light, (See Rainbow Family Tribal Council).

Rainbow Family Tribal Council (*Communal*), P.O. Box 5577, Eugene, OR 97405.

Rainbow Island Sanctuary for Evolution (*Psychic*), P.O. Box 1986, Lihue, Kauai, HI 96766.

Rainbow Revival Church, Inc. (*Pentecostal*), 890 South Crenshaw Blvd., Los Angeles, CA 90005.

Rainbow Tribe Gathering (*New Age*), 4417$^{1}/_{2}$ East 72nd Street, Tacoma, WA 98443.

Rajneesh Meditation Centers (*Hindu*), c/o Ananda Rajneesh Meditation Center, 29 East 28th Street, New York, NY 10016.

Raj-Yoga Math and Retreat (*Hindu*), c/o Yogi Satchakrananda, P.O. Box 547, Deming, WA 98244.

Ramakrishna Monastery (*Hindu*), Trabuco Canyon, CA 92678.

Ramakrishna — Vivekananda Center (*Hindu*), 17 East 94th Street, New York, NY 10028.

Ramapo Trust (*Jewish*), 100 East 42nd Street — Room 1020, New York, NY 10017.

Raskob Foundation for Catholic Activities, Inc., Kennett Pike and Montchanin Road, P.O. Box 4019, Wilmington, DE 19807.

Rationalist Association, Inc., 2001 St. Clair Avenue, St. Louis, MO 63144.

Ray Mossholder Ministries, Inc., P.O. Box 832, Chatsworth, CA 91311.

Reach Out Ministries, 3117 Majestic Circle, Avondale Estates, GA 30002.

Real Yoga Society (*Hindu*), c/o Swami Shiva, 47 Harrison Street, Oak Park, IL 60304.

Reba Place Fellowship and Associated Communities, 727 Reba Place, Evanston, IL 60202.

Reconstructionist Federation of Congregations and Fellowships (*Jewish*), 432 Park Avenue South, New York, NY 10016.

Reconstructionist Fellowship of Congregations (*Jewish*), (See Reconstructionist Federation of Congregations and Fellowships).

Recovered Alcoholic Clergy Association, P.O. Box 95, Albion, IL 62806.

Redwind Native American Spiritual Center, Santa Margarita, CA 93453.

Reform Jewish Appeal, 838 5th Avenue, New York, NY 10021.

Reformation Translation Fellowship, 207 Darlington Road, Beaver Falls, PA 15010.

Reformed Baptists, c/o Rev. Jon Zens, P.O. Box 498, Malin, OR 97632.

Reformed Church in America, 475 Riverside Drive, New York, NY 10115.

Reformed Church in the United States, c/o Rev. Steven Work, Clerk, Route 3, Garner, Ia 50438.

Reformed Druids of North America (*Neo-Paganism*), c/o Isaac Bonewits, P.O. Box 9398, Berkeley, CA 94709.

Reformed Ecumenical Synod, 1677 Gentian, S.E., Grand Rapids, MI 49508.

Reformed Episcopal Church, c/o Rev. D. Ellsworth Raudenbush, Secretary, 560 Fountain Street, Havre de Grace, MD 21078.

Reformed Fellowship, Inc., 4855 Starr Street, S.E., P.O. Box 7383, Grand Rapids, MI 49510.

Reformed Mennonite Church, c/o Bishop Earl Basinger, 1036 Lincoln Heights Avenue, Ephrata, PA 17522.

Reformed Mennonites (Reforming Mennonite Society), (See The Missionary Church).

Reformed Methodist Church (*Holiness*), (See Churches of Christ in Christian Union).

Reformed Methodist Union Episcopal Church, c/o Rev. Eugene Davis, Jr., Secretary, 1219 Carnegie Avenue, Charleston, SC 29407.

Reformed Presbyterian Church, Evangelical Synod, c/o Rev. Paul R. Gilchrist, Stated Clerk, 107 Hardy Road, Lookout Mountain, TN 37350.

Reformed Presbyterian Church in North America, General Synod, (See Reformed Presbyterian Church, Evangelical Synod).

Reformed Presbyterian Church of North America, c/o Louis D. Hutmire, Stated Clerk, 7418 Penn Avenue, Pittsburgh, PA 15208.

Reformed Zion Union Apostolic Church, c/o James C. Feggins, Secretary, 416 South Hill Avenue, South Hill, VA 23970.

Regional Education Council of the Christian Brothers (*Catholic*), Christian Brothers Council, Romeoville, IL 60441.

Regions Beyond Missionary Union (*Interdenominational Foreign Mission Association of North America*), 8102 Elberon Avenue, Philadelphia, PA 19111.

Regis College Lay Apostolate (*Catholic*), Regis College, Weston, MA 02193.

Regular Baptists (*Calvinist/Arminian*), c/o Elder Sherman Essex, Route 1 — Box 246A, Pittsboro, IN 46167.

Reincarnation Research and Education Foundation (*New Age*), P.O. Box 5520, Santa Monica, CA 90405.

Reincarnation Research Lab, P.O. Box 1046, Palos Verdes Estates, CA 90274.

Release, Incorporated, c/o Norman K. Elliott, Executive Director, 1571 Grand Avenue, St. Paul, MN 55105.

Release the World for Christ Foundation (*Pentecostal*), P.O. Box 4275, Houston, TX 77210.

The Relief Society of The Church of Jesus Christ of Latter-day Saints, c/o Barbara Smith, General President, 50 East North Temple Street, Salt Lake City, UT 84103.

Religio-Psychiatric Clinic, (See Institutes of Religion and Health).

Religion Analysis Service, Inc., 2708 East Lake Street — Suite 231, Minneapolis, MN 55406.

Religion and Ethics Institute, Inc., P.O. Box 664, Evanston, IL 60204.

Religion in American Life, Inc., 815 Second Avenue — Suite 200, New York, NY 10017.

Religion in Media Association, 1776 North Gower, Hollywood, CA 90028.

Religion Newswriters Association, 231 Madison Avenue, New York, NY 10016.

The Religion Publishing Group, c/o Eve F. Roshevsky, Doubleday & Co., Inc., 245 Park Avenue, New York, NY 10017.

Religious Action Center (*Jewish*), 2027 Massachusetts Avenue, N.W., Washington, DC 20036.

Religious Arts Guild (*Unitarian Universalist*), 25 Beacon Street, Boston, MA 02108.

Religious Committee on SALT, 118 Maryland Avenue, N.E., Washington, DC 20002.

Religious Convention Managers Association, c/o L. G. Wymore, Corresponding Secretary, P.O. Box 39456, Cincinnati, OH 45239.

Religious Department, Farmers Federation, (See Lord's Acre Plan).

Religious Education Association, 409 Prospect Street, New Haven, CT 06510.

Religious Education / CCD (*Catholic*), 1312 Massachusetts Avenue, N.W., Washington, DC 20005.

Religious Formation Conference (*Catholic*), 1234 Massachusetts Avenue, N.W., Washington, DC 20005.

Religious Instruction Association, (See Public Education Religion Studies Center).

Religious News Service, 43 West 57th Street, New York, NY 10019.

Religious Newswriters Association, (See Religion Newswriters Association).

The Religious Public Relations Council, Inc., 475 Riverside Drive — Room 1031, New York, NY 10115.

Religious Publicity Council, (See The Religious Public Relations Council, Inc.).

The Religious Research Association, Inc., P.O. Box 303, Manhattanville Station, New York, NY 10027.

Religious Research Center, P.O. Box 3, Alta Loma, CA 91701.

Religious Research Fellowship, (See The Religious Research Association, Inc.).

Religious Roundtable, 422 Maple Avenue East, Vienna, VA 22180.

The Religious School of Natural Hygiene (*New Age*), P.O. Box 5963, San Jose, CA 95150.

Religious Science International (*New Thought*), P.O. Box 486, Fillmore, CA 93015.

Religious Society of Friends (*Conservative*), c/o Robert Berquist, R.R. No. 1, West Branch, IA 52358.

Religious Task Force of the Mobilization for Survival, c/o Lafayette Avenue Presbyterian Church, 85 South Oxford Street, Brooklyn, NY 11217.

Religious Zionists of America (*Jewish*), 25 West 26th Street, New York, NY 10010.

The Remnant Church, 7293 Monterey Street, Gilroy, CA 95020.

Remnant of Israel, 11303 East Seventh Avenue, Opportunity, WA 99206.

Renaissance Church of Beauty, (See The Renaissance Community, Inc.).

The Renaissance Community, Inc. (*New Age*), 71 Avenue A, Turners Falls, MA 01376.

The Renovated Church of Jesus Christ, c/o Monastery of the Apostles, P.O. Box 308, Saint Jovite, Quebec JOT 2HO, Canada.

Reorganized Church of Jesus Christ of Latter-Day Saints (*Mormon*), The Auditorium, Independence, MO 64051.

Reorganized Tradition Gwyddonic Order of Wicca (*Witchcraft*), 2525 Date Street — No. 2405, Honolulu, HI 96826.

Reparation Society of the Immaculate Heart of Mary (*Catholic*), 100 East 20th Street, Baltimore, MD 21218.

Research Center for Religion and Human Rights in Closed Societies, 475 Riverside Drive, New York, NY 10115.

Research Foundation for Jewish Immigration, Inc., 570 7th Avenue, New York, NY 10018.

Restoration Ministries, Inc. (*Pentecostal*), P.O. Box 4677, Springfield, MO 65804.

The Restorers, P.O. Box 8011, Boise, ID 83707.

Rev. Al and Prayer Family, (See United Faith Foundation).

Rev. Ike, Prayer Tower, (See United Church and Science of Living Institute).

Revival Fires Ministries, 1200 North Main Street, Joplin, MO 64801.

"Revolutionaries for Jesus", (See Children of God).

The Rex Humbard Ministry, P.O. Box 100, Akron, OH 44331.

RHEMA Bible Church, (See Kenneth Hagin Ministries).

Rhode Island State Council of Churches, Two Stimson Avenue, Providence, RI 02906.

The Ridgefield Foundation (*Jewish*), 245 Park Avenue, New York, NY 10017.

Rinzai-ji, Inc. (*Buddhist*), 2505 Cimarron Street, Los Angeles, CA 90018.

Rissho Kosei Kai (*Buddhist*), 2280 Auhuhu Street, Honolulu, HI 96800.

Rivendell, Inc., RFD 8 — Box 375, Concord, NH 03301.

River Brethren, (See Brethren in Christ Church).

River of Life Ministry, (See Truth Station).

Riverside Church Disarmament Program, 490 Riverside Drive, New York, NY 10027.

Roandoak of God, 455A Chorro Creek Road, Morro Bay, CA 93442.

Robert Burke Foundation, (See Institute of Esoteric Transcendentalism).

Robert H. Schuller Institute for Successful Church Leadership, 12141 Lewis Street, Garden Grove, CA 92640.

Robert Schuller Ministries, P.O. Box 100, Garden Grove, CA 92642.

Robin's Return (*New Age*), 1008 Lamberton Street, Grand Rapids, MI 49505.

Rocky Mountain Dharma Center (*Buddhist*), Route 1, Livermore, CO 80536.

Rocky Mountain Yearly Meeting of Friends, c/o Arthur James Ellis, 3343 East 114th Drive, Thornton, CO 80233.

The Rod of God Ministries, Inc., 200 Dogwood Lane, Easley, SC 29640.

Roddis Foundation (*Episcopal*), (See Hamilton Roddis Foundation, Inc.).

Roloff Evangelistic Enterprises, Inc., P.O. Box 1177, Corpus Christi, TX 78403.

The Roman Catholic Church, National Conference of Catholic Bishops, 1312 Massachusetts Avenue, N.W., Washington, DC 20005.

The Roman Catholic Legation of Utrecht, P.O. Box 269, Venice, CA 90291.

Roman Catholic Peace Fellowship, (See Catholic Peace Fellowship).

Roman Catholic Union of the Knights of St. John, (See Knights of St. John Supreme Commandery).

Romanian Apostolic Pentecostal Church of God of North America, c/o Rev. Petru Tivadan, Sr., 7794 Rosemont, Detroit, MI 48228.

Romanian Baptist Association of the United States, c/o Valentin Popovici, Executive Director, 1451 North LeClaire Avenue, Chicago, IL 60651.

Romanian Jewish Federation, c/o Dr. Charles Kremer, 210 West 101st Street, New York, NY 10025.

Romanian Missionary Society, c/o Dr. Peter Trutza, President, 801 South Ocean Drive, Hollywood, FL 33019.

The Romanian Orthodox Church in America, c/o Rt. Rev. Bishop Victorin, 19959 Riopelle Street, Detroit, MI 48203.

The Romanian Orthodox Episcopate of America, 2522 Grey Tower Road, RFD 7, Jackson, MI 49201.

Romanian Orthodox Missionary Episcopate in America, (See The Romanian Orthodox Church in America).

Ronald E. Short Evangelistic Association, Inc., 110 Jackeye Street, Idabel, OK 74745.

Roosevelt Spiritual Memorial Benevolent Association (*Spiritualist*), c/o Rev. Nellie M. Pickens, P.O. Box 68-313, Miami, FL 33168.

Rosary Altar Society (Confraternity of the Most Holy Rosary) (*Catholic*), 141 East 65th Street, New York, NY 10021.

Rosary League (*Catholic*), c/o Franciscan Sisters of the Atonement, Graymoor / Garrison, NY 10524.

Rose of Sharon Foundation, Inc., G.P.O. Box AM, San Juan, PR 00936.

Rosenhaus Peace Foundation, Inc. (*Jewish*), (See The Sarah and Matthew Rosenhaus Peace Foundation, Inc.).

The Rosicrucian Anthroposophic League, c/o R. A. Straughn, 226 West 138th Street, New York, NY 10030.

The Rosicrucian Fellowship (*Occult*), 2222 Mission Avenue, P.O. Box 713, Oceanside, CA 92054.

Rosicrucian Fraternity (*Occult*), Beverly Hall, P.O. Box 220, Quakertown, PA 18951.

The Rosicrucian Order (AMORC) (*Occult*), (See Ancient and Mystic Order of Rosae Crucis).

Roundlick Primitive Baptist Association, c/o Charles L. West, Route 1, Carthage, TN 37030.

The Roundtable of the Light Centers, Inc. (*New Age*), 1801 Southwest 82nd Place, Miami, FL 33155.

The Rowan Tree (*Neo-Paganism*), P.O. Box 8814, Minneapolis, MN 55408.

Roxanne Brant Crusades, Inc., P.O. Box 1000, O'Brien, FL 32071.

Rudolf Steiner Institute (*Anthroposophic*), Route 2 — Box 199, Phoenixville, PA 19460.

Rudrananda Ashrams (*Hindu*), 316 North Washington Avenue, Bloomington, IN 47401.

Ruhani Satsang (*Sikhism*), (Divine Science of the Soul), 211 West Broadway, Anaheim, CA 92805.

Runic Society (*Neo-Paganism*), c/o N. J. Templin, P.O. Box 2811, Milwaukee, WI 53219.

Russia for Christ, Inc., P.O. Box 30,000, Santa Barbara, CA 93105.

Russian Gospel Association, (See Slavic Gospel Association, Inc.).

Russian Orthodox Catholic Mutual Aid Society of U.S.A., 100 Hazle Street, Wilkes-Barre, PA 18702.

Russian Orthodox Catholic Women's Mutual Aid Society, 975 Greentree Road, Pittsburgh, PA 15220.

The Russian Orthodox Church Abroad, (See The Russina Orthodox Church Outside of Russia).

Russian Orthodox Church in the U.S.A., (See Patriarchal Parishes of the Russian Orthodox Church in the U.S.A.).

The Russian Orthodox Church Outside of Russia, 75 East 93rd Street, New York, NY 10028.

Russian Orthodox Greek Catholic Church of North America, (See The Orthodox Church in America).

Russian-Ukrainian Evangelical Baptist Union of the U.S.A., Inc., c/o Dr. Ivan A. Kmeta, President, Roosevelt Blvd. & Seventh Street, Philadelphia, PA 19120.

Sabaean Religious Order of Am'n (*Neo-Paganism*), 2447 North Halsted, Chicago, IL 60614.

Sabbatsmeet Council (*Witchcraft*), c/o Earth Church of Amargi, Route 3 — Box 596, Bonne Terre, MO 63628.

Sabian Assembly (*Occult*), c/o Marc Edmund Jones, Stanwood, WA 98292.

Sabian Temple of Arcane and Astrological Research (*Occult*), 23150 North Woodward Avenue, Ferndale, MI 48220.

S.A.C. Vocation Information Center (*Catholic*), P.O. Box 1930, Cherry Hill, NJ 08034.

The Sacramental Order of Mystic Christians, P.O. Box 1015, Mountain View, CA 94042.

Sacred Heart League (*Catholic*), c/o Rev. Gregory Bezy, Walls, MS 38680.

Sacred Mountain Ashram (*Hindu*), Gold Hill, Salina Star Route, Boulder, CO 80302.

Sacred Society of the Eth, Inc. (*Psychic*), P.O. Box 3, Forks of Salmon, CA 96031.

Sadhana Foundation (*New Age*), 32100 Page Mill Road, Los Altos, CA 94022.

Sadhana Society, 1535 Private Road, Prescott, AZ 86301.

Safe House Ministry, 8200 Grand Avenue South, Minneapolis, MN 55420.

Sahaj Marg (*Hindu*), c/o James Metz, 18 Sargent Street, Cambridge, MA 02140.

S.A.I. Foundation (*Hindu*), 7911 Willoughby Avenue, Los Angeles, CA 90046.

St. Ansgar's Scandinavian Catholic League, 40 West 13th Street, New York, NY 10011.

St. Anthony's Guild (*Catholic*), c/o Rev. Salvator Fink, O.F.M., Paterson, NJ 07509.

St. Apollonia Guild (*Catholic*), 2186 Draper Avenue, St. Paul, MN 55113.

St. Basil's Center for Eastern Christian Studies, 1111 West Main, Houston, TX 77006.

St. Boniface Mission League, Inc. (*Catholic*), c/o Teresa E. Muech, President, 2768 North 70th, Milwaukee, WI 53210.

St. Davids Christian Writers' Conference, Route 2, Cochranville, PA 19330.

St. David's Society, 71 West 23rd Street, New York, NY 10010.

St. Dominic Savio Classroom Club (*Catholic*), (See Savio Club National Office).

St. Francis Indian Mission, St. Francis, SD 57572.

St. George Association of the U.S.A., 83 Christopher Street, New York, NY 10014.

St. Joan's International Alliance (*Catholic*), 435 West 119th Street, New York, NY 10027.

St. Jude League (*Catholic*), 221 West Madison Street, Chicago, IL 60606.

St. Lawrence Institute for Death Education, c/o Professor Varre A. Cummins, Director, St. Lawrence University, Canton, NY 13617.

St. Madonna's Temple of Light (*Psychic*), c/o Rev. Jennie Easterling, 406 South Poplar, Kankakee, IL 60901.

St. Margaret of Scotland Guild, Inc. (*Catholic*), Graymoor/Garrison, NY 10524.

St. Martin de Porres Guild (*Catholic*), 141 East 65th Street, New York, NY 10021.

St. Paul's Church of Aquarian Science (*Spiritualist*), 312 South Texas Blvd., Weslaco, TX 78596.

St. Paul's Guild (*Psychic*), Graniteville, VT 05654.

St. Thomas Aquinas Foundation of the Dominican Fathers of the United States (*Catholic*), c/o Very Rev. Thomas H. McBrien, O.P., Providence College, Providence, RI 02908.

St. Thomas More Society (*Catholic*), c/o St. Francis Xavier Church, 30 West 16th Street, New York, NY 10011.

St. Timothy's Abbey Church, (See Church of Essential Science).
Saiva Siddhanta Church (*Hindu*), P.O. Box 10, Kapaa, HI 96746.
Sakya Tegchen Choling Center (*Buddhist*), 4416 Burke Avenue North, Seattle, WA 98103.
Salamanca Ecumenical Summer Institute, c/o American Secretary, 150 Greeves Street, Kane, PA 16735.
Salem Acres (*Communal*), R.R. 1 — Box 175A, Rock City, IL 61070.
Salesian Missions (*Catholic*), P.O. Box 1975, Mamaroneck, NY 10543.
Salomon Korteniemi Lutheran Society, (See Apostolic Lutheran Church of America).
Salvation Army (*Holiness*), 120 West 14th Street, New York, NY 10011.
Samaritan Order of Many Affections (SOMA), 526 Green Street, Cambridge, MA 02139.
Samaritan's Purse, P.O. Box 3000, Arcadia, CA 91006.
Samuel A. Fryer Educational Research Foundation (*Jewish*), 229 Park Avenue South, New York, NY 10003.
Samuel Blank and Family Foundation (*Jewish*), 11077 N.W. 36th Avenue, P.O. Box 680310, Miami, FL 33168.
Samuel Friedland Family Foundation (*Jewish*), 222 South Marginal Road, Fort Lee, NJ 07024.
San Francisco Grove of the Reformed Druids of North America (*Neo-Paganism*), c/o Chris Sherback, 2345 Post Street — No. 21, San Francisco, CA 94115.
Sanatana Dharma Foundation (*Hindu*), 3100 White Sulphur Springs Road, St. Helena, CA 94574.
Sanatana Dharma Information Committee of Los Angeles (*Hindu*), c/o Marlin Sennett, 47 Clubhouse Avenue, Venice, CA 90291.
Sanctified Church of Christ (*Holiness*), 2715 18th Avenue, Columbus, GA 31901.
Sanctuary of the Master's Presence (*Psychic*), c/o Mrs. Mary Myneta, Two Lakin Road, Scarsdale, NY 10583.
Sanctuary of Truth (*New Thought*), 507 North Granada Avenue, Alhambra, CA 91801.
Sanders Christian Foundation, P.O. Box 384, South Hamilton, MA 01982.
Sant Bani Ashram (*Sikhism*), Osgood Road, Sanbornton, NH 03269.
Santal Mission (*Lutheran*), (See World Mission Prayer League).
The Sarah and Matthew Rosenhaus Peace Foundation, Inc. (*Jewish*), 767 Fifth Avenue, New York, NY 10022.
Sat Veda Rajneesh Center (*Hindu*), 1846 North Wilton Place, Hollywood, CA 90028.
Satanic Church of America, c/o Anton Szander LaVey, 6114 California Street, San Francisco, CA 94121.
Sathya Sai Baba Center (*Hindu*), (See S.A.I. Foundation).
Satmar Hasidim (*Jewish*), c/o Howard J. Rubenstein Associates, 1345 Avenue of the Americas, New York, NY 10019.
Satyam Shivam Sundaram (*Hindu*), P.O. Box 3016, Princeton, NJ 08540.
The Satyartha Rajneesh Meditation Center (*Hindu*), c/o Swami Anand Prasthan, 8933 National Blvd., Los Angeles, CA 90034.
Savio Club National Office (*Catholic*), Filors Lane, West Haverstraw, NY 10993.
Saviour of All Fellowship, P.O. Box 468, Montclair, CA 91763.

Savitria (*New Age*), 2405 Ruscombe Lane, Baltimore, MD 21209.

Sawan Kirpal Meditation Center (*Sikhism*), Route 1 — Box 24, Bowling Green, VA 22427.

Sawan Kirpal Ruhani Mission (*Sikhism*), c/o T. S. Khanna, 8807 Lea Lane, Alexandria, VA 22309.

Scandinavian Alliance Mission of North America, (See The Evangelical Alliance Mission).

Scandinavian Evangelical Lutheran Augustana Synod of North America, (See Lutheran Church in America).

Scandinavian Free Baptist Society of the U.S.A., (See Independent Baptist Church of America).

Scandinavian Independent Assemblies of God (*Pentecostal*), (See Independent Assemblies of God International; see also The Fellowship of Christian Assemblies).

Scandinavian Independent Baptist Denomination of the U.S.A., (See Independent Baptist Church of America).

School for Esoteric Studies (*New Age*), 40 East 49th Street — Suite 1903, New York, NY 10017.

School for Sufi Studies, 65 Norwich Street, San Francisco, CA 94110.

School of Esoteric Christianity (*New Thought*), 130 East Girard, Englewood, CO 80110.

School of Inner Sense Development (*New Age*), P.O. Box 15538, Durham, NC 27704.

School of Light and Realization (SOLAR) (*New Age*), Route 1 — Box 72, Suttons Bay, MI 49682.

School of Metaphysics, Inc., 1111 East 62nd Street, Kansas City, MO 64110.

School of Natural Science (*Spiritualist*), 25355 Spanish Ranch Road, Los Gatos, CA 95030.

The School of Spiritual Healing, c/o The Sufi Healing Order Secretariat, Route 2 — Box 166, Leicester, NC 28748.

School of the Natural Order, P.O. Box 578, Baker, NV 89311.

School of Wholeistic Education (*New Age*), c/o William Butler, President, 7315 Kentland Avenue, Canoga Park, CA 91307.

School of Wicca (*Witchcraft*), P.O. Box 1502, New Bern, NC 28560.

The Schowalter Foundation, Inc. (*Mennonite*), 716 Main Street, Newton, KS 67114.

Schwenkfelder Church, One Seminary Street, Pennsburg, PA 18073.

Scientific Consciousness Group (*New Age*), 1933 Boulder Drive, Indianapolis, IN 46260.

Scientology, (See Church of Scientology).

Scripture Memory Fellowship International, P.O. Box 24551, St. Louis, MO 63141.

Scripture Union, 1716 Spruce Street, Philadelphia, PA 19103.

Seamen and International House (*Lutheran*), 123 East 15th Street, New York, NY 10003.

Seamen's Church Institute of America, (See Seamen's Church Institute of New York).

Seamen's Church Institute of New York (*Episcopal*), 15 State Street, New York, NY 10004.

Search and Prove (*New Age*), P.O. Box K, St. Paul Park, MN 55071.

Search Institute, c/o Dr. Merton P. Strommen, Director, 122 West Franklin Avenue, Minneapolis, MN 55404.

Searchlight Seminars, Inc. (*New Age*), P.O. Box 5552, Walnut Creek, CA 94596.

Seattle Coalition Task Force on Women and Religion, 4759 15th Avenue, N.E., Seattle, WA 98105.

Seax-Wica (*Witchcraft*), c/o Dr. Raymond Buckland, P.O. Box 5149, Virginia Beach, VA 23455.

Second Coming, Inc., Kent Road, Huntingdon Valley, PA 19006.

Second Cumberland Presbyterian Church in the United States, c/o Rev. R. Stanley Wood, Stated Clerk, 226 Church Street, Huntsville, AL 35801.

Second Foundation (*Sufism*), P.O. Box 370, Nevada City, CA 95959.

Secretariat for Catholic-Jewish Relations, 1312 Massachusetts Avenue, N.W., Washington, DC 20005.

Secretariat for Hispanic Affairs, National Conference of Catholic Bishops, 1312 Massachusetts Avenue, N.W., Washington, DC 20005.

Secretariat for the Spanish Speaking (*Catholic*), (See Secretariat for Hispanic Affairs).

Seeds of Universal Light, 1907 Talpeco Road, Tallahassee, FL 32303.

Seekers After Truth (SAT) (*New Age*), 89 Kensington Road, Kensington, CA 94707.

Seekers of Enlightenment and Enrichment (*New Age*), P.O. Box 2245, Merced, CA 95340.

The Seeker's Quest Ministry, (See Christ Ministry Foundation).

Seicho-No-Ie Truth of Life Movement (*New Thought*), 14527 South Vermont Avenue, Gardena, CA 90247.

Sekai Kyusei Kyo, (See Church of World Messianity).

Self-Enlightenment Meditation Society (*Hindu*), 745 31st Street, Boulder, CO 80303.

Self-Improvement Institute (*New Age*), c/o Dr. Elan Z. Neev, Director, P.O. Box 6300, Beverly Hills, CA 90212.

Self-Realization Fellowship (*Hindu*), 3880 San Rafael Avenue, Los Angeles, CA 90065.

Self-Revelation Church of Absolute Monism (*Hindu*), Golden Lotus Temple, 4748 Western Avenue, N.W., Washington, DC 20016.

Self-Sufficiency Institute (*New Age*), 2545 Ferdinand Avenue, Honolulu, HI 96822.

Separate Baptists in Christ, c/o Floyd Wilson, Clerk, 59 Greensprings Road, Indianapolis, IN 46224.

Sephardic Jewish Brotherhood of America, 97-29 64th Road, Rego Park, New York, NY 11374.

Seraphic Society for Vocations (*Catholic*), c/o Rev. Clarence Chambers, Vocations Director, 3320 Robert Kingery Highway, Oak Brook, IL 60521.

Serbian Eastern Orthodox Church for the U.S.A. and Canada, c/o St. Sava Monastery, P.O. Box 519, Libertyville, IL 60048.

Serenity Spiritualist Association, P.O. Box 137, Forest Knolls, CA 94933.

Serra International (*Catholic*), 22 West Monroe Street, Chicago, IL 60603.

Servants of Christ the King (*Episcopal*), P.O. Box 42, Mendham, NJ 07945.

The Servants of the Good Shepherd, Inc. (*Western Rite Orthodox*), 1529 Pleasant Valley Blvd., Altoona, PA 16602.

Servants of the Word, Inc. (*Pentecostal*), 49 Trottingham Road, Saratoga Springs, NY 12866.

Servers of the Great Ones (*New Age*), 47 Roslin Street, Boston, MA 02124.

Service Committee for Orthodox Charismatic Renewal, P.O. Box 98, East Lansing, MI 48823.

Seventh-day Adventist Church, 6840 Eastern Avenue, N.W., Washington, DC 20012.

Seventh-day Adventist Reform Movement, 3031 Franklin Blvd., Sacramento, CA 95818.

Seventh-day Adventist World Service, c/o Howard Burbank, Executive Director, General Conference of Seventh-day Adventists, 6840 Eastern Avenue, N.W., Washington, DC 20012.

Seventh Day Baptist General Conference, Seventh Day Baptist Bldg., 510 Watchung Avenue, Plainfield, NJ 07060.

Seventh Day Baptist Historical Society, 510 Watchung Avenue, Plainfield, NJ 07060.

The Seventh Day Baptist Missionary Society, c/o Rev. Leon R. Lawton, Executive Vice President, 401 Washington Trust Bldg., Westerly, RI 02891.

Seventh Day Christian Conference (*Adventist*), 252 West 138th Street, New York, NY 10030.

The Seventh Day Church of God (*Adventist*), c/o Elder M. L. Ogren, P.O. Box 804, Caldwell, ID 83605.

The Seventh Day Pentecostal Church of the Living God, 1443 Euclid Avenue, N.W., Washington, DC 20009.

Shafenberg Research Foundation, Inc. (*Psychic*), P.O. Box 806, Kingfisher, OK 73750.

Shaker Museum Foundation, 95 Shaker Museum Road, Old Chatham, NY 12136.

Shakers, (See United Society of Believers in Christ's Second Appearing).

Shalom, Incorporated, (See The Messianic Jewish Movement International).

Shanti Yogi Institute (*Hindu*), 943 Central Avenue, Ocean City, NJ 08226.

Share the Care International, c/o Kenneth J. Stroman, President, P.O. Box 485, Pasadena, CA 91102.

Shared Ministry in Utah, (See Ecumenical Media Resource Center).

Sharing Of Ministries Abroad (*Anglican*), c/o Episcopal Renewal Ministries, 769 Wye Road, Bath, OH 44210.

Shekinah Fellowship, 119½ South Kenwood Street, Glendale, CA 91205.

Shepherd's Bush, 5416 Gaston Avenue, Dallas, TX 75214.

Shepherds Fold Ministries, 1324 El Rancho Drive, Santa Cruz, CA 95060.

Shiloh Christian Fellowship, 520 Ann Street, East Lansing, MI 48823.

Shiloh Christian (Retreat) Ministries, Inc., P.O. Box B, Hamilton, MT 59840.

Shiloh True Light Church of Christ, c/o Elder James R. Purser, 4001 Sheridan Drive, Charlotte, NC 28205.

Shiloh Trust (*Communal*), c/o Rev. James Janisch, Sulphur Springs, AR 72768.

Shingon Mission (*Buddhist*), 915 Sheridan Street, Honolulu, HI 96814.

Shinreikyo (*Shinto*), c/o Mr. Kameo Kiyota, 310C Uulani Street, Hilo, HI 96720.

Shinyo-En (*Buddhist*), c/o Bishop J. Kuriyama, 2348 South Beretania Street, Honolulu, HI 96826.

Shiva Fellowship, (See Psychedelic Venus Church).

Shivalila, P.O. Box 11781, San Francisco, CA 94101.
Sholem Aleichem Folk Institute (*Jewish*), 3301 Bainbridge Avenue, Bronx, NY 10467.
Shomrim Society (*Jewish*), 235 East 20th Street, New York, NY 10003.
Short Terms Abroad, (See Intercristo).
Shree Gurudev Ashram California (*Hindu*), 113 Friar Way, Campbell, CA 95008.
Shree Gurudev Rudrananda Yoga Ashram (*Hindu*), 88 East Tenth Street, New York, NY 10003.
Shree Gurudev Siddha Yoga Ashram (*Hindu*), (See Siddha Yoga Dham of America).
Shri Narayana Association, Inc. (*Hindu*), c/o N. Damanan, President, P.O. Box 2269, Astoria, L.I., NY 11102.
"Sicilian Strege", (See Witches International Craft Associates).
Siddha Yoga Dham of America (*Hindu*), 113 Friar Way, Campbell, CA 95008.
Siddhartha Foundation (*New Age*), 91 Dobbins Street, Waltham, MA 02154.
Siebert Lutheran Foundation, Inc., 2600 North Mayfair Road, Wauwatosa, WI 53226.
The Sikh Center of the Gulf Coast Area, Inc., 8819 Prairie Drive, Houston, TX 77064.
Sikh Cultural Society, Inc., 9530 118th Street, Richmond Hill, NY 11419.
Sikh Dharma Brotherhood of the Western Hemisphere, 1620 Preuss Road, Los Angeles, CA 90035.
Sikh Foundation, 2126 Greenway Drive, Woodside, CA 94062.
Sikh Religious Society, c/o Mr. Balwant Hansra, 406 West Burr Oak, Arlington Heights, IL 60004.
Sikh Study Circle, c/o Dr. A. S. Marwah, 1966 North Vermont Avenue, Hollywood, CA 90027.
The Sikh Temple, Inc., 3911 Military Road, N.W., Washington, DC 20015.
Sikh Temple of Yuba City, 2468 Tierra Buena, P.O. Box 1353, Yuba City, CA 95991.
The Simon Wiesenthal Center for Holocaust Studies, Yeshiva University of Los Angeles, 9760 West Pico Blvd., Los Angeles, CA 90035.
Simplicity of Life (*New Age*), P.O. Box 6018, San Diego, CA 92106.
Single Christian Fellowship International, P.O. Box 187, Hinsdale, IL 60521.
Sino-American Buddhist Association, 1731 15th Street, San Francisco, CA 94103.
Sisterhood of the Holy Nativity (*Episcopal*), 101 East Division Street, Fond du Lac, WI 54935.
Sisterhood of the Moon (*Neo-Paganism*), P.O. Box 119, Daly City, CA 94016.
Sisters-of-the-Amber, (See The Dena Foundation).
Sisters Uniting (*Catholic*), c/o Sister Maria Iglesias, 2140 Homer Avenue, Bronx, NY 10473.
Sivananda Conservatory of Yoga One Science, (See Holy Shankaracharya Order).
Sivananda Yoga Vedanta Center (*Hindu*), 243 West 24th Street, New York, NY 10011.
SKY Foundation, (See Swami Kuvalayananda Yoga Foundation).
Slavic Gospel Association, Inc., P.O. Box 1122, Wheaton, IL 60187.

Slavic Missionary Service, Inc. (*Russian-Ukrainian Evangelical Baptist Union of U.S.A.*), c/o Rev. A. J. Overton, Jr., Chairman, P.O. Box 307, South River, NJ 08882.
Slovak Catholic Federation, c/o Rev. Joseph V. Adamec, 2555 Wieneke Road, Saginaw, MI 48603.
Slovak Catholic Federation of America, (See Slovak Catholic Federation).
Slovak Catholic Sokol, 205 Madison Street, Passaic, NJ 07055.
Slovak Evangelical Lutheran Church, (See The Lutheran Church-Missouri Synod).
Slovak Evangelical Lutheran Synod of the United States of America, (See The Lutheran Church-Missouri Synod).
Slovak Evangelical Union, (See United Lutheran Society).
Snite Foundation (*Catholic*), (See Fred B. Snite Foundation).
Social Brethren, c/o Rev. John Hancock, 195 South Monroe, Bradley, IL 60915.
Society for Humanistic Judaism, 28611 West Twelve Mile Road, Farmington, MI 48018.
Society for Jewish Youth Education in the Middle East and North Africa, (See Ozar Hatorah).
Society for Pentecostal Studies, c/o Horace S. Ward, 6901 North Maple Avenue, Fresno, CA 93710.
Society for Propagating the Gospel Among the Indians and Others in North America (*Unitarian Universalist*), 200 Beacon Street, Boston, MA 02116.
Society for Providing Evangelical Religious Literature for the Blind, (See John Milton Society for the Blind).
Society for Religion in Higher Education, (See Society for Values in Higher Education).
Society for the Advancement of Continuing Education for Ministry, 855 Locust Street, Collegeville, PA 19426.
Society for the Advancement of Judaism, 15 West 86th Street, New York, NY 10024.
Society for the Arts, Religion and Contemporary Culture, 619 Lexington Avenue, New York, NY 10022.
Society for the History of Czechoslovak Jews, 87-08 Santiago Street, Hollis Station, Jamaica, NY 11423.
Society for the Preservation of the Book of Common Prayer (*Episcopal*), (See The Prayer Book Society).
Society for the Propagation of the Faith (*Catholic*), 366 Fifth Avenue, New York, NY 10001.
Society for the Scientific Study of Religion, c/o Wade Clark Roof, Executive Secretary, Department of Sociology, University of Massachusetts, Amherst, MA 01003.
Society for the Study of Natural Order (*New Age*), P.O. Box 326, Brooklyn, NY 11224.
Society for the Teaching of the Inner Christ, Inc., (See Teaching of the Inner Christ).
Society for Values in Higher Education, 363 St. Ronan Street, New Haven, CT 06511.
The Society Mass League (*Catholic*), c/o Society of St. Pius X, 8 Pond Place, Oyster Bay, NY 11771.

Society of African Missions (*Catholic*), 23 Bliss Avenue, Tenafly, NJ 07670.

Society of Biblical Literature, c/o Kent H. Richards, Executive Secretary, Iliff School of Theology, Denver, CO 80210.

Society of Biblical Literature and Exegesis, (See Society of Biblical Literature).

Society of Brothers, (Hutterian Society of Brothers), Rifton, NY 12471.

Society of Catholic College Teachers of Sacred Doctrine, (See College Theology Society).

Society of Christ, Inc. (*Spiritualist*), 3061 Harrington Avenue, Los Angeles, CA 90006.

Society of Christian Ethics, c/o Joseph L. Allen, Executive Secretary, Perkins School of Theology, Southern Methodist University, Dallas, TX 75275.

Society of Christian Philosophers, c/o Janine Marie Idziak, Department of Philosophy and Religion, Eastern Kentucky University, Richmond, KY 40475.

Society of Christian Poets, c/o Patti Garr, P.O. Box 214, Van Buren, AR 72956.

Society of Descendants of Schwenkfeldian Exiles, (See Descendants of Schwenk-feldian Exiles).

Society of Evangelical Agnostics, P.O. Box 515, Auberry, CA 93602.

Society of Helpers (*Catholic*), 11 East 89th Street, New York, NY 10028.

Society of Jewish Bibliophiles, c/o Hebrew Union College, 3101 Clifton Avenue, Cincinnati, OH 45220.

Society of Jewish Science, 825 Round Swamp Road, Old Bethpage, Hicksville, NY 11804.

Society of King Charles the Martyr (*Anglican*), c/o Mrs. Eleanor E. Langlois, Secretary, 110 Devonshire Court, Rochester, NY 14619.

Society of Missionaries of Africa (*Catholic*), (See White Fathers of Africa).

Society of Orthodox Youth Organizations (*Eastern Orthodox*), 358 Mountain Road, Englewood, NJ 07631.

Society of Pragmatic Mysticism (*New Thought*), 200 West 58th Street — Suite 9-B, New York, NY 10019.

Society of Rosicrucians, 321 West 101st Street, New York, NY 10025.

Society of Saint Francis (*Episcopal*), P.O. Box 399, Mount Sinai, NY 11766.

Society of St. Gregory of America (*Catholic*), (See Church Music Association of America).

Society of St. John the Evangelist (*Episcopal*), 980 Memorial Drive, Cambridge, MA 02138.

Society of Saint Margaret (*Episcopal*), 17 Louisburg Square, Boston, MA 02108.

Society of Saint Paul (*Episcopal*), P.O. Box 100, Sandy, OR 97055.

Society of St. Peter the Apostle for Native Clergy (*Catholic*), 366 Fifth Avenue, New York, NY 10001.

The Society of Saint Pius X (*Catholic*), 8 Pond Place, Oyster Bay Cove, NY 11771.

Society of St. Vincent De Paul (*Catholic*), 4140 Lindell Blvd., St Louis, MO 63108.

Society of Separationists, Inc., (See American Atheists).

Society of the Bible in the Hands of Its Creators (*Jewish*), c/o Moses Guibbory, Director, 65 Bluff Avenue, Rowayton, CT 06853.

The Society of the Catholic Apostolate, P.O. Box 32, Collingswood, NJ 08108.

Society of the Companions of the Holy Cross (*Episcopal*), c/o Ruth S. Leonard, Byfield, MA 01922.

Society of the Descendants of the Colonial Clergy, c/o Mrs. Robert H. Lubker, 30 Leewood Road, Wellesley, MA 02181.

Society of the Devotees of Jerusalem (*Jewish*), 1282 49th Street, Brooklyn, NY 11219.

Society of the Evening Star (*Neo-Paganism*), P.O. Box 558, East Greenwich, RI 02818.

Society of the Little Flower (*Catholic*), 11343 South Michigan Avenue, Chicago, IL 60628.

Society of the Magians, P.O. Box 46, Cathedral City, CA 92234.

Society of the Silver Bow (*Witchcraft*), P.O. Box 24, Beckley, WV 25801.

Society of the Study of Religion and Communism, P.O. Box 601, Elgin, IL 60120.

Society of the Universal Living Christ (*New Thought*), c/o Mrs. H. E. Johnson, Secretary, 3880 Mayfield Road — Apt. 306, Cleveland, OH 44121.

Society to Preserve the Heritage of the Episcopal Church, Inc., 1745 Huntington Avenue, Jacksonville, FL 32223.

Sodality Movement and Queens Work (*Catholic*), (See U.S. National Federation of Christian Life Communities).

Sojiji Foreign Guest Department of the Dai Hon Zen Sojiji (*Buddhist*), (See Zen Mission Society).

Sojourners, 1309 L Street, N.W., Washington, DC 20005.

Sol Center Foundation (*Psychic*), 704 South Broadway, Santa Ana, CA 92701.

Sol Nusbaum Family Foundation, Inc. (*Jewish*), 21170 West Eight Mile Road, Southfield, MI 48075.

Solar Light Retreat (*Psychic*), c/o Aleuti Francesca, 7700 Avenue of the Sun, Central Point, OR 97501.

Soldiers of Jesus Christ, Inc., P.O. Box 25, Spring Valley, WI 54767.

The Solid Rock, 435 East 700 South, Brigham City, UT 84302.

Sologa, Inc. (*New Age*), P.O. Box 759, Melbourne, FL 32901.

Sons of Jewish War Veterans of the United States of America, 1712 New Hampshire Avenue, N.W., Washington, DC 20009.

Sought Out Church of God in Christ and Spiritual House of Prayer, Inc. (*Pentecostal*), Brunswick, GA 31520.

Soul Assurance Prayer Plan (*Catholic*), P.O. Box 1632, Chicago, IL 60690.

Soulcraft Fellowship, Inc. (*Occult*), P.O. Box 192, Noblesville, IN 46060.

Sounds of Truth Ministries, 2616 Cardenas, N.E., Albuquerque, NM 87110.

South America Indian Mission, (See South America Mission).

South America Mission, 5217 South Military Trail, P.O. Box 769, Lake Worth, FL 33460.

South American Crusades, Inc., c/o Rev. Bruce Woodman, Executive Director, P.O. Box 5664, Ft. Lauderdale, FL 33310.

South American Mission Prayer League (*Lutheran*), (See World Mission Prayer League).

South Carolina Baptist Fellowship, c/o Faith Baptist Church, 1605 Greenwood Road, Laurens, SC 29360.

South Louisiana Primitive Baptist Association, (No address available; group in fellowship with the Union Primitive Baptist Association of Old School or Predestinarian Faith and Order).

The Southeast Kansas Fire Baptized Holiness Association, (See The Fire Baptized Holiness Church — Wesleyan).

Southeastern Yearly Meeting (*Friends*), c/o James O. Bond, 1705 North Oregon Circle, Tampa, FL 33612.

Southern Appalachian Association of Friends, c/o Lucretia Evans, 301 Hayes Street, Crossville, TN 38555.

Southern Appalachian Yearly Meeting of Friends (*Unaffiliated*), 17 Foxfire Lane, Hendersonville, NC 28739.

Southern Association of Baptist Colleges and Schools, (See Association of Southern Baptist Colleges and Schools).

Southern Baptist Convention, 460 James Robertson Parkway, Nashville, TN 37219.

Southern Baptist Convention, Brotherhood Commission, 1548 Poplar Avenue, Memphis, TN 38104.

Southern Baptist Convention Flyers, P.O. Box 22005, Denver, CO 80222.

Southern Baptist Convention, Foreign Mission Board, P.O. Box 6597, 3806 Monument Avenue, Richmond, VA 23230.

Southern Baptist Convention, Radio and Television Commission, 6350 West Freeway, Fort Worth, TX 76116.

Southern Baptist Fellowship, (See Southwide Baptist Fellowship).

Southern Baptist Foundation, 460 James Roberston Parkway, Nashville, TN 37219.

Southern Baptist Historical Society, (See Historical Commission, Southern Baptist Convention).

Southern Baptist Press Association, 460 James Robertson Parkway, Nashville, TN 37219.

Southern California Council of Churches, 813 South Hope Street — Room 31, Los Angeles, CA 90017.

Southern Christian Leadership Conference, 334 Auburn Avenue, N.E., Atlanta, GA 30303.

Southern Episcopal Church, c/o Bishop B. H. Webster, 420 Mid-State Medical Center, Nashville, TN 37203.

Southern Hebrew Mission, c/o Barry Rubin, Executive Director, P.O. Box 587, Chattanooga, TN 37401.

Southern Methodist Church, c/o Rev. Julian B. Gamble, President, P.O. Box 132, Orangeburg, SC 29115.

Southwest Literature Crusade, P.O. Box 22093, Phoenix, AZ 85028.

Southwest Volunteer Apostolate (*Catholic*), P.O. Box 1338, Gallup, NM 87301.

Southwestern Center of Light and Truth (*New Age*), P.O. Box 3695, Tucson, AZ 85722.

Southwide Baptist Fellowship, c/o Dr. Walter Handford, Southside Baptist Church, 2315 Augusta Road, Greenville, SC 29605.

Sovereign Grace Baptist Movement, c/o Calvary Baptist Church, P.O. Box 7464, Pine Bluff, AR 71611.

The Sovereign Military Hospitaller Order of St. John of Jerusalem of Rhodes and of Malta (*Catholic*), *Eastern Association*: c/o J. Peter Grace, 1011 First Avenue, New York, NY 10022. *Southern Association*: c/o Edward A. McDermott, 815 Connecticut Avenue, N.W., Suite 500, Washington, DC 20006. *Western Association*: c/o John A. Minehan, 555 South Flower Street, Suite 901, Los Angeles, CA 90071.

Sovereign Order of Saint John of Jerusalem, c/o Salvatore T. Messineo, Lieutenant Grand Master, Church Lane — R.D. 3, Reading, PA 19606.

Sovereign Order of St. John of Jerusalem, Knights Hospitaller, (See Hospitaller Order of St. John of Jerusalem).
SOYO (*Eastern Orthodox*), (See Society of Orthodox Youth Organizations).
Spanish Baptist Missions, Inc., 2031 Ruiz Street, San Antonio, TX 78207.
Spanish World Gospel Mission, P.O. Box 542, Winona Lake, IN 46590.
Special Ministries Board, Wisconsin Evangelical Lutheran Synod, 3512 West North Avenue, Milwaukee, WI 53208.
Spertus Museum of Judaica, 618 South Michigan Avenue, Chicago, IL 60605.
Spiritual Advancement of the Individual Foundation, Inc., 7720 Sunset Blvd., Los Angeles, CA 90046.
Spiritual Advisory Council, 2500 East Curry Ford Road, Orlando, FL 32806.
Spiritual Arts Society, P.O. Box 1543, Green Island, NY 12183.
Spiritual Book Associates (*Catholic*), Notre Dame, IN 46556.
Spiritual Counterfeits Project, P.O. Box 2418, Berkeley, CA 94702.
Spiritual Dawn Community, Inc. (*New Age*), c/o John Swann, P.O. Box 4, Sugar Grove, NC 28679.
Spiritual Development Center (*New Age*), Pleasant Hill Road, P.O. Box 179-A, Tuskegee, AL 36083.
Spiritual Development Center, 11105 66th Avenue, Forest Hills, NY 11375.
Spiritual Frontiers Fellowship, 10819 Winner Road, Independence, MO 64052.
Spiritual Hierarchy Information Center (*Psychic*), 2220 North 47th Avenue, Hollywood, FL 33021.
Spiritual Life Institute of America (*Catholic*), R.R. 3, Sedona, AZ 86336.
Spiritual Life Line (*New Age*), 8570 Wilshire Blvd., Beverly Hills, CA 90211.
Spiritual Outreach Society, (See First Century Church).
Spiritual Regeneration Movement, (See International Meditation Society).
Spiritual Regeneration Movement Foundation of America, (See International Meditation Society).
Spiritual Research Fellowship (*New Age*), 326 Tunxis Avenue, Bloomfield, CT 06002.
Spiritual Research Society (*New Age*), 740 Hubbard, N.E., Grand Rapids, MI 49505.
Spiritual Research Society (*New Age*), (Spiritual Advisory Council), 2500 East Curry Ford Road, Orlando, FL 32806.
Spiritual Science Mother Church, Inc., c/o Rev. Glenn Argal, Carnegie Hall — Studio 1010, West 56th Street & Seventh Avenue, New York, NY 10019.
Spiritual Unity Movement (*New Age*), 9575 Canterbury, Arleta, CA 91331.
Sports Ambassadors, P.O. Box 66, Santa Clara, CA 95052.
Sri Aurobindo Center (*Hindu*), (See Matagiri Sri Aurobindo Center).
SRI Centre International (*Hindu*), 45 East 51st Street, New York, NY 10022.
Sri Chinmoy Centres (*Hindu*), P.O. Box 32433, Jamaica, NY 11431.
Sri Guru Singh Sabha, Inc. (*Hindu*), P.O. Box 772, Paramus, NJ 07652.
Sri Ma Anandamayi Monastery (*Hindu*), c/o Swami Nirmalananda Giri, 1835 N.W. 16th Street, Oklahoma City, OK 73106.
Sri Meenakshi Temple Society of Houston (*Hindu*), 11415 Sagemorgan Drive, Houston, TX 77089.
Sri Ram Ashrama (*Hindu*), P.O. Drawer AR, Benson, AZ 85602.
Sri Venkateswara Temple (*Hindu*), 1620 Branning Road, Pittsburgh, PA 15235.
Stamps for Bibles, c/o Joyce Wells, National Coordinator, 11764 Fowler Avenue, Tampa, FL 33617.

Standing Commission on Church Music (*Episcopal*), 865 Madison Avenue, New York, NY 10021.

Standing Conference of the Canonical Orthodox Bishops in the Americas (*Eastern Orthodox*), c/o Rev. Paul Schneirla, 8005 Ridge Blvd., Brooklyn, NY 11209.

Star of Enchantment (*Witchcraft*), 4037 Martin, S.W., Albuquerque, NM 87105.

Star of Truth Foundation (*Psychic*), 118 West Sparks Street, Galena, KS 66739.

Starcross Monastery, (An Inter-Faith Community), Annapolis, CA 95412.

Stauffer Mennonite Church, c/o Bishop Jacob S. Stauffer, Route 3, Ephrata, PA 17522.

STEER, Inc., c/o LaRue Goetz, Executive Director, P.O. Box 1236, Bismarck, ND 58501.

The Stelle Group (*New Age*), Stelle, Illinois, Cabery P.O. 60919.

Stern Foundation (*Jewish*), (See Max Stern Foundation, Inc.).

Stewards Foundation (*Plymouth Brethren*), c/o J. Wilson McCracken, 218 Willow Street, Wheaton, IL 60187.

Stewardship Services, Inc. (*Catholic*), 1234 Massachusetts Avenue, N.W. — Suite 913, Washington, DC 20005.

Stillpoint Institute (*Buddhist*), 604 South 15th Street, San Jose, CA 95112.

Stonecroft, 10121 Grandview Road, Kansas City, MO 64137.

"Strategic Prayer Program for Russia", (See Slavic Gospel Association, Inc.).

Student Foreign Missions Fellowship, (See Student Missions Fellowship).

Student Missions Fellowship, 233 Langdon Street, Madison, WI 53703.

Student Struggle for Soviet Jewry (*Jewish*), 200 West 72nd Street — Suites 30-31, New York, NY 10023.

Students' International Meditation Society, 17310 Sunset Blvd., Pacific Palisades, CA 90272.

Students of Esoteric Thought, Inc. (*New Age*), 265 South Broadway, Hicksville, NY 11801.

Students of the Ascended Masters Committee (*New Age*), c/o Laura Girrard, 2027 N.E. 104th Street, Seattle, WA 98125.

Subcommission for Catholic-Jewish Relations, (See Secretariat for Catholic-Jewish Relations).

Subramuniya Yoga Order (*Hindu*), 108 Mill Street, Virginia City, NV 89440.

Subud U.S.A., 1932 1st Avenue — Suite 802, Seattle, WA 98101.

Successful Life Ministries, 925 Arthur Godfrey Road, Miami Beach, FL 33140.

Sudan Interior Mission, Cedar Grove, NJ 07009.

Sufi Healing Order, c/o The Secretariat, Route 2 — Box 166, Leicester, NC 28748.

Sufi Islamia Ruhaniat Society, 410 Precita Avenue, San Francisco, CA 94110.

Sufi Order, P.O. Box 587, Lebanon Springs, NY 12114.

Sufism Reoriented, 1300 Boulevard Way, Walnut Creek, CA 94595.

The Summit Lighthouse (*New Age*), (Church Universal and Triumphant, Inc.), P.O. Box A, Malibu, CA 90265.

Summit Ministries, c/o Dr. David A. Noebel, Director, 935 Osage, P.O. Box 207, Manitou Springs, CO 80829.

Summit Youth Ministries, (See Summit Ministries).

Sunday League, c/o Dr. Robert S. Womer, 279 Highland Avenue, Newark, NJ 07104.

Sunray Meditation Society (*New Age*), RFD — Box 26, Huntington, VT 05462.

Sunrise Church of the Golden Age (*Psychic*), 3054 Telegraph Avenue, Berkeley, CA 94705.

Superet Light Center (*Psychic*), 2512-16 West Third Street, Los Angeles, CA 90057.

Supreme Council of the Independent Associated Spiritualists, 7230 4th Street North — No. 2304, St. Petersburg, FL 33702.

Supreme Council of the Western Catholic Union, (See Western Catholic Union).

Supreme Ladies Auxiliary Knights of St. John (*Catholic*), 11 Christian Drive, Cheektowaga, NY 14225.

SURATAO (*New Age*), (School of Universal Religious Arts, the Aquarian Order), P.O. Box 19847, Los Angeles, CA 90019.

Susan B. Anthony Coven (*Witchcraft*), P.O. Box 42121, Los Angeles, CA 90042.

Susana Yeiktha Meditation Center and Buddhist Society, (See Stillpoint Institute).

Swami Kuvalayananda Yoga Foundation (*Hindu*), 601 St. George's Road, Philadelphia, PA 19119.

Swaminarayan Hindu Temple, 43-38 Bowne Street, Flushing, NY 11355.

Swedenborg Foundation, Inc., 139 East 23rd Street, New York, NY 10010.

Swedenborgians, (See Churches of the New Jerusalem).

Swedish Baptist General Conference, (See Baptist General Conference).

Swedish Evangelical Free Mission, (See The Evangelical Free Church of America).

Sword of the Lord Foundation, P.O. Box 1099, Murfreesboro, TN 37130.

SYDA Foundation (*Hindu*), P.O. Box 2157, Santa Monica, CA 90406.

Symphony of Life (*New Age*), 2921 Carlisle Blvd., N.E., Albuquerque, NM 87110.

Synagogue Council of America (*Jewish*), 327 Lexington Avenue, New York, NY 10016.

Synod of Evangelical Lutheran Churches, (See The Lutheran Church-Missouri Synod).

Syrian Antiochian Orthodox Archdiocese of New York and North America, (See The Antiochian Orthodox Christian Archdiocese of North America).

Syrian Orthodox Church of Antioch (Archdiocese of the U.S.A. and Canada), c/o Archbishop MarAthanasius Y. Samuel, 49 Kipp Avenue, Lodi, NJ 07644.

The Syrian Orthodox Church of Malabar, (The Orthodox Syrian Church of India), c/o Very Rev. K. M. Simon, 12 Edwin Street, Ridgefield Park, NJ 07660.

Syrian Orthodox Youth Organization, (See Society of Orthodox Youth Organizations).

Syro-Chaldean Church of North America, c/o Rt. Rev. Bertram A. Schlossberg, Six Tanglewood Lane, Bolton, CT 06040.

The Tabernacle of God, Route 1 — Box 956, Gastonia, NC 28052.

Tabernacle Presbyterian Church, (See Pentecostal Holiness Church, Inc.).

Tail of the Tiger Buddhist Community, (Karme-Choling), Star Route, Barnet, VT 05821.

Tainan Evangelical Mission, c/o Frank Lin, Director, 4606 Avenue H, Lubbock, TX 79404.

Taishakyo-Hawaii Izumo Taisho (*Shinto*), 215 North Kukui Street, Honolulu, HI 96817.

Tananbaum Foundation (*Jewish*), (See Martin Tananbaum Foundation, Inc.).
Taoist Sanctuary, P.O. Box 27806, Tempe, AZ 85282.
Taoist Sanctuary of San Diego, 3351 Adams Avenue, San Diego, CA 92116.
Tara Center, P.O. Box 6001, North Hollywood, CA 91603.
Task Force for Moral Alternatives and Politics, (See Moral Alternatives).
Task Force on Women (*United Presbyterian Church in the U.S.A.*), (See Council on Women and the Church).
Tasseraluk Institute (*Unitarian Universalist Association*), Koviashuvik, The Brooks Range, Via Bettles Field, AK 99726.
Te Deum International (*Catholic*), 611 South 6th Street, Springfield, IL 62701.
Teaching of the Inner Christ (*New Age*), 3869 42nd Street, San Diego, CA 92105.
The Teachings of the Angelic Host Within the Kingdom of Heaven (*New Age*), c/o Mary L. Myers, 3427 Denson Place, Charlotte, NC 28215.
Teachings of the New Age, (See The Teachings of the Angelic Host Within the Kingdom of Heaven).
Teen Challenge, Inc., 444 Clinton Avenue, Brooklyn, NY 11238.
"Teens for Christ", (See Children of God).
Temple Dar-I-Afar (*Zoroastrian*), c/o Rev. Daena Louise Durkin, 471 Ellis Street, San Francisco, CA 94102.
Temple of Bacchus (*Neo-Paganism*), c/o Bishop H. Carlisle Estes, R.D. 2 — Box 51, Wells, ME 04090.
Temple of Cosmic Religion (*Hindu*), 174 Santa Clara Avenue, Oakland, CA 94610.
The Temple of Esoteric Science (*New Age*), 7046 Hollywood Blvd., Los Angeles, CA 90028.
Temple of Golden Light (*New Age*), P.O. Box 3787, San Diego, CA 92103.
Temple of Kriya Yoga (*Hindu*), 2414 North Kedzie, Chicago, IL 60647.
The Temple of Lotus Flowers, 2322 Broadway, San Francisco, CA 94115.
The Temple of Man (*New Age*), 1439 Cabrillo Avenue, Venice, CA 90291.
Temple of Power (*Occult*), P.O. Box 134, Deerfield, IL 60015.
Temple of the Golden Calf (*Neo-Paganism*), P.O. Box 4322, Berkeley, CA 94704.
Temple of the Night (*Neo-Paganism*), P.O. Box 14593, Aurora, CO 80014.
Temple of the Pagan Way (*Neo-Paganism*), P.O. Box 60151, Chicago, IL 60660.
Temple of Tiphereth, (See Lady Sara's Coven).
The Temple of Understanding, Wainwright House, 260 Stuyvesant Avenue, Rye, NY 10580.
Temple of Wicca (*Witchcraft*), P.O. Box 1302, Findlay, OH 45840.
Temple Zurvan (*Pre-Christian Gnosticism*), 3230 North Clark Street, Chicago, IL 60657.
Tennessee Association of Churches, 5428 Dogwood Road, N.E., Knoxville, TN 37918.
Tennessee-Georgia Christian Camps, P.O. Box 9363, Chattanooga, TN 37412.
Tenrikyo (*Shinto*), 2727 East First Street, Los Angeles, CA 90033.
Tensho Kotai Jingu Kyo (*Shinto*), 253 Margarita Avenue, Palo Alto, CA 94306.
Teutonic Temple (*Neo-Paganism*), P.O. Box 681, The Dalles, OR 97058.
Texas Conference of Churches, 2704 Rio Grande, Austin, TX 78705.
Thea Jones Evangelistic Association, Inc., 858 North Broad Street, Philadelphia, PA 19130.
Thee Satanic Church, P.O. Box 1123, Melrose Park, IL 60161.

Thee Satanic Church of Nethilum Rites, c/o Terry Taylor, High Priest, 3109 North Central Avenue, Chicago, IL 60634.

Thelemic Catholic Church (*Neo-Paganism*), P.O. Box 606, Shasta, CA 96087.

Theocentric Foundation (*Psychic*), 3341 East Cambridge Avenue, Phoenix, AZ 85008.

Theodor Herzl Institute (*Jewish*), 515 Park Avenue, New York, NY 10022.

THEOS Foundation, 10521 Lindberg Avenue, Pittsburgh, PA 15235.

Theological Students Fellowship, c/o Mark Lau Branson, General Secretary, 233 Langdon, Madison, WI 53703.

The Theosophical Society, P.O. Bin C, Pasadena, CA 91109.

Theosophical Society in America, 1926 North Main Street, Wheaton, IL 60187.

Theosophists: Reunite, P.O. Box 672, Belmont, CA 94002.

Theresians of America (*Catholic*), 5326 East Pershing Avenue, Scottsdale, AZ 85254.

Theta Association, c/o Psychical Research Foundation, P.O. Box 3356, Chapel Hill, NC 27514.

Third Civilization (*Shinto*), P.O. Box 2506, Santa Fe, NM 87501.

This Testimony, c/o Ernest L. Chase, Atlantic States Christian Convention, 1370 Ray Street, Norfolk, VA 23502.

Thomas Institute of Metaphysical Research (*New Age*), 659 South Saint Andrews Place, Los Angeles, CA 90005.

Thomas Merton Community, c/o Humanitas, P.O. Box 2324, Santa Cruz, CA 95063.

Thomas Merton Foundation, c/o Kenneth M. Rofrano, American Institute for Research and Education in Naturopathy, N.Y.C. Community College, 300 Jay Street, Brooklyn, NY 11201.

Thomas Merton Studies Center (*Catholic*), Bellarmine College, Newburg Road, Louisville, KY 40205.

Thomas More Association (*Catholic*), 180 North Wabash Avenue, Chicago, IL 60601.

Threefold Foundation (*Anthroposophic*), c/o Threefold Center for Adult Education, 262 Hungry Hollow Road, Spring Valley, NY 10977.

3HO Foundation (*Sikhism*), (See Healthy, Happy, Holy Organization).

The Tibet Society (*Buddhist*), 101 Goodbody Hall, Indiana University, Bloomington, IN 47401.

Tibetan Aid Project (*Buddhist*), 2425 Hillside Avenue, Berkeley, CA 94704.

Tibetan Nyingmapa Meditation Center (*Buddhist*), 2425 Hillside Avenue, Berkeley, CA 94704.

Timely Messenger Fellowship, c/o R.B. Shiflet, P.O. Box 473, Mineral Wells, TX 76067.

Tioga River Christian Conference, 35 Schiller Street, Binghamton, NY 13905.

Todaiji Hawaii Bekkaku Honzan (*Buddhist*), c/o Bishop Tatsucho Hirai, 426 Luakini Street, Honolulu, HI 96817.

Today Center (*New Age*), 3005 West Markham Street, Little Rock, AR 72205.

Today Church (*New Thought*), c/o Bud and Carmen Moshier, 5002 West Lovers Lane, Dallas, TX 75209.

Tokyo Gospel Mission, Inc., c/o Dr. Hugh Moreton, Executive Director, 1402 Magnolia, Norman, OK 73069.

The Tolerants, (See Association of Churches of The Tolerants).

T.O.M. Religious Foundation (*Spiritualist*), P.O. Box 52, Chimayo, NM 87522.

Tom Skinner Associates, 505 Eighth Avenue, New York, NY 10018.

Tomorrow Enterprises (*New Age*), 303 5th Avenue — Suite 1306, New York, NY 10016.

Tony and Susan Alamo Christian Foundation, P.O. Box 398, Alma, AR 72921.

Torah Umesorah National Society for Hebrew Day Schools (*Jewish*), 229 Park Avenue South, New York, NY 10003.

Totonac Bible Center, Inc., P.O. Box 2050, Orange, CA 92669.

Trailing the Son Ministries, Route 1 — Box 124, Victor, MT 59875.

Trans World Radio, 560 Main Street, Chatham, NJ 07928.

Transcendental Meditation, (See International Meditation Society).

Trans-National Association of Christian Schools, c/o Dr. G. Edwin Miller, Christian Heritage College, 2100 Greenfield Drive, El Cajon, CA 92021.

Transport for Christ International, P.O. Box 1562, Akron, OH 44309.

Tree of Knowledge Centre of Higher Consciousness (*New Age*), 9838 West Roosevelt Road, Westchester, IL 60153.

Tree of Life Fellowship & Institute, 25 West 43rd Street, New York, NY 10036.

Trinity Christian Community, 1619 Prytania Street, New Orleans, LA 70130.

Tri-State Interfaith Development Enterprises, Inc., 122 West Franklin Avenue, Minneapolis, MN 55404.

Triumph the Church and Kingdom of God in Christ (*Holiness*), Route 4 — Box 386, Birmingham, AL 35210.

True Believer Fellowship Church, P.O. Box 13501, Philadelphia, PA 19101.

True Bible Society International, (See True Church of Christ, International).

True Church of Christ, International (*Psychic*), P.O. Box 2, Station G, Buffalo, NY 14213.

True Church of Jesus Christ (Cutlerite) (*Mormon*), Clitherall, MN 56524.

The True Church of Jesus Christ Restored, Inc. (*Mormon*), 1533 East Mechanic, Independence, MO 64050.

True Fellowship Pentecostal Church of America, Inc., c/o Rt. Rev. Charles E. Waters, 4238 Pimlico Road, Baltimore, MD 21215.

True Gospel Ministries, Inc., P.O. Box 488, Fremont, CA 94537.

True Grace Memorial House of Prayer for All People (*Pentecostal*), 205 V Street, N.W., Washington, DC 20001.

The True Light Church of Christ, (See True Light Church of Christ of the Living God).

True Light Church of Christ of the Living God, c/o Bishop Herman Flake Braswell, Monroe, NC 28110.

Trust Funds, Inc. (*Catholic*), One Embarcadero Center — Suite 2201, San Francisco, CA 94111.

Truth Consciousness (*Hindu*), c/o Swami Amar Jyoti, Gold Hill, Salina Star Route, Boulder, CO 80302.

Truth for Today, Route 2, Warsaw, IN 46580.

Truth of Life Center, (See Seicho-No-Ie Truth of Life Movement).

Truth Station, P.O. Box 2085, Hesperia, CA 92345.

Tuatha De Danann Pagan Council, 1445 Seminole Road, North Brunswick, NJ 08902.

Twentieth Century Church of God (*Adventist*), P.O. Box 129, Vacaville, CA 95688.

20th Century Reformation Hour, 756 Haddon Avenue, Collingswood, NJ 08108.

Tyler Crusades, Inc., c/o Dr. Glenn E. Tyler, P.O. Box 14025, Orlando, FL 32857.

Tyndale House Foundation, 336 Gundersen Drive, P.O. Box F, Wheaton, IL 60187.

Ukrainian Autocephalic Church of North and South America, 2224 Liberty Street West, Allentown, PA 18104.

Ukrainian Catholic Students of the United States, c/o Cathedral of the Immaculate Conception, 816 North Franklin, Philadelphia, PA 19123.

Ukrainian Evangelical Alliance of North America, 5610 Trowbridge Drive, Dunwoody, GA 30338.

Ukrainian Evangelical Baptist Convention, 690 Berkeley Avenue, Elmhurst, IL 60126.

Ukrainian Evangelical Reformed Church in Exile, 22146 Kelly Road, East Detroit, MI 48021.

Ukrainian Orthodox Church in the U.S.A., c/o Most Rev. Mstyslav S. Skrypnyk, P.O. Box 595, South Bound Brook, NJ 08880.

Ukrainian Orthodox Church of America (Ecumenical Patriarchate), c/o Most Rev. Andrei Kuschak, St. Andrew's Ukrainian Orthodox Diocese, 90-34 139th Street, Jamaica, NY 11435.

Ultrajectine Ordinariate, Holy Catholic Church, 1418 Second Street, Santa Monica, CA 90401.

Unarius — Science of Life (*Psychic*), P.O. Box 1042, El Cajon, CA 92022.

UNDA — USA, 3015 4th Street, N.E., Washington, DC 20017.

Undenominational Church of the Lord (*Holiness*), 11545 Helmick Road, Monmouth, OR 97361.

Underground Evangelism, P.O. Box 250, Glendale, CA 91209.

Understanding, Inc. (*Psychic*), P.O. Box 206, Merlin, OR 97532.

Unevangelized Fields Mission, 306 Bala Avenue, Bala-Cynwyd, PA 19004.

Unicorn Coven (*Witchcraft*), P.O. Box 691, Central, NM 88026.

Unification Association of Christian Sabbath Keepers (*Adventist*), 145-151 Central Park North, New York, NY 10026.

The Unification Church, 1611 Upshur Street, N.W., Washington, DC 20011.

The Unified Family, (See The Unification Church).

Union American Methodist Episcopal Church, c/o Bishop David E. Hackett, 4411 Fielding Road, Brandywine Hill, Wilmington, DE 19802.

Union Assembly of the Church of God, Inc. (*Pentecostal*), (See Church of God of the Union Assembly, Inc.).

The Union Bible Study Association, P.O. Box 284-5, Winter Park, FL 32789.

Union of American Hebrew Congregations (*Jewish-Reform*), 838 5th Avenue, New York, NY 10021.

Union of Black Clergy and Laity of the Episcopal Church, (See Union of Black Episcopalians).

Union of Black Episcopalians, c/o Rt. Rev. John M. Burgess, President, 401 Whitney Avenue, New Haven, CT 06511.

Union of Councils for Soviet Jews, 2920 Arlington Blvd., Arlington, VA 22204.

Union of Orthodox Jewish Congregations of America, 116 East 27th Street, New York, NY 10016.

Union of Orthodox Jewish Congregations of America, Women's Branch, c/o Leah G. Stern, Executive Vice President, 84 5th Avenue, New York,NY 10011.

Union of Orthodox Rabbis of the U.S. and Canada, 235 East Broadway, New York, NY 10007.

Union of Polish Women in America (*Catholic*), 2636-38 East Allegheny Avenue, Philadelphia, PA 19134.

Union of Russian Evangelical Christians, 261 East Sixth Street, Erie, PA 16507.

Union of Sephardic Congregations (*Jewish*), Eight West 70th Street, New York, NY 10023.

Union Primitive Baptist Association of Old School or Predestinarian Faith and Order, c/o Pilgrim Church, Palestine, TX 75801.

Union Saint-Jean-Baptiste (*Catholic*), One Social Street, Woonsocket, RI 02895.

Unitarian and Universalist Genealogical Society, 10605 Lakespring Way, Cockeysville, MD 21030.

Unitarian Educational Directors Association, (See Liberal Religious Education Directors Association).

Unitarian Historical Society, (See Unitarian Universalist Historical Society).

Unitarian Service Committee, (See Unitarian Universalist Service Committee).

Unitarian Universalist Association, 25 Beacon Street, Boston, MA 02108.

Unitarian Universalist Association — Washington Office for Social Concern, 100 Maryland Avenue, N.E. — Room 106, Washington, DC 20002.

Unitarian Universalist Black Affairs Council, c/o Louis J. Gothard, 6503 Lincoln Drive, Philadelphia, PA 19119.

Unitarian Universalist Christian Fellowship, c/o Dr. Charles C. Forman, Executive Director, 347 Marlborough Street, Boston, MA 02115.

Unitarian Universalist Gay Caucus, c/o David Fanning, 1187 Franklin Street, San Francisco, CA 94109.

Unitarian Universalist Historical Society, 25 Beacon Street, Boston, MA 02108.

Unitarian Universalist Ministers Association, 25 Beacon Street, Boston, MA 02108.

Unitarian Universalist Ministers' Mates Association, 25 Beacon Street, Boston, MA 02108.

Unitarian Universalist Ministry to Migrant Farm Workers, c/o Rev. Howard G. Matson, 1148 Cragmont Avenue, Berkeley, CA 94708.

Unitarian Universalist Psi Symposium, c/o Rev. Richard Fewkes, 644 Main Street, Norwell, MA 02061.

Unitarian Universalist Service Committee, 78 Beacon Street, Boston, MA 02108.

Unitarian Universalist Society for Alcohol Education, c/o Dwight S. Strong, President, 223 West Springfield Street, Boston, MA 02118.

Unitarian Universalist United Nations Office, Inc., 777 United Nations Plaza — Room 7D, New York, NY 10017.

Unitarian Universalist Women's Federation, 25 Beacon Street, Boston, MA 02108.

Unitarian Universalists for Black and White Action, c/o Dr. Glover Barnes, Immunology Laboratory, University of Washington, Seattle, WA 98105.

United American Free Will Baptist Church, 1000 University Street, Kinston, NC 28501.

United Andean Indian Mission, (See Ecuador Concerns Committee).

United Bible Societies, c/o Dr. Oswald C. J. Hoffmann, President, 2185 Hampton Avenue, St. Louis, MO 63139.

United Black Christians (*United Church of Christ*), c/o Harold Cotton, 1905 Lutheran Street, Greensboro, NC 27401.

United Black Churchmen (*United Church of Christ*), (See United Black Christians).

United Board for Christian Colleges in China, (See United Board for Christian Higher Education in Asia).

United Board for Christian Higher Education in Asia, 475 Riverside Drive, New York, NY 10115.

United Brethren in Christ, 302 Lake Street, P.O. Box 650, Huntington, IN 46750.

The United Catholic Group Insurance Trust, National Headquarters, Trevose, PA 19048.

United Charity Institutions of Jerusalem (*Jewish*), 1141 Broadway, New York, NY 10001.

United Christian Church, c/o Elder Henry C. Heagy, Lebanon R.D. 4, Lebanon County, PA 17042.

United Christian Church, Inc., 117 Rose Lane, New Hyde Park, NY 11040.

The United Christian Church of America, (See United Christian Church, Inc.).

United Christian Evangelistic Association, P.O. Box 1000, Boston, MA 02103.

United Christian Ministerial Association (*Pentecostal*), P.O. Box 754, Cleveland, TN 37311.

The United Christian Missionary Society (*Disciples of Christ*), 222 South Downey Avenue, P.O. Box 1986, Indianapolis, IN 46206.

United Church and Science of Living Institute (*New Thought*), c/o Dr. Frederick Eikerenkoetter (Rev. Ike), G.P.O. Box 50, New York, NY 10116.

United Church Board for Homeland Ministries (*United Church of Christ*), 132 West 31st Street, New York, NY 10001.

United Church Board for World Ministries (*United Church of Christ*), 475 Riverside Drive, New York, NY 10115.

United Church Foundation, Inc. (*United Church of Christ*), 132 West 31st Street, New York, NY 10001.

United Church of Christ, 105 Madison Avenue, New York, NY 10016.

United Church of Christ Gay Caucus, P.O. Box 25005, Philadelphia, PA 19147.

United Church of Christ Historical Council, 105 Madison Avenue, New York, NY 10016.

United Church of Christ Ministers for Racial and Social Justice, c/o Rev. Marvin Morgan, Chairman, First Congregational United Church of Christ, 105 Courtland Street, N.E., Atlanta, GA 30303.

The United Church of Jesus Christ (*Pentecostal*), c/o W. C. Gibson, Highway 68, Sweetwater, TN 37874.

United Church of Religious Science (*New Thought*), 3251 West Sixth Street, Los Angeles, CA 90020.

United Church of the Apostles, 246 East Granada Avenue, Lindenhurst, NY 11757.

United Churches of Revelations, Inc., 1741 Superior Avenue, Costa Mesa, CA 92627.

United Community Church, 213 South Kenwood, Glendale, CA 91205.

United Council of Church Women, (See Church Women United).

United Council of Spiritual Churches of America, P.O. Box 38028, Detroit, MI 48238.

United Danish Evangelical Lutheran Church in America, (See The American Lutheran Church).

United Episcopal Church, c/o Bishop Russell G. Fry, Schwenksville, PA 19473.

The United Episcopal Church of The United States of America, c/o Archbishop C. Dale David Doren, 2293 Country Club Drive, Upper St. Clair, PA 15241.

United Evangelical Churches (*Pentecostal*), P.O. Box 28, Monrovia, CA 91016.

United Evangelical Lutheran Church, (See The American Lutheran Church).

United Evangelical Mennonites, (See The Missionary Church).

United Evangelism to the Chinese, 800 West Colorado Blvd., Los Angeles, CA 90041.

United Faith Foundation, (The Ministry of Rev. Al), P.O. Box 707, Fresno, CA 93761.

United Fellowship for Christian Service, (See Bible and Medical Missionary Fellowship).

United Focus, P.O. Box 5019, Seattle, WA 98105.

United Foursquare Women (*International Church of the Foursquare Gospel*), 11661 Firestone Blvd., Norwalk, CA 90650.

The United Free Will Baptist Church, Kinston College, 1000 University Street, Kinston, NC 28501.

United Fundamentalist Church, Inc., P.O. Box 28, Los Angeles, CA 90053.

United Hebrew Charities, (See Jewish Family Service).

United Hebrew Congregation (*Black Jews*), c/o Rabbi Naphtali Ben Israel, 131 West 74th Street, Chicago, IL 60621.

United Hebrew Trades of the State of New York (*Jewish*), 853 Broadway, New York, NY 10003.

United HIAS Service (*Jewish*), (See HIAS).

The United Hindu Temple of New Jersey, Inc., c/o Mrs. H. Lakshmi Anand, Secretary, 690 Vail Road, Parsippany, NJ 07054.

United Holiness Church, c/o Wesleyan Bible Institute, Cedar Springs, MI 49319.

United Holiness Convention (*Pentecostal*), (See United Holy Church of America, Inc.).

United Holy Church of America, Inc. (*Pentecostal*), P.O. Box 19846, Philadelphia, PA 19143.

United House of Prayer for All People (*Pentecostal*), 601 M Street, N.W., Washington, DC 20001.

The United House of Prayer for All People, Church on the Rock of the Apostolic Faith, Inc. (*Pentecostal*), (See United House of Prayer for All People).

United Israel Appeal (*Jewish*), 515 Park Avenue, New York, NY 10022.

United Israel World Union (*Jewish*), 507 5th Avenue — Room 903, New York, NY 10017.

United Jewish Appeal, Inc., 1290 Avenue of the Americas, New York, NY 10019.

United Libertarian Fellowship, 7220 Larnel Place, Los Altos, CA 94022.

United Lodge of Theosophists, 347 East 72nd Street, New York, NY 10021.

United Lodge of Theosophists, 3766 El Cajon Blvd., San Diego, CA 92105.

United Lutheran Church in America, (See Lutheran Church in America).

United Lutheran Church Women, (See Lutheran Church Women).

United Lutheran Society, 233 East Main Street, Ligonier, PA 15658.

United Mennonites, (See The Missionary Church).

The United Methodist Church, 475 Riverside Drive, New York, NY 10115.

The United Methodist Church, General Commission on Religion and Race, 100 Maryland Avenue, N.E., Washington, DC 20002.

United Methodist Committee on Overseas Relief, (See United Methodist Committee on Relief).

United Methodist Committee on Relief, 475 Riverside Drive, New York, NY 10115.

United Methodist Council on Youth Ministry, (See National Youth Ministry Organization).

United Methodist Gay Caucus, Two Jannsen Place, Kansas City, MO 64109.

United Methodist Renewal Services Fellowship, P.O. Box 50086, Nashville, TN 37205.

United Ministries in Education, c/o American Baptist Churches in the U.S.A., Valley Forge, PA 19481.

United Ministries in Higher Education, (See United Ministries in Education).

United Missionary Church, (See The Missionary Church).

United Missionary Fellowship, P.O. Box 214095, Sacramento, CA 95821.

United Monthly Meetings (*Friends*), (See Philadelphia Yearly Meeting of the Religious Society of Friends).

United Nations and International Ministries (*Southern Baptist*), 236 West 72nd Street, New York, NY 10023.

United Norwegian Lutheran Church in America, (See The American Lutheran Church).

United Order True Sisters (*Jewish*), 150 West 85th Street, New York, NY 10024.

United Overcomers International (*Pentecostal*), 2020 Bell Avenue, Des Moines, IA 50315.

United Pentecostal Church, International, 8855 Dunn Road, Hazelwood, MO 63042.

United Prayer Force, P.O. Box 30289, Washington, DC 20014.

The United Prayer Tower, (Camps Farthest Out), 5516 Lyndale Avenue South — Room 108, Minneapolis, MN 55419.

The United Presbyterian Church in the United States of America, 475 Riverside Drive — Room 1201, New York, NY 10115.

The United Presbyterian Church of North America, (See The United Presbyterian Church in the United States of America).

United Presbyterian Health, Education and Welfare Association, 475 Riverside Drive — Room 1268, New York, NY 10115.

United Presbyterian Peace Fellowship, P.O. Box 271, Nyack, NY 10960.

United Research (*New Age*), c/o James V. Goure, P.O. Box 1146, Black Mountain, NC 28711.

United Roumanian Jews of America, 31 Union Square, New York, NY 10003.

United Russian Orthodox Brotherhood of America, 333 Boulevard of the Allies, Pittsburgh, PA 15222.

United Secularists of America, Inc., 377 Vernon Street, Oakland, CA 94610.

United Service for New Americans (*Jewish*), (See HIAS).

United Seventh Day Brethren, c/o Myrtle Ortig, President, P.O. Box 225, Enid, OK 73701.

United Societies of U.S.A. (*Catholic*), 613 Sinclair Street, McKeesport, PA 15132.

United Society of Believers in Christ's Second Appearing (*Communal*), Canterbury, NH 03224.

United Society of Christian Endeavor, (See International Society of Christian Endeavor).

United Sons of Israel (*Jewish*), 41 Union Square, New York, NY 10003.

United Spiritualist Church, 813 West 165th Place, Gardena, CA 90247.

U.S. Apostolic Delegation (*Catholic*), 3339 Massachusetts Avenue, N.W., Washington, DC 20008.

United States Army Chaplain Board, Building 209, Ft. Wadsworth, Staten Island, NY 10305.

United States Catholic Conference, 1312 Massachusetts Avenue, N.W., Washington, DC 20005.

U.S. Catholic Historical Society, St. Joseph's Seminary, Dunwoodie, Yonkers, NY 10704.

United States Catholic Mission Council, 1302 18th Street, N.W., Washington, DC 20036.

U.S. Center for the Catholic Biblical Apostolate, 1312 Massachusetts Avenue, N.W., Washington, DC 20005.

U.S. Center for World Mission, 1605 East Elizabeth Street, Pasadena, CA 91104.

The United States Conference for the World Council of Churches, 475 Riverside Drive — Room 1062, New York, NY 10115.

United States Conference of Secular Institutes (*Catholic*), 7007 Bradley Blvd., Bethesda, MD 20014.

United States Interreligious Committee on Peace, (See World Conference on Religion and Peace).

U.S. National Federation of Christian Life Communities (*Catholic*), 3721 Westminster Place, St. Louis, MO 63108.

The United Stewardship Council, (See the National Council of Churches of Christ in the U.S.A).

United Synagogue Commission on Jewish Education, 155 Fifth Avenue, New York, 10010.

United Synagogue of America (*Jewish-Conservative*), 155 Fifth Avenue, New York, NY 10010.

United Synagogue Youth (*Jewish-Conservative*), c/o United Synagogue of America, 155 Fifth Avenue, New York, NY 10010.

United Synod of the Evangelical Lutheran Church in the South, (See Lutheran Church in America).

United Tiberias Institutions Relief Society (*Jewish*), 195 Henry Street, New York, NY 10002.

United Wesleyan Methodist Church of America, c/o Rev. David S. Bruno, President, 270 West 126th Street, New York, NY 10027.

United World (*New Age*), 3103 Palmer Drive, Los Angeles, CA 90065.

United World Mission, P.O. Box 8000, St. Petersburg, FL 33738.

United Zion Church, c/o Amos Weidman, RD 2, Manheim, PA 17545.

United Zionists (*Jewish*), (See Herut-USA).

United Zion's Children, (See United Zion Church).

Unity Church Worldwide, P.O. Box 1709, Palm Desert, CA 92260.

Unity Fellowship, P.O. Box 1277, Burlington, NC 27215.

Unity-in-Diversity Council (*New Age*), World Trade Center, 350 South Figueroa Street — Suite 370, Los Angeles, CA 90071.

Unity of the Brethren, c/o Rev. Milton Maly, 2205 Carnation Lane, Temple, TX 76501.

Unity School of Christianity (*New Thought*), Unity Village, MO 64063.

Universal Awareness Research Center (*Psychic*), 252 Tunxis Road, West Hartford, CT 06107.

Universal Brotherhood (*Psychic*), P.O. Box 366, Grand Central Station, New York, NY 10017.

Universal Buddhist Fellowship, P.O. Box 1079, Ojai, CA 93023.

Universal Christ Church, Inc. (*Spiritualist*), 1704 West Venice Blvd., Los Angeles, CA 90006.

Universal Christian Churches of America, 8648 Oakleigh Road, Baltimore, MD 21234.

Universal Christian International Catholic Church, c/o His Holiness M. Zidones Hamatheite, 30 Malta Street, Brooklyn, NY 11207.

Universal Christian Movement, P.O. Box 195, Glencoe, IL 60022.

Universal Church of Psychic Science, Inc. (*Spiritualist*), 4740 Tacony Street, Philadelphia, PA 19124.

Universal Church of Scientific Truth (*New Thought*), 1250 Indiana Street, Birmingham, AL 35224.

Universal Church of Spiritual Science, P.O. Box 188, Fern Park, FL 32730.

Universal Church of the Master (*New Age*), 399 West San Carlos Street, P.O. Box 692, San Jose, CA 95106.

Universal Connection Foundation (*New Age*), P.O. Box 2541, Tucson, AZ 85702.

Universal Faithists of Kosmon (*Psychic*), c/o Kosmon Service Center, P.O. Box 392, Vernal, UT 84078.

Universal Fellowship of Metropolitan Community Churches, 5300 Santa Monica Blvd. — No. 304, Los Angeles, CA 90029.

Universal Goddess Center, Inc. (*Psychic*), P.O. Box 3814, San Diego, CA 92103.

Universal Great Brotherhood, Solar Line (*New Age*), P.O. Box 9154, St. Louis, MO 63117.

Universal Harmony Association (*New Age*), 5903 Seminole Blvd., Seminole, FL 33542.

The Universal Industrial Church of the New World Comforter (One World Family) (*Communal*), 345 West Clay Street, Stockton, CA 95206.

The Universal Institute of Applied Ontology, (See Ontological Society).

Universal Life Alliance (*New Age*), 1031 West Washington Blvd., Venice, CA 90291.

The Universal Life Church, 1335 Seabright Avenue, Santa Cruz, CA 95062.

Universal Light Church, P.O. Box 26623, Houston, TX 77207.

The Universal Listening Post (*New Age*), P.O. Box 68, Sarahsville, OH 43779.

Universal Metaphysical Church, Inc., P.O. Box 19549, Los Angeles, CA 90019.

Universal Peace Mission, (Founded by Father Divine), 1600 Oxford Street West, Philadelphia, PA 19121.

Universal Prayer Group, P.O. Box 42, Mira Loma, CA 91752.

Universal Psychic Science Association, (See Universal Harmony Association).

Universal Shrine of Divine Guidance, c/o Most Rev. Mark Athanasios G. Karras, 730 Barron Avenue — No. 77, Redwood City, CA 94063.

Universal Spiritualist Association, c/o Pauline Swann, P.O. Box 158, Chesterfield, IN 46017.

Universal World Church (*Pentecostal*), 123 North Lake Street, Los Angeles, CA 90026.

Universalist Church of America, (See Unitarian Universalist Association).

Universalist Historical Society, (See Unitarian Universalist Historical Society).

Universalist Service Committee, (See Unitarian Universalist Service Committee).

Universalist Youth Fellowship, (See Liberal Religious Youth).

Universariun Foundation, Inc. (*Psychic*), 3600 S.E. 84th Avenue, Portland, OR 97266.

The Universe Society (*New Age*), 6153 Lexington Avenue, Hollywood, CA 90038.

University of Life Church (*Psychic*), c/o Rev. Richard Ireland, 5600 Sixth Street South, Phoenix, AZ 85040.

University of Oriental Studies (*Buddhist*), 939 South New Hampshire Avenue, Los Angeles, CA 90006.

University of the Trees (*New Age*), P.O. Box 644, Boulder Creek, CA 95006.

Unorganized Italian Christian Church in the United States (*Pentecostal*), (See Christian Church of North America).

Upper Midwest Regional Charismatic Service Committee (*Catholic*), 705 S.E. 12th Avenue, Minneapolis, MN 55414.

Upper Triad Association (*New Thought*), P.O. Box 1370, Manassas, VA 22110.

Urantia Foundation (*Psychic*), 533 Diversey Parkway, Chicago, IL 60614.

Us Unlimited (*New Age*), 3405 Mono Way, Sonora, CA 95370.

Utah Christian Association, P.O. Box 21052, Salt Lake City, UT 84121.

Utah Christian Mission, P.O. Box 511, Orem, UT 84057.

Utah Christian Tract Society (*Mormon*), P.O. Box 725, La Mesa, CA 92041.

Utah Commission for Ministry in Higher Education, 232 University Street, Salt Lake City, UT 84102.

Utah Missions, Inc., P.O. Box 348, Marlow, OK 73055.

Vairatker Prediction Centre, (Modern Occult Science Bureau), 817 Foster Avenue, Bartlett, IL 60103.

Vajradhatu (*Buddhist*), 1345 Spruce Street, Boulder, CO 80302.

Vajrapani Institute (*Buddhist*), P.O. Box 82, Boulder Creek, CA 95006.

Vajrapani Institute for Wisdom Culture (*Buddhist*), Sera House, 1140 7th Street, Santa Monica, CA 90403.

Vanguard Presbytery, (See Presbyterian Church in the United States).

Vedanta Centre (*Hindu*), 130 Beachwood Street, Cohasset, MA 02025.

Vedanta Society (*Hindu*), 34 West 71st Street, New York, NY 10023.

Vedanta Society of Greater Washington, Inc. (*Hindu*), 7430 Tower Street, Falls Church, VA 22046.

Vedanta Society of Northern California (*Hindu*), 2323 Vallejo Street, San Francisco, CA 94123.

Vedanta Society of Southern California (*Hindu*), 1946 Vedanta Place, Hollywood, CA 90068.

Vedic Cultural Society, Inc. (*Hindu*), 2610 East-West Highway, Chevy Chase, MD 20015.

Vedic Society of America (*Hindu*), c/o Vedic Publishing House, P.O. Box 926, Pacific Palisades, CA 90272.

Vellore Christian Medical College Board (USA), Inc., 475 Riverside Drive — Room 243, New York, NY 10115.

Veneration Society of Sanctity, Inc. (*Catholic*), 1322 Cranwood Square South, Columbus, OH 43229.

Vermont Ecumenical Council and Bible Society, 30 Elmwood Avenue, P.O. Box 593, Burlington, VT 05402.

Vernacular Society (*Catholic*), P.O. Box 207, Passaic, NJ 07055.

Viking Brotherhood (*Neo-Paganism*), P.O. Box 2552, Wichita Falls, TX 76307.

Villa Cristi (*New Age*), P.O. Box 6043, Evansville, IN 477712.

Villa Serena (*New Age*), 8201 Willow Street, Sarasota, FL 33580.

Vipassana Fellowship of America (*Buddhist*), 32 Tufts Street, Cambridge, MA 02139.

Virginia Council of Churches, Inc., 2321 Westwood Avenue, Richmond, VA 23230.

Vishwa Hindu Parishad of America, 438 Foote Road, South Glastonbury, CT 06033.

Vivekananda Medical Mission (*Hindu*), 80 Hillsdale Road, Old Bridge, NJ 08857.

Vivekananda Monastery (*Hindu*), Route 2, 122nd Avenue, Fennville (Ganges Township) MI 49408.

Vocation Central (*Catholic*), c/o Bro. Joe Pfeiffer, Donaldson, IN 46513.

Voice of Calvary Ministries, 1655 St. Charles Street, Jackson, MS 39209.

Voice of Elijah, c/o Carl Parke, P.O. Box 3455, Spokane, WA 99220.

Voice of Faith Fellowship, c/o Rev. Merton Jannusch, Fourth and Maple Streets, Green Bay, WI 54303.

Voice of Miracles and Missions, Inc. (*Pentecostal*), 4740 South Buckner Blvd., Dallas, TX 75227.

Voice of Tangier, (See Trans World Radio).

Voice of The Nazarene Association of Churches, Inc. (*Holiness*), P.O. Box 1, Finleyville, PA 15332.

Volunteers of America (*Holiness*), 3939 North Causeway Blvd. — Suite 202, Metairie, LA 70002.

The Vortex Institute (*New Age*), (See Philosophical Heritage Institute).

The W. O'Neil Foundation (*Catholic*), One General Street, Akron, OH 44329.

Waikiki Beach Chaplaincy, P.O. Box 15488, Honolulu, HI 96815.

Wailua University of the Contemplative Arts, (See Subramuniya Yoga Order).

Wainwright House Center for Development of Human Resources (*New Age*) 260 Stuyvesant Avenue, Rye, NY 10580.

Waldensian Church, 127 East 82nd Street, New York, NY 10028.

"The Walk", (See The Church of the Living Word).

Walk Thru the Bible Seminars, 1190 Winchester Parkway — Suite 203, Smyrna, GA 30080.

War Relief Services — National Catholic Welfare Conference, (See Catholic Relief Service — U.S. Catholic Conference).

Warner Pacific College Christian Writers Conference, c/o Dr. Dale W. Mark, 2219 S.E. 68th Avenue, Portland, OR 97215.

Warren Foundation (*Catholic*), (See The William K. Warren Foundation).

Warsaw Ghetto Resistance Organization (*Jewish*), 871 Seventh Avenue, New York, NY 10019.

Washington Association of Churches, 4759 15th Avenue, N.E., Seattle, WA 98105.

Washington Ethical Society, 7750 16th Street, N.W., Washington, DC 20012.

Washington Friends Seminar Program, (See William Penn House).

Watchman Fellowship, P.O. Box 7681, Columbus, GA 31908.

Watchtower Bible and Tract Society, Inc., (See Jehovah's Witnesses).

The Way Biblical Research Center, P.O. Box 328, New Knoxville, OH 45871.

The Way Maker, P.O. Box 152, Miami Springs, FL 33166.

Way of the Cross Church (*Pentecostal*), 19th & D Streets, N.E., Washington, DC 20002.

Way of the Light, (See Kealaokalamalama Church).

The Way of the Magus (*Psychic*), 7046 Hollywood Blvd., Los Angeles, CA 90028.

WE CARE Ministries, (See Missionary Revival Crusade).

Well Being (*New Age*), P.O. Box 887, San Anselmo, CA 94960.

Wellspring Renewal Center, P.O. Box 332, Philo, CA 95466.

Welsh Sons and Daughters of the Isle of Great Britain, (See Association of Cymry Wicca).

"Wendish Lutherans", (See Lutheran Church-Missouri Synod).

Wesak Festival (*New Age*), c/o Lucis Trust, 866 United Nations Plaza — Suite 5667, New York, NY 10017.

The Wesleyan Church (*Holiness*), P.O. Box 2000, Marion, IN 46952.

Wesleyan Connection of Churches (*Holiness*), (See Bible Methodist Connection of Churches).

Wesleyan Holiness Association of Churches, 108 Carter Avenue, Dayton, OH 45405.

The Wesleyan Methodist Church of America, (See The Wesleyan Church).

Wesleyan Tabernacle Association (*Holiness*), c/o Rev. Thomas Reed, Moderator, 9841 South 82nd Avenue, Palos Hills, IL 60465.

Wesleyan Theological Society, c/o Dr. Wayne E. Caldwell, 215 East 43rd Street, Marion, IN 46952.

West Indies Mission, c/o J. Allen Thompson, General Director, P.O. Box 343038, Coral Gables, FL 33134.

West Virginia Council of Churches, 612 Virginia Street East, Charleston, WV 25301.

Western Bible Students, 12739 26th Avenue, N.E., Seattle, WA 98125.

Western Bohemian Catholic Union, (See Catholic Workman).

Western Catholic Union, 506 Maine Street, Quincy, IL 62301.

Western Prayer Warriors, (See International Church of Spiritual Vision).

Western Young Buddhist League, c/o Buddhist Churches of America, 1710 Octavia Street, San Francisco, CA 94109.

Westminster Biblical Fellowship, c/o Rev. Earl Pinckney, 205 Orchard Drive, Bristol, TN 37620.

WFLK Fountain of the World (*Communal*), Route 5 — Box 61, Canoga Park, CA 91305.

Wheat Ridge Foundation (*Lutheran*), Seven South Dearborn, Chicago, IL 60603.

Which Bible? Society, Inc., c/o Dr. David Otis Fuller, 605 Deming Street, S.E., P.O. Box 7096, Grand Rapids, MI 49510.

White Fathers of Africa (*Catholic*), 777 Belvidere Avenue, Plainfield, NJ 07062.

White Lotus Study Center (*Neo Taoist*), 3878 43rd Street, San Diego, CA 92105.

White Star (*Psychic*), P.O. Box 307, Joshua Tree, CA 92252.

Whitworth Institute of Ministry, c/o Dr. Ronald G. Frase, Whitworth College, Spokane, WA 99251.

Whole Life Learning Center (*New Age*), 1545 Gilpin, Denver, CO 80218.

169

Wider Episcopal Fellowship, 815 Second Avenue, New York, NY 10017.
Wider Quaker Fellowship, 1506 Race Street, Philadelphia, PA 19102.
"Wilburites", (See Religious Society of Friends — Conservative).
William J. Kerby Foundation (*Catholic*), Syracuse-Kemper Bldg. — Room 814, Syracuse, NY 13202.
The William K. Warren Foundation (*Catholic*), P.O. Box 45372, Tulsa, OK 74145.
William Penn House (*Religious Society of Friends*), 515 East Capitol Street, Washington, DC 20003.
The Winant and Clayton Volunteers, Inc., c/o St. Bartholomew Community Club, 109 East 50th Street, New York, NY 10022.
Winds of New Birth (*New Age*), c/o Sylvanus Kaystosik, 1257 Meloy Road, Kent, OH 44240.
Winged Heart Coven (*Witchcraft*), c/o Gerald Brunson, 329 Turney Street, Sausalito, CA 94965.
Wings of Healing, Inc. (*Pentecostal*), 6615 Allston Street, Los Angeles, CA 90022.
Wisconsin Conference of Churches, 1955 West Broadway — Suite 104, Madison, WI 53713.
Wisconsin Evangelical Lutheran Synod, 3512 West North Avenue, Milwaukee, WI 53208.
Wisdom Institute of Spiritual Education (*New Thought*), 1236 South Marlborough, Dallas, TX 75208.
Witchcraft and Pagan Institute, c/o Phyllis Ammirati, 69 Strathmore Village Drive, South Setauket, NY 11733.
Witches Antidefamation League, (See Witches International Craft Associates).
Witches Encounter Bureau, (See Witches International Craft Associates).
Witches International Craft Associates, 153 West 80th Street — Suite 1B, New York, NY 10024.
Witches Liberation Movement, (See Witches International Craft Associates).
Witness, Inc., P.O. Box 597, Clayton, CA 94517.
Witnessing Watchmen Association (*Psychic*), P.O. Box 1556, Lenoir, NC 28645.
Wolfowski Foundation, Inc. (*Jewish*), One State Street Plaza, New York, NY 10004.
Woltman Foundation (*Lutheran*), (See B. M. Woltman Foundation).
Woman's American Baptist Foreign Mission Society, (See American Baptist Foreign Mission Society).
Women in Metaphysics, c/o Rev. Joanna Byers, P.O. Box 926, Tijeras, NM 87059.
Women in Spiritual Education, 1130 Keeler Avenue, Berkeley, CA 94708.
Women of the Church Coalition (*Catholic*), 22 East Van Buren, Chicago, IL 60605.
Women's Aglow Fellowship, P.O. Box 1, Lynnwood, WA 98036.
Women's American ORT (*Jewish*), 1250 Broadway, New York, NY 10001.
Women's Catholic Order of Foresters, (See National Catholic Society of Foresters).
Women's Caucus in Religion Studies, c/o Carol Bohn, Boston Theological Institute, 210 Herrick Road, Newton Centre, MA 02159.
Women's International Religious Fellowship, c/o Norma E. Boyd, 1602 Webster Street, N.W., Washington, DC 20011.

Women's League for Conservative Judaism, 48 East 74th Street, New York, NY 10021.

Women's League for Israel (*Jewish*), 1860 Broadway, New York, NY 10023.

Women's League for Palestine (*Jewish*), (See Women's League for Israel).

Women's League of the United Synagogue of America, (See Women's League for Conservative Judaism).

Women's Mission Society of the American Evangelical Lutheran Church, (See Lutheran Church Women).

Women's Missionary Federation (*Lutheran*), (See American Lutheran Church Women).

Women's Missionary Society (*Lutheran*), (See American Lutheran Church Women).

Women's Ordination Conference, 34 Monica Street, Rochester, NY 14619.

Women's Organization of Hapoel Hamizrachi (*Jewish*), (See Emunah Women of America).

Women's Supreme Council (*Jewish*), (See B'nai B'rith Women).

Won Gak Sa (*Buddhist*), 40 East 20th Street, New York, NY 10003.

The Word Foundation, Inc., P.O. Box 769, Forest Hills, NY 11375.

Word of God Institute (*Catholic*), 487 Michigan Avenue, N.E., Washington, DC 20017.

Word of Life Fellowship, c/o Jack Wyrtzen, President, Schroon Lake, NY 12870.

Words of Life, Inc. (*Pentecostal*), P.O. Box 2156, Austin, TX 78768.

The Work of God, Inc. (*Catholic*), (See Opus Dei).

Work of the Chariot (*Jewish*), P.O. Box 2226, Hollywood, CA 90028.

The Worker Sisters for the Holy Spirit (*Episcopal*), P.O. Box 5972, Kansas City, MO 64111.

World Alliance of Reformed Churches, (See World Alliance of Reformed Churches — Presbyterian and Congregational).

World Alliance of Reformed Churches (*Presbyterian and Congregational*), c/o Rev. James E. Andrews, North American Secretary, 341 Ponce de Leon Avenue, N.E., Atlanta, GA 30308.

World Baptist Alliance, 1628 Sixteenth Street, N.W., Washington, DC 20009.

World Baptist Fellowship, 3001 West Division Street, Arlington, TX 76012.

World Bible Society, P.O. Box 495, Brentwood, TN 37027.

World Christian Fundamentals Association, (See Slavic Gospel Association, Inc.).

World Christian Liberation Front, (See Berkeley Christian Coalition).

The World Community of Islam in the West (*Black Muslims*), 7351 South Stoney Island Avenue, Chicago, IL 60649.

World Concern, c/o Arthur L. Beals, Executive Director, 19303 Fremont Avenue North, Seattle, WA 98133.

World Conclave of Light (*New Age*), P.O. Box 1042, El Cajon, CA 92022.

World Confederation of General Zionists (*Jewish*), (See World Confederation of United Zionists).

World Confederation of Jewish Community Centers, 15 East 26th Street, New York, NY 10010.

World Confederation of United Zionists (*Jewish*), 595 Madison Avenue, New York, NY 10022.

World Conference on Religion and Peace, 777 United Nations Plaza, New York, NY 10017.

World Convention of Churches of Christ, 8609 Northwest Plaza Drive — Suite 405, Dallas, TX 75225.
World Council of Christians, c/o Rev. Peter P. S. Ching, President, 144-25 Roosevelt Avenue, Flushing, NY 11354.
World Council of Churches, (See The United States Conference for the World Council of Churches).
World Council of Clergy, c/o Rev. Peter P.S. Ching, 144-25 Roosevelt Avenue, Flushing, NY 11354.
World Council of Synagogues (*Jewish-Conservative*), 155 5th Avenue, New York, NY 10010
World Evangelical Fellowship, P.O. Box 670, Colorado Springs, CO 80901.
World Evangelism, c/o Dr. Morris Cerullo, P.O. Box 700, San Diego, CA 92138.
World Federation of Bergen-Belsen Associations (*Jewish*), P.O. Box 333, New York, NY 10021.
World Federation of Hungarian Jews, 136 East 39th Street, New York, NY 10016.
World Federation of Jews of Hungarian Descent, (See World Federation of Hungarian Jews).
World Federation of Polish Jews, American Section, (See American Federation of Polish Jews).
World Federation of YMHAS and Jewish Community Centers, (See World Confederation of Jewish Community Centers).
World Fellowship of Religions, 722 Tompkins Avenue, Staten Island, NY 10305.
World Fellowship of Slavic Evangelical Christians, P.O. Box 35220, Chicago, IL 60635.
World For Christ Crusade, 1005 Union Valley Road, West Milford, NJ 07480.
World Fundamental Missionary Fellowship, (See World Baptist Fellowship; see also Baptist Bible Fellowship, International).
World Goodwill, 866 United Nations Plaza — Suite 566-7, New York, NY 10164.
World Gospel Crusades (*Evangelical Foreign Missions Association*), P.O. Box 3, Upland, CA 91786.
World Gospel Mission (*Christian Holiness Association*), P.O. Box 948, 3783 State Road, 18 East, Marion, IN 46952.
World Harvest, (See Lester Sumrall Evangelistic Association, Inc.).
The World Healing Foundation for Wholistic Universal Oneness and Conscious Enlightenment (*New Age*), c/o Dr. Marvin P. Farber, 8379 Westview, Spring Branch, TX 78070.
World Healing Ministry (*New Age*), c/o Dr. Marion Dickes, Director, Inner Christ Administration Center, 3869 42nd Street, San Diego, CA 92105.
World Home Bible League, 16801 Van Dam Road, South Holland, IL 60473.
World Impact, Inc., 2001 South Vermont Avenue, Los Angeles, CA 90007.
World Insight International, P.O. Box 35, Pasadena, CA 91102.
World Institute of Avasthology (*New Age*), 107 North Ventura Street, Ojai, CA 93023.
World Involvement Ministry, (See Campus Crusade for Christ International).
World Jewish Congress, One Park Avenue — Suite 418, New York, NY 10016.
World Literature Crusade, P.O. Box 1313, Studio City, CA 91604.

World Medical Missions, Inc., 702 State Farm Road, Boone, NC 28607.
World Mercy Fund, Inc., 121 South St. Asaph Street, Alexandria, VA 22314.
World Messianity (*New Age*), Los Angeles Central Church, 3068 San Marino, Los Angeles, CA 90006.
World Methodist Council, P.O. Box 518, Lake Junaluska, NC 28745.
World Methodist Historical Society, 39 Lakeshore Drive, Lake Junaluska, NC 28745.
World Ministry of Prayer (*United Church of Religious Science*), P.O. Box 75127, Los Angeles, CA 90075.
World Mission Prayer League (*Lutheran*), 232 Clifton Avenue, Minneapolis, MN 55403.
World Missionary Assistance Plan (*Pentecostal*), 900 North Glenoaks Blvd., Burbank, CA 91502.
World Missionary Evangelism, Inc., P.O. Box 4326, Dallas, TX 75208.
World Missions Fellowship (*Interdenominational Foreign Missions Association*), P.O. Box 1048, Grants Pass, OR 97526.
World Missions, Inc., 837 Centre Street, P.O. Box 24496, Dallas, TX 75224.
World Missions to Children, (See World Missions Fellowship).
World Neighborhood, 635 North Hampton, Dallas, TX 75208.
World New Religion, 2475 West Seventh Street, Cleveland, OH 44113.
World Opportunities International, c/o Dr. Roy McKeown, President, 1415 North Cahuenga Blvd., Hollywood, CA 90028.
World Outreach International, 2215 West Beltline Road, Garland, TX 75042.
World Plan Executive Council, (See International Meditation Society).
World Prayer Foundation, P.O. Box 6072, Bend, OR 97701.
World Prophetic Ministry, Inc., P.O. Drawer 907, Colton, CA 92324.
World Radio Missionary Fellowship (*Interdenominational Foreign Missionary Association*), 20201 N.W. 37th Avenue, Opa-Locka, FL 33056.
World Redemption (*Mormon*), P.O. Box 1925, Independence, MO 64055.
World Relief (*National Association of Evangelicals*), Wheaton, IL 60187.
World Resort Chaplaincies, P.O. Box 15488, Waikiki Beach, HI 96815.
World Student Christian Federation, P.O. Box 9098, Berkeley, CA 94709.
World Union for Progressive Judaism, 838 Fifth Avenue, New York, NY 10021.
World University Roundtable (*New Age*), P.O. Box 40638, University Station, Tucson, AZ 85717.
World Vision International, P.O. Box 0, Pasadena, CA 91109.
World Zionist Organization — American Section, Inc., 515 Park Avenue, New York, NY 10022.
World's Christian Endeavor Union, 1221 East Broad Street, P.O. Box 1110, Columbus, OH 43216.
World's Evangelical Alliance, (See World Evangelical Fellowship).
The World's Faith Missionary Association, (See The Evangelical Church Alliance).
Worldshakers For Christ, P.O. Box 9664, Tulsa, OK 74107.
World Wide Baraca-Philathea Union, Tower House, Mt. Vernon, VA 22121.
Worldwide Church of God (*Adventist*), 300 West Green Street, Pasadena, CA 94303.
Worldwide Discipleship Association, Inc., 1001 Virginia Avenue — Suite 315, Atlanta, GA 30354.

Worldwide European Fellowship, Inc., c/o Rev. Henry Heijermans, General Director, P.O. Box 307, Langhorne, PA 19047.

World-Wide Evangelists, 714 Claremont Drive, Republic, MO 65738.

Worldwide Evangelization Crusade, 709 Pennsylvania Avenue, Fort Washington, PA 19034.

World-Wide Missionary Crusader, Inc., 4606 Avenue H, Lubbock, TX 79404.

World-Wide Missions, Inc. (*Pentecostal*), P.O. Box 6, 1593 East Colorado Blvd., Pasadena, CA 91109.

World-Wide Orthodox Renewal for Christ, Inc., c/o George J. Tzangas, 454 Citizens Savings Bldg., 110 Central Plaza South, Canton, OH 44702.

World-Wide Prayer and Missionary Union, 6821 North Ottawa Avenue, Chicago, IL 60631.

World-Wide Revival Crusades, Inc. (*Pentecostal*), P.O. Box 4446, Dallas, TX 75208.

Worship Arts Clearing House (*Unitarian Universalist Association*), 25 Beacon Street, Boston, MA 02108.

"Wotanism", (See Runic Society).

Wurzweiler Foundation (*Jewish*), (See The Gustav Wurzweiler Foundation, Inc.).

Wycliffe Associates, Inc., P.O. Box 2000, Orange, CA 92669.

Wycliffe Bible Translators, 19891 Beach Blvd., Huntington Beach, CA 92648.

Wyoming Church Coalition, c/o Mrs. Ema Bixler, 407 South 24th Street, Laramie, WY 82070.

Xavier Society for the Blind (*Catholic*), 154 East 23rd Street, New York, NY 10010.

Yahshua's Army, (See The True Church of Jesus Christ Restored, Inc.).

Yavneh — National Religious Jewish Students Association, 25 West 26th Street, New York, NY 10010.

Yes Educational Society (*New Age*), c/o Lee Lewis, 1047 31st Street, N.W., Washington, DC 20007.

Yeshe Nyingpo (*Buddhist*), 19 West 16th Street, New York, NY 10011.

Yeshua Ministries, (A Christian Mission to Southern Jews), P.O. Box 1845, Decatur, GA 30031.

Yivo Institute for Jewish Research, 1048 Fifth Avenue, New York, NY 10028.

Yoga Center of California (*Hindu*), 445 East 17th Street, Costa Mesa, CA 92627.

Yoga Research Foundation (*Hindu*), 6111 S.W. 74th Avenue, Miami, FL 33143.

Yoga Retreat (*Hindu*), 12 East Grand Avenue, Chicago, Il 60611.

Yoga Society of Rochester (*Hindu*), 93 Spruce Avenue, Rochester, NY 14611.

Yoga Society of San Francisco (*Hindu*), 2872 Folsom Street, San Francisco, CA 94110.

Yogashakti Ashram Mission, Inc. (*Hindu*), 827 South Federal Highway, Deerfield Beach, FL 33441.

Yogi Gupta Association (*Hindu*), 127 East 56th Street, New York, NY 10022.

Yogiraj Sect (*Hindu*), (Swami Swanandashram), c/o Arnold Ralph, 606 McCarthy Street, Easton, PA 18042.

Yokefellows International Prison Ministry, 230 College Avenue, Richmond, IN 47374.

Yoruba Religion (*Voodoo*), Oyo-Tienji, Beaufort County, SC 29902.

You Institute, Inc. (*New Age*), P.O. Box 10057, Glendale, CA 91209.

Young Calvinist Federation, 1333 Alger, S.E., P.O. Box 7244, Grand Rapids, MI 49510.

Young Christian Students Movement (*Catholic*), 7436 West Harrison, Forest Park, IL 60130.

Young Judaea (*Jewish*), (See Hashachar).

Young Ladies' Institute (*Catholic*), 50 Oak Street, San Francisco, CA 94102.

Young Life, 720 West Monument Street, Colorado Springs, CO 80904.

Young Men's and Women's ORT (*Jewish*), (See Business and Professional ORT).

Young Men's and Young Women's Hebrew Association (*Jewish*), 1395 Lexington Avenue, New York, NY 10028.

Young Men's Christian Association, (See National Council of the Young Men's Christian Associations of the United States of America).

Young Men's Hebrew Association (*Jewish*), (See Young Men's and Young Women's Hebrew Association).

Young Men's Institute (*Catholic*), 50 Oak Street, San Francisco, CA 94102.

Young Messianic Jewish Alliance of America, c/o Messiah College, Grantham, PA 17027.

Young Peoples Christian Union Workers, c/o Rev. Johnny Albertson, General Superintendent, Route 1 — Box 91, Palestine, AR 72372.

Young People's Missionary Movement, (See Commission on Education for Mission).

Young Peoples Pagan Association, (See Alternative Religions Center).

Young Women of The Church of Jesus Christ of Latter-day Saints (*Mormon*), c/o Elaine Cannon, General President, 50 East North Temple Street, Salt Lake City, UT 84103.

Young Women's Christian Association of the U.S.A., 600 Lexington Avenue, New York, NY 10022.

Young Women's Hebrew Association (*Jewish*), (See Young Men's and Young Women's Hebrew Association).

Youth for Christ, 360 South Main Place, Carol Stream, IL 60187.

Youth Mission for the Immaculata (*Catholic*), 8000 39th Avenue, Kenosha, WI 53142.

Youth With A Mission ((YWAM), 7085 Battlecreek Road, S.E., Salem, OR 97302.

Zeirei Agudath Israel (*Jewish-Orthodox*), Five Beekman Street, New York, NY 10038.

Zen Buddhist Association of Hawaii, (See Diamond Sangha).

Zen Buddhist Temple of Chicago, 2230 North Halsted Street, Chicago, IL 60614.

Zen Center of Los Angeles (*Buddhist*), 927 South Normandie Avenue, Los Angeles, CA 90006.

The Zen Center of Rochester (*Buddhist*), Seven Arnold Park, Rochester, NY 14607.

Zen Center of San Francisco (*Buddhist*), 300 Page Street, San Francisco, CA 94102.

Zen Mission Society (*Buddhist*), Shasta Abbey, P.O. Box 478, Mt. Shasta, CA 96067.

Zen Studies Society (*Buddhist*), Dai Bosatsu Zendo, Beecher Lake, Star Route, Livingston Manor, NY 12758.

The Zen Studies Society, Inc. (*Buddhist*), 223 East 67th Street, New York, NY 10021.

Zenshuji Soto Mission (*Buddhist*), 123 South Hewitt Street, Los Angeles, CA 90012.

Zion Coptic Church (*Communal*), c/o Brother Michael Madison, RFD, Soldiers Grove, WI 54655.

Zionist Archives and Library of Jewish Agency — American Section, (See Zionist Archives and Library of World Zionist Organization — American Section).

Zionist Archives and Library of Palestine Foundation Fund (*Jewish*), (See Zionist Archives and Library of World Zionist Organization — American Section).

Zionist Archives and Library of World Zionist Organization — American Section (*Jewish*), 515 Park Avenue, New York, NY 10022.

Zionist Organization of America (*Jewish*), Four East 34th Street, New York, NY 10016.

Zionists Revisionists of America (*Jewish*), (See Herut-USA).

Zion's First International Church (*Mormon Protestants*), c/o Phillip J. Hart, Secretary, 6837 West 3500 South, West Valley City, UT 84120.

Zion's Order of the Sons of Levi (*Mormon*), c/o William A. Hilles, Secretary, South Range Ranch, RFD 2, Mansfield, MO 65704.

Zoroastrian Association of Metropolitan Chicago, 626 West 56th Street, Hinsdale, IL 60521.

Zoroastrian Association of Southern California, c/o Roshan Motivala, 5061 Ambrose Avenue, Los Angeles, CA 90027.

Zotheria, (See Neo-Pythagorean Gnostic Church).